D0236704

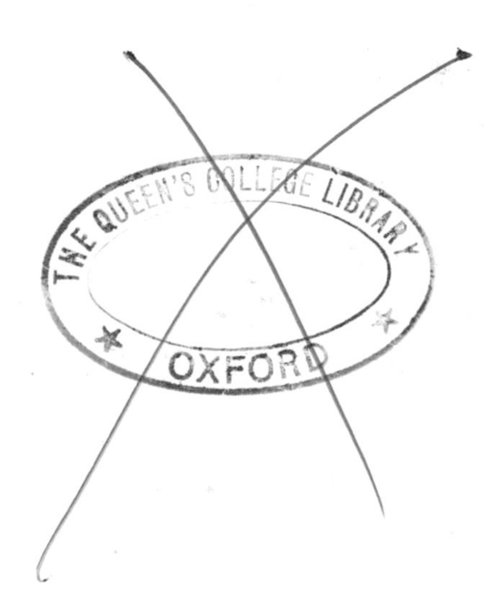
THE QUEEN'S COLLEGE LIBRARY
OXFORD

The Story of Chemical Industry in Basle

The Story of Chemical Industry in Basle

Published by CIBA Limited
on the Occasion of its 75th Anniversary

Urs Graf Publishers Olten and Lausanne 1959

THE QUEEN'S COLLEGE LIBRARY
4 JAN 1960
OXFORD

Foreword

Within the modest precincts of the city-canton Basle are domiciled the majority of enterprises that constitute the Swiss organic-chemical industry. The contribution which they have made to the scientific and technical progress of chemistry is a significant one. Many developments of far-reaching importance in this science derive from discoveries made by the Basle firms. Their business activity, above all the production and marketing of pharmaceuticals and dyes, is maintained either directly or through numerous subsidiaries abroad and is considerable in volume. They are in the forefront of world commerce with such products.

These are quite astonishing facts. For Basle, in its natural situation, does not boast one essential advantage which might have offered industrial chemistry a special chance. On the contrary, the prerequisites for successful large-scale industrial operations, such as the proximity of raw materials or the backing of a market able to absorb manufactures, are lacking. I have often been asked how the extensive and sustained success of this industry was possible. The answer calls forth considerations which take us beyond the conventional notion of place and situation as these affect economic development.

Now in reality the so-called objective factors inhering in a locale have a decisive influence on long-term industrial success only under very definite conditions. Their impact will always be less pronounced wherever, as in the present case, we are concerned with the conduct of an industry whose fate largely depends on the possibility of keeping pace, actively and creatively, with constant and rapid technical advance. Basle well illustrates the extent to which man and the institutions which he has established and upheld are able to tip the balance, even in a decidedly unfavorable situation.

It has become difficult to get an overall picture of the compass of chemical knowledge. Chemistry as a technique of research and as a method of producing commodities permeates every sphere of our lives nowadays.

Its history, as old as that of civilization itself, is both remarkable and instructive. The ideas underlying men's explanations of natural phenomena change with the philosophical systems which mark the different epochs of history. The chemical art itself took on practical importance only at that moment when the intellectual foundations were laid for a rational (as we would say today) preoccupation with nature in her many aspects. That evolution is the subject of this book. How did modern technology come about; what kind of forces unleashed it; where is it taking us? Such questions, directed to examining how technology originated and was turned to effect, are at the heart of the present work. And its peculiarity: the subject is treated by taking Basle as an exemplar – a town which, thanks to an unusual destiny, has had a part in every major chapter of cultural achievement in the West.

I should not like to anticipate the text. Only in one regard does this investigation of the background of industrial chemistry in Basle call for a supplementary remark or two. The cultural record of Basle reveals, in impressive fashion, all essential characteristics of the development which led from the scholasticism of the Middle Ages to the rational-scientific method of thinking and its practical consequences in our technological age. This fact is due neither to chance nor to circumstances willed, as it were, by nature. The reasons are to be found, rather, outside of the economic realm as such. They were never simply present. An admirable display of talent and of fibre was necessary to create them, and then to re-constitute them again and again, in the midst of a highly insecure environment.

The course of the story that is told in these pages has been enhanced in vividness, and thus rendered clearer to the reader, by means of carefully selected illustrations. The profusion of source material available in the university library and in the public archives and those of the various enterprises invited this enrichment. The possibility of presenting an unbroken documentation of a subject stretching so far back in time and of such great intrinsic interest is among the numerous advantages which accrue when a polity has remained intact for hundreds of years. But this good fortune did not fall into the lap of Basle; it is the fruit of astute statesmanlike accomplishment. In saying this, I touch on one of those imponderable special circumstances to which Basle owes the striking continuity between scientific performance and the commercial success linked with it. In relation to the size of the town's body politic, these successes are outstanding.

It is not easy to appraise the position of Basle among those towns of the Middle Ages that belonged to the old Holy Roman Empire. In our perspective, it is important that the high point of Basle's municipal development occurred at the end of the middle period, with the great Ecumenical Council, the founding of the university, and the introduction of printing. These events marked the entry of Basle into the phase of its history with which this book is particularly concerned. A close relationship existed between the university and the printers' ateliers. In that period both institutions distinguished themselves with brilliant achievements, making of Basle a spiritual anchorage in a time of extreme upheavals. One effect of their activities may be seen in the stand which Basle took with regard to the Reformation. Amidst the dramatic train of events which that convulsion set in motion, the town became a refuge of the persecuted and thus, for a time, a forum where the spiritual and intellectual resources of the West could be re-established.

That was undoubtedly the time when the abiding character of Basle was formed. Gone from then on were those halcyon days of the bishopric which the chronicler has sung:

> Spyer das andächtigst,
> Strasburg das edelst,
> Costentz das grossest,
> Basel das lustigst
> Bistum am Rhein.

Or in English: Speyer most pious,
Strasbourg most noble,
Constance the largest,
Basle the gayest
See on the Rhine.

The Puritanical attitude, that strange mixture of strict discipline and piety with a pronounced bent for the acquisition of this world's goods, dominated public life. In practice its effects were mitigated by the broad vein of humanism, to which Basle was thenceforward indebted for its finest achievements.

The splendor that radiated from Basle in the Reformation period proved to be transitory. Yet the citizenry, proud of the new consciousness brought by that epoch, zealously cultivated the seeds that had been planted – and has gone on doing so to the present day. The university was and remained a privilege to be carefully watched over. The names of scholars and whole dynasties of learned men which shone again and again in the succeeding generations established its renown and implanted it solidly in the hearts of the citizens. Nor was their contribution limited to ways and means of giving it material support. Not a few of the men whose names distinguish the history of the university came from the ranks of the community itself.

The great figures of intellectual and cultural life in Basle appear in this book, to be sure, only insofar as a close connection with the subject permits. What we have, then, is a detail from a most fascinating panorama. The relationship of that canvas to the main theme of the book should therefore be viewed with certain reservations. There is, for example, no relation which one can point to between the work of the great 18th century mathematicians in Basle and the subsequent technological exploitation of scientific knowledge. On the contrary, the triumph of mathematics was bound to entail, initially, a definite preference for deductive reasoning, which proceeds from the general to the specific. The price was a neglect of inductive experimental research, with the consequence that the time was not yet ripe in that century for the most important discoveries of natural science to flourish. Only in the 19th, the century of invention, did the preparation of dyes come to be an object of scientific investigation. With an economic base in the textile industry, it became a key component of industrial chemistry. The successful outcome of this development is due without any doubt to Basle's scientific heritage, the result of the indefatigable cultivation of all branches of learning. This nexus is explicitly presented in the book and stands out beautifully.

Now, the brilliant scientific background depicted does not of itself suffice to explain the industrial performance played out against it. There are cities whose names are far more conspicuously bound up with the progress of science than is Basle's, and yet they have no notable rôle in the great play of industrial forces today. Others which represent powerful concentrations of industrial potential have no tradition comparable to Basle's to offer. The conjunction of the two phenomena – the fusion of scientific tradition with the capability of industrial development – evidently depends on other qualities, on a catalyst, so to speak, which can bridge the tensions between these two manifestations of human endeavor, so disparate in purpose. In our case, I see this function fulfilled through two traits specially characteristic of Basle. I mean its natural hospitality and an uncommon power of assimilation.

We need only recall that the bearers of those illustrious names which adorn the history of Basle were often either immigrants themselves or the descendants of emigrant families; or that the founders of the textile industry were religious refugees who sought sanctuary here, and that among the pioneers of the modern chemical industry the names of people originally native elsewhere predominate by far. These things we have but to remember in order to appreciate the importance of Basle's readiness to admit what is novel and even different. The farther we go back into the past, the more truly – and more commendably – this appears to have been so. For in recent times the rules regarding exclusion have been changed and the former maxims gradually obliterated. In the name of aid to less developed countries, the old principle has ended by being converted into its antipode. In this matter, however, we must guard against falling prey to a deception! A fundamental willingness to tolerate the idea in need of protection and to absorb new impulses from outside is a feature only of individual commonwealths which, like Basle, gained their inner and outer freedom at an early date and maintained it through all vicissitudes.

With Dr. Arthur Wilhelm, my friend and colleague in the management of CIBA, I have often reflected on how we might use the occasion of our 75th anniversary as a means of expressing the thanks which we owe to Basle for the unique industrial opportunities it has offered. The present portrayal of the genealogy and the shape of industrial chemistry in Basle attempts to meet this keenly felt need. Every one of us who had anything to do with the production of the book is aware, however, that so compact an outline of a complex and immeasurable development must inevitably be more or less fragmentary.

The text was written by two CIBA chemists, Dr. George Leo Huber and Dr. Karl Menzi. Their thorough knowledge of the problems involved in modern chemistry and their eager interest in the origins of this science made them uniquely qualified for the task. Dr. A. Eschenmoser and Dr. E. Heilbronner, faculty members of the Swiss Federal Institute of Technology in Zurich, served as consultants for the chapter concerned with recent developments in chemical theory. The editors were assisted in their work by the following institutions in Basle: the library of the University, the Public Records Office, the Swiss Museum of Pharmaceutical History, the Anthropological Museum, the Swiss Museum for European Ethnology, the Historical Museum, and the Basle Art Gallery. Their co-operation in making available documents and objects for purposes of study and reproduction was also of valuable help.

Finally, we should like to emphasize the kind assistance given the authors, both in the form of documentation and of counsel, by J.R.Geigy S.A., Sandoz Limited, Durand & Huguenin Limited, and F. Hoffmann-LaRoche & Co., Limited.

Dr. Robert Käppeli
President and Chairman of the Board
CIBA Limited, Basle

Basle, April 1959

Table of Contents

Basle's Passage to the Age of Technology

Basle in the Setting of the Late Middle Ages

Politically, the Middle Ages were as agitated as any other epoch: wars were won and lost, borders were drawn up and then rearranged, empires arose and disappeared. More important for the fate of the Occident than all these vicissitudes, however, was the advent of two institutions: around the year 1200, and almost simultaneously, the universities and the gilds came into being in various European countries.
The first universities grew out of the institutions which gave clerics, physicians, and jurists their education. The term "universitas" as now construed dates from the year 1208. Pope Innocent III used it for the first time in connection with the cathedral school of Notre-Dame in Paris, grouping together under this heading the masters and scholars of various disciplines. The University of Paris, endowed with its own rights by king and pope, was organized in its main outlines in 1231. In the "facultates superiores", theology, law and medicine were taught, while in the "facultas inferior" the arts were pursued as preparatory disciplines.

Left: Medicine as taught in the old centres of learning. From the "Cyrurgia" of Henri de Mondeville, 1314. MS. fr. 2030; Bibliothèque Nationale, Paris.
Above: Universities north of the Alps were modelled on Paris. Seal of the University of Paris from the 13th century, in the collection of the Bibliothèque Nationale.

ἀληθές· ὁμοίως δὲ καὶ κατηγορικῆς οὔσης τῆς καθ-
όλου προτάσεως τῆς δ' ἐν μέρει στερητικῆς· ἐγχωρεῖ γὰρ τὸ α τῷ μὲν β μηδενί· τῷ δὲ γ παντὶ
ἕπεσθαι· καὶ τὸ β τινὶ τῷ γ μὴ ὑπάρχειν· οἷον ζῷον
ἐπιστήμῃ μὲν οὐδεμιᾷ· ἀνθρώπῳ δὲ παντὶ ἕπεται· ἡ δὲ
ἐπιστήμη οὐ παντὶ ἀνθρώπῳ· ἐὰν οὖν ληφθῇ τὸ α τῷ
μὲν β ὅλῳ ὑπάρχειν· τῷ δὲ γ τινὶ μή· αἱ
μὲν προτάσεις ψευδεῖς· τὸ δὲ συμπέρασμα ἀληθές·:·
περὶ τῶν ἐν τῷ γ σχήματι ἐκ ψευδῶν ἀληθῶν συλλογισμῶν·
Ἔσται δὲ καὶ ἐν ἐσχάτῳ σχήματι διὰ ψευδῶν ἀληθές·
καὶ ἀμφοτέρων ψευδῶν οὐσῶν ὅλων· καὶ ἐπὶ
τι ἑκατέρας· καὶ τῆς μὲν ἑτέρας ἀληθοῦς ὅλης
τῆς δ' ἑτέρας ψευδοῦς· καὶ τῆς μὲν ἐπί τι ψευδοῦς
τῆς δ' ὅλης ἀληθοῦς· καὶ ἀνάπαλιν· καὶ ὁσαχῶς
ἄλλως ἐγχωρεῖ μεταλαβεῖν τὰς προτάσεις· οὐδὲν
γὰρ κωλύει μήτε τὸ α μήτε τὸ β μηδενὶ τῷ γ ὑπάρ-
χειν· τὸ μέντοι α τινὶ τῷ β ὑπάρχειν· οἷον οὔτ' ἄνθρωπος
οὔτε πεζὸν οὐδενὶ ἀψύχῳ ἕπεται· ἄνθρωπος μέντοι τινὶ
πεζῷ ὑπάρχει· ἐὰν οὖν ληφθῇ τὸ α καὶ τὸ β παντὶ
τῷ γ ὑπάρχειν· αἱ μὲν προτάσεις ὅλαι ψευδεῖς· τὸ
δὲ συμπέρασμα ἀληθές· ὡσαύτως δὲ καὶ τῆς μὲν στε-
ρητικῆς τῆς δὲ καταφατικῆς οὔσης· ἐγχωρεῖ
γὰρ τὸ μὲν β μηδενὶ τῷ γ ὑπάρχειν· τὸ δὲ α παντί·
καὶ τὸ α τινὶ τῷ β μὴ ὑπάρχειν· οἷον τὸ μέλαν οὐδενὶ κύκνῳ· ζῷον δὲ παντί· καὶ τὸ ζῷον οὐ παντὶ μέλανι· ὥστ' ἂν ληφθῇ τὸ μὲν β παντὶ τῷ γ· τὸ

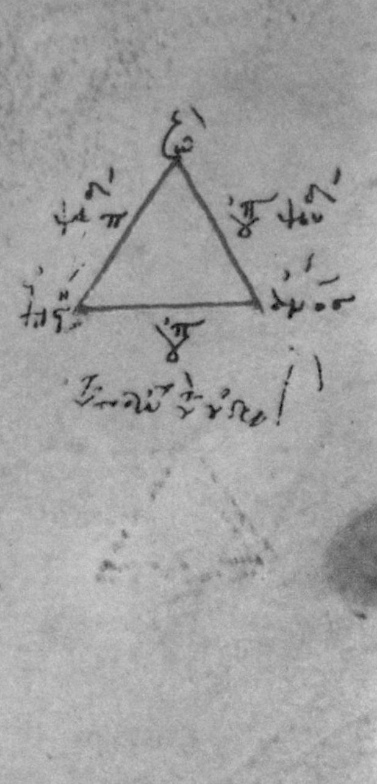

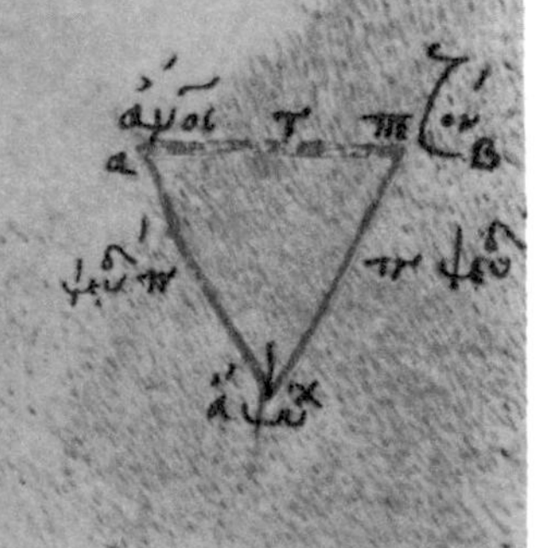

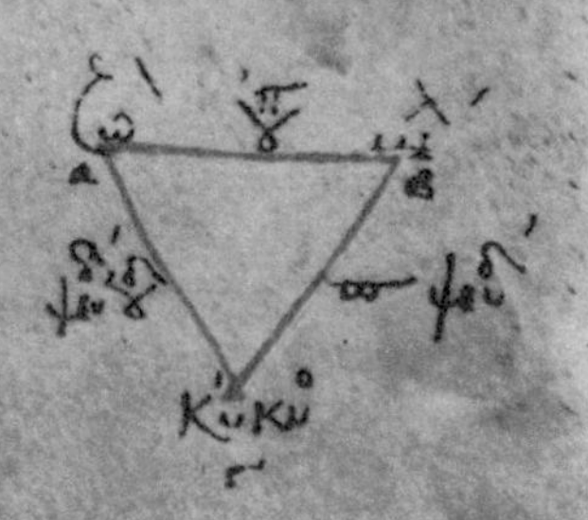

et · b · et · c · toti inee · et · b · aliquod · c · n̄ se
qui · ut genus speciem et differentiam ·
Nam an̄l omnem hominem · et totū gressi
bile sequitur · homo uero nō omne gres
sibile · Quare si sumatur · a · b · quidē toti
inee · c · autē alicui nō inee · uniuersalis qui
dem ppō uera · particularis aū falsa · cō
autē uera · Manifestū autē quā et
ex utrisque falsis conclusio uera erit · si q̄
dem contingit · a · et · b · et · c · huic quid oi
illi uero nulli · b · uero aliqd · c · nō seq̄ ·
Nam sūpto · a · b · quidem nulli · c · autē
alicui inee · ppōnes quidē ambe false ·
conclusio aū uera · Similiter aū et contraria
fuerit uniuersalis ppō · particularis autē priua
tiua · possibile est n · a · b · quidē nullam
c · aū omnē sequi · et · b · alicui · c · nō inee ·
ut an̄l disciplinam quidē nullam · hoīē
autē omnem sequitur · disciplina uō nō o
nē hominem · Si ergo sumatur · a · b · toti inee ·
c · aū quoddā nō sequi · ppōes quidē false ·
conclusio quidem uera ·

Erit aū et in posteriora figura p
falsas totas et in aliquo utramque
et altā quidem uera · alterā aū falsa ·
et hac quidē in aliquo falsa · illa aū
tota uera · et conuerso · et quotcumque modis
aliter contingit transsumere ppōnes · Nich
· n · prohibet nec · a · neque · b · nulli · c · inee
· a · aū alicui · b · inee · ut neque homo
neque gressibile · nullū inanimatū sequitur
hō autē alicui gressibili inest · Si ergo su
matur · a · et · b · omni · c · inee · ppōnes quō
tote false sunt · conclusio aū uera · Simili
ter autem et cum hec quidē est priuatiua
illa uero affirmatiua · euenit · n · b ·
quidē nulli · c · inee · a · aū omni · c · et · a ·
alicui · b · nō inee · ut nigrū nulli cig
no · an̄al autē omni · et an̄l nō omni nigro
Quare si sumatur · b · quidē omni · c · a · uō nul
li : a · alicui · b · nō inerit · et conclusio quō
uera est · ppōnes autē false · Et si in
aliquo sit utraque falsa · erit conclusio uā
Nichil · n · prohibet · et · a · et · b · alicui
· c · inee · et · a · alicui · b · ut albū et pul
crū · alicui an̄li inest · et albū alicui
pulchro · Si ergo ponatur · a · et · b · omni
· c · inee · ppōnes quidē in aliquo fal
se sunt · conclusio aū uera · Et priuati
ua · a · c · posita similiter · Nichil · n · p
hibet · a · quidē alicui · c · non inee · b · uō
alicui inee · et · a · non omni · b · inee · ut
pulcrū alicui an̄li nō inest · albū aū
alicui inest · et pulcrum nō omni albo ·
Quare si sumatur · a · quidē nulli · c · b ·
aū omni · utreque quidē ppōnes in aliquo
false sunt · conclusio autē uera · Similiter
autē et hac quidē tota falsa · illa
aū tota uera sūpta · possibile est · n ·
et · a · et · b · omne · c · sequi · et · a · alicui
· b · non inee · ut an̄l · et albū omnem
cignū sequitur · et an̄l nō omni albo inest ·
Positis ergo his terminis : si sumatur · b ·
quidem toti · c · inee · a · uō toti n̄ inee ·

The university idea spread rapidly. Students of the Paris institution founded the University of Oxford, the earliest documentary reference to which is dated 1240. In 1231 the medical school of Salerno, a cross-roads of cultures which went back to the 11th century, was accorded official recognition by the King of Sicily. Its students established the University of Montpellier, a stronghold of medical studies first mentioned in a record dated 1220 and granted the papal privilege in 1289. In the course of the 12th century the school of law at Bologna also developed into a centre at which the "studium generale" (another technical title given to the university program in those days) was fostered, although it was not organized into a university as such until the following century.

All these university foundations are the visible reflection of a revolution in attitudes then taking place. The traditional Christian view of the universe, Platonic in character ever since Augustine, was faced by the more empirical doctrines of the other great Greek philosopher, Aristotle of Stagira. His works were absorbed into the culture of Islam in the 11th and 12th centuries through the commentaries on them written by Avicenna the Persian and Averroes the Moor. Soon thereafter, together with other philosophical and scientific works of Greek as well as Islamic origin, they were translated into Latin and thus made accessible to Christian scholars. Three such early mediators of Graeco-Arabian thought were Constantinus Africanus of Monte Cassino, Gerard of Cremona in Toledo, and Adelard of Bath.

The effect of Aristotelian philosophy on the high Middle Ages was a powerful one. It obliged thinkers to re-cast their conceptions of the universe. The theological and philosophical "summae" of the 13th century are the literary outcome of this spiritual contention. At the centre of the turmoil stood three professors of the University of Paris: the Aristotelian Thomas Aquinas and the Neo-Platonists Bonaventura and John Duns Scotus.

The idea of a personal Creation is not to be found in Aristotle's cosmology. The "unmoved mover" who keeps the machinery of the world in motion is not older than the universe itself. The inscrutable will of this "mover" governs nature.

As Christians, the scholastic thinkers of the late 13th century prefaced their interpretation of nature with the notion of the Creation of the World. But in the new view, once the world had been created its machinery operated eternally according to natural laws, without intervention of the "mover". With the significant exception of man's free will, nature is determined through and through, ruled by order rather than chance.

By fusing the conception of a created universe with Aristotelian philosophical method, the West took what was probably the most decisive step in its intellectual history, for the way was now open to a rational comprehension of the world. Thus Etienne Gilson writes: "Although the men of that time may have had but a poor knowledge of nature, nevertheless they did not mistake the essential characteristics which constitute the object of our rational knowledge."

Preceding pages: Specimen pages from Aristotle's Analytics.
Left: Greek version. 12th century manuscript owned at one time by John Stoikovič of Ragusa, later in the Dominican monastery in Basle. University Library, Basle; MS. F II 21.
Right: Latin version of same text in a French manuscript of the mid-14th century, formerly also in the Dominican monastery. University Library, Basle; MS. F I 25.

Opposite: Thomas Aquinas incorporated Aristotle into Christian doctrine, making reason an instrument to supplement faith. This is the beginning of his "Summa Theologica" as it appears in a richly illuminated manuscript done in a French scriptorium around 1460. Its owner, John Heynlin de Lapide, bequeathed the document to the library of the Carthusians in Basle. University Library, Basle; MS. A I 14.

QUESTIO PRIMA

QUIA KATHOLICE VERITATIS DOCTOR
non solum provectos debet instruere Sed ad eum
et ptinet incipientes erudire sm illud apli
primo ad cor. tercio Tamqz parvulis in xpo
lac vobis potum dedi non escam. Propositum nre
intentionis in hoc ope est ea que ad xpianam
religionem ptinet eo modo tradere sm qd congruit
eruditioni incipientium. Consideravimus naqz huius
doctrine novitios ab his que a diversis
conscripta sunt plurimum impediri. ptim quidem ppt multi
tudinem inutilium questionum articulorum et argumentorum. ptim
etiam qz ea que sunt necessaria talibus ad sciendum non traduntur
sm ordinem discipline s sm qd requirebat librorum
expositio vel sm qd se pbebat occasio disputandi. ptim
quidem qz frequens eorundem repetitio et fastidium et
confusionem generabat in animis auditorum. Hec
igitur et alia huiusmodi evitare studentes temptabimus
cum confidentia divini auxilii ea que ad sacram doc
trinam ptinent breviter ac dilucide psequi sm
qd materia patietur. Et ut intentio nra sub ali
quibus certis limitibus comprehendatur necessarium est pri
mo de ipsa sacra doctrina investigare qualis sit
et ad que se extendat. Circa quam querenda sunt
decem. primo de necessitate huius doctrine. Secundo
Utrum sit scientia. Tercio Utrum sit una vel
plures. Quarto Utrum sit speculativa vel practica.
Quinto de comparatione eius ad alias scientias. Sexto
Utrum sit sapientia. Septimo quid sit subiectum eius.
Octavo Utrum sit argumentativa. Nono Utrum
uti debeat metaphoricis aut simbolicis locutioni
bus. Decimo Utrum sit scriptura sacra huius doctrine
sm plures sensus exponenda.

Ad primum sic proceditur. Videtur quod non sit
necessarium preter philosophicas disciplinas aliam
doctrinam haberi. Ad ea enim que supra rationem sunt homo
non debet conari sm illud Eccl. iii. Altiora te ne quesie
ris. Sed ea que rationi subduntur sufficienter traduntur in philosophicis
disciplinis. Superfluum igitur videtur preter philosophicas disci
plinas aliam disciplinam haberi. Preterea doctrina non
potest esse nisi de ente. Nichil enim scitur nisi verum quod
cum ente convertitur. Sed de omnibus entibus tractatur
in philosophicis disciplinis etiam de deo. Unde quedam
pars philosophie dicitur theologia sive scientia divina ut
patet per philosophum in sexto methaphisice. non fuit igitur ne
cessarium preter philosophicas disciplinas aliam doctrinam fieri
seu haberi. Sed contra est quod dicitur ii. thimo
iii. Omnis scriptura divinitus inspirata utilis est
ad docendum ad arguendum ad corripiendum
ad erudiendum ad iusticiam. Scriptura autem
divinitus inspirata non pertinet ad philosophicas disciplinas que sunt sm
rationem humanam invente. Utile igitur est preter
disciplinas philosophicas aliam esse scientiam divinitus inspiratam.
Respondeo dicendum quod necessarium fuit ad humanam sa
lutem esse doctrinam quandam sm revelationem divinam
preter philosophicas disciplinas que ratione humana investigantur. Primo
quidem quia homo ordinatur a deo ad quendam finem qui
rationis comprehensionem excedit sm illud Ysa. lxiiii. Oculus
non vidit deus absque te que preparasti diligentibus
te. Finem autem oportet esse precognitum hominibus qui
suas intentiones et actiones debent ordinare in
finem. Unde necessarium fuit homini ad salutem quod
ei nota fierent quedam per revelationem divinam que
rationem humanam excedunt. Ad ea etiam que de deo
ratione humana investigari possunt necessarium fuit hominem
instrui revelatione divina quia veritas de deo
per rationem investigata a paucis et per longum tempus
cum admixtione multorum errorum homini proveniret
a cuius veritatis cognitione dependet tota hominis
salus que in deo est. Ut igitur salus hominibus convenientius
et securius proveniat necessarium fuit quod de divinis per
divinam revelationem instruantur. necessarium igitur fuit
et preter philosophicas disciplinas que per rationem investi
gantur sacram doctrinam per revelationem haberi.

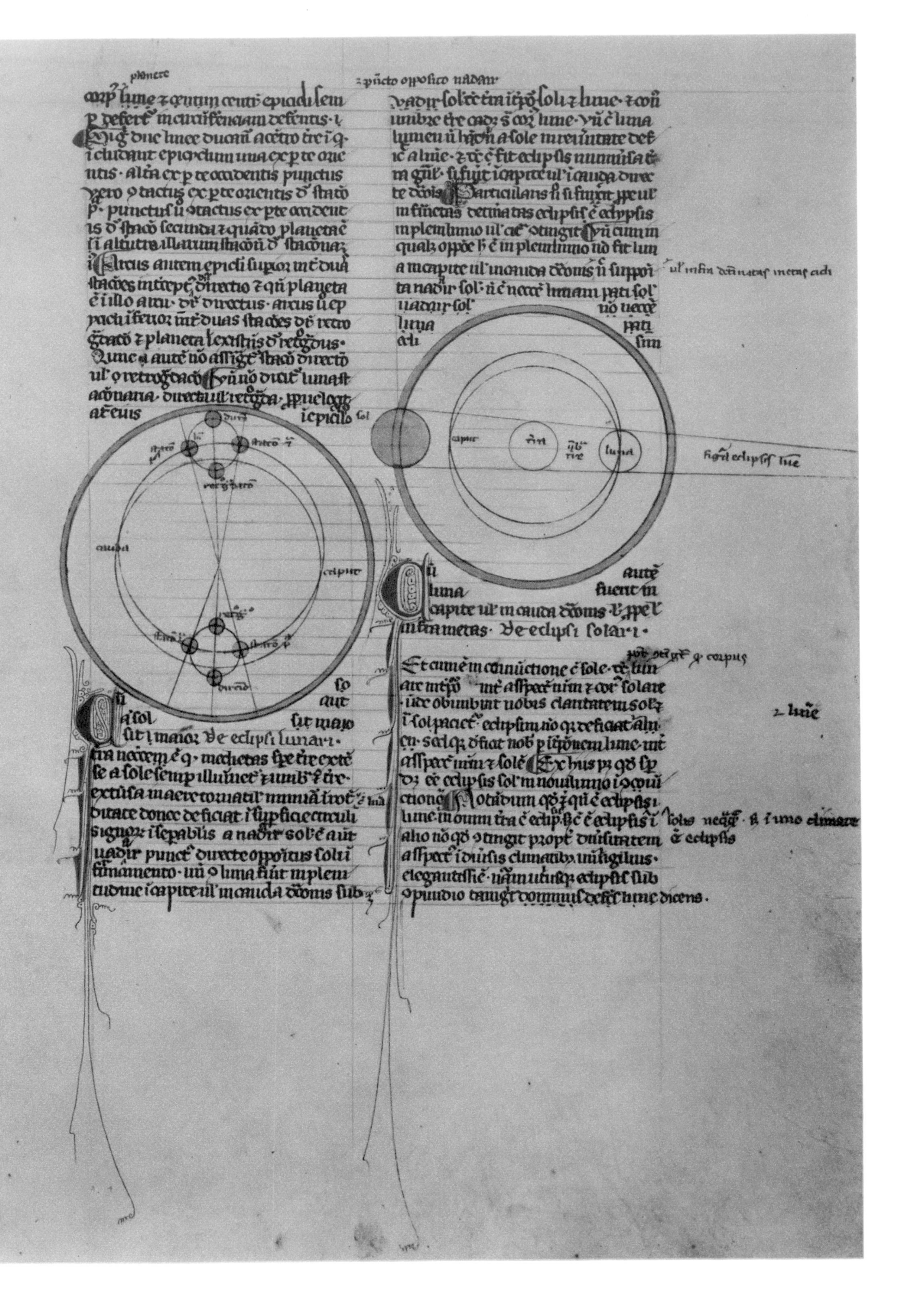

Opposite: Solar and lunar eclipses as depicted in a 14th century manuscript. Originally a work of the Englishman John of Sacrobosco, who wrote it in Paris in the first part of the 13th century, this document contains mathematical and astronomical disquisitions which remained widely current up to the 17th century. Formerly in the Dominicans' library, now in the University Library, Basle; MS. O II 7.

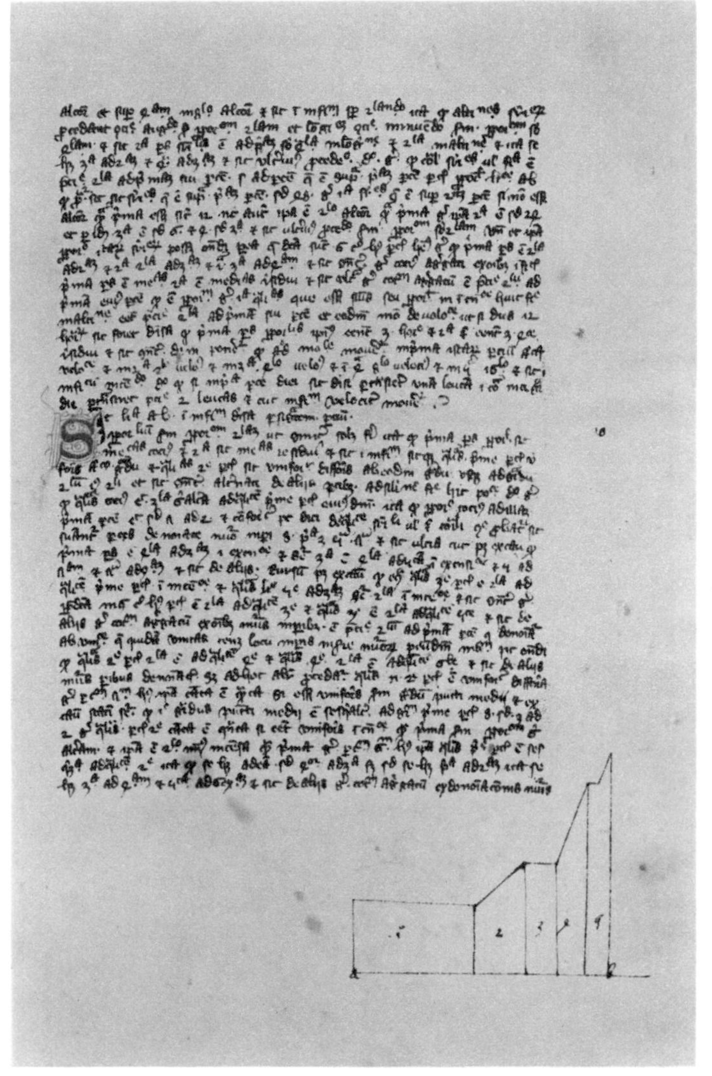

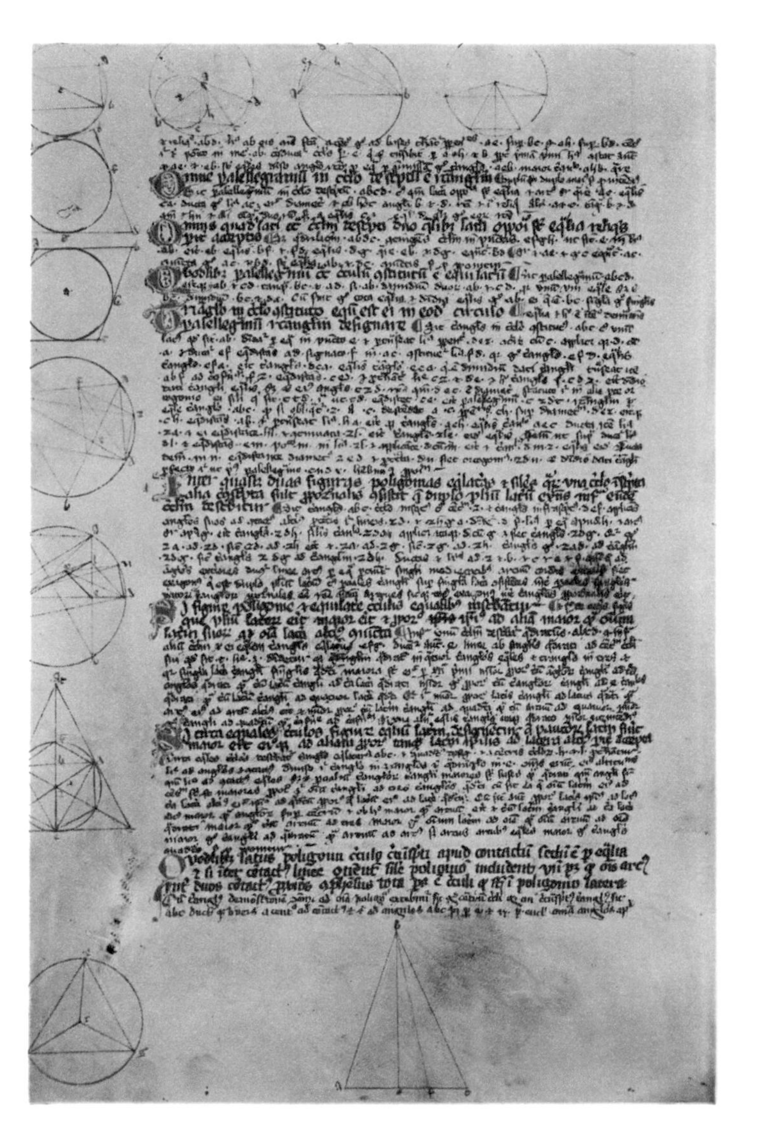

Left: Page from Jordanus de Nemore's work on triangles. Building on Greek knowledge, Jordanus laid the groundwork of Western mathematics and mechanics around 1200. Manuscript from the first half of the 15th century. University Library, Basle; MS. F II 33.
Above: Page from the "De Uniformitate et Difformitate Intensionum" of Nicholas Oresme, who used co-ordinates for plotting paths of motion. The diagram on lower margin illustrates determination of speed by means of surfaces. Oresme's method of interpreting curves was a forerunner of differential calculus. 14th century manuscript from the Dominican monastery in Basle. University Library, Basle; MS. F III 31.

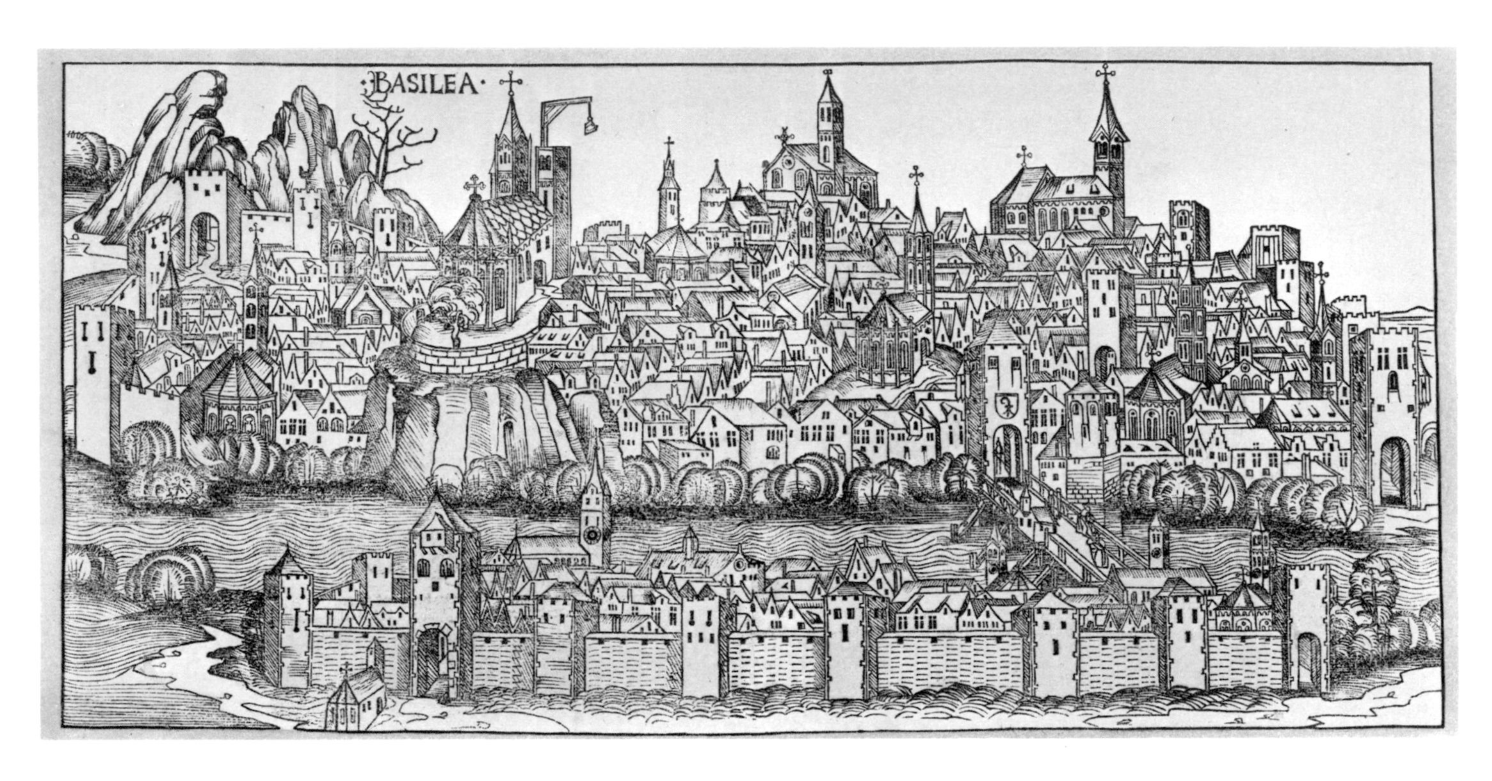

Basle around 1500. Although certain topographical details are not true to nature, this woodcut by Wilhelm Pleydenwurff gives a good idea of how the town looked at that time. From Hartmann Schedel's "World Chronicle"; Nuremberg, 1493.

The first faint beginning of the renaissance in science, of the age of technology, is to be found, then, in the 13th century.

This also explains why we may look for the beginning of "modern" mathematics in that age. Leonardo of Pisa expounds in his works algebraic equations of the first and second degree. Jordanus de Nemore, a professor at the University of Paris, laid the foundations of mechanics in the West with his studies of bodies at rest and in motion.

In England, where the "quadrivium" held sway, mathematics received a strong impetus from Roger Bacon in the 13th century and Richard Wallingford in the following one. Wallingford is generally known as the originator of trigonometry. In the field of statics and dynamics, three figures of the 14th century made signal contributions in Paris. Jean Buridan explained the concepts of motion and impulse; Albert of Saxony, later a professor at the University of Vienna, defined the centre of gravity and acceleration; and Nicole Oresme projected the system of co-ordinates for recording the path of bodies in motion. His view that the earth is not the stationary centre of a universe in motion, but rather revolves like other planets around the sun, was advocated anew by Nicholas of Cusa in the 15th century, Copernicus in the 16th, and finally by Galileo Galilei in the 17th century.

Two other men from the beginnings of the university age call for our regard: Bartholomew the Englishman, founder of the University of Paris, and Albert the Great, one of the greatest teachers of that institution. Their encyclopaedias are voluminous compilations embracing all that was known at that time concerning natural history and medicine. Albert, the "Universal Doctor", is remarkable for another reason too: he not only represented the rational, experimental attitude

A depiction of the Grande Chartreuse, part of a mural in the cloisters of the Basle Carthusian monastery, today an orphan asylum. The paintings were probably done in the mid-15th century and have undergone frequent restoration since. Of all the orders in Basle, the Carthusians' establishment possessed the richest store of manuscripts and incunabula.

then in the ascendant, but was also a credulous adept of alchemy, the doctrine of matter imbued with magical and mystical influences. He resembles another figure who, three centuries later, showed a similarly compounded double nature, one part rational, one part mystical: Paracelsus, who gave such a powerful stimulus to the advance of medicine.

Basle, too, was caught up by the intellectual revolution of the 13th century. Basle theologians, jurists and

12th century monks at their work of transcription. Before the invention of printing, the literate world depended on ecclesiastical and secular scriptoria for dissemination of the written word. Miniature from a book of scriptural readings of the monastery at Echternach. State Library, Bremen; MS. b 21.

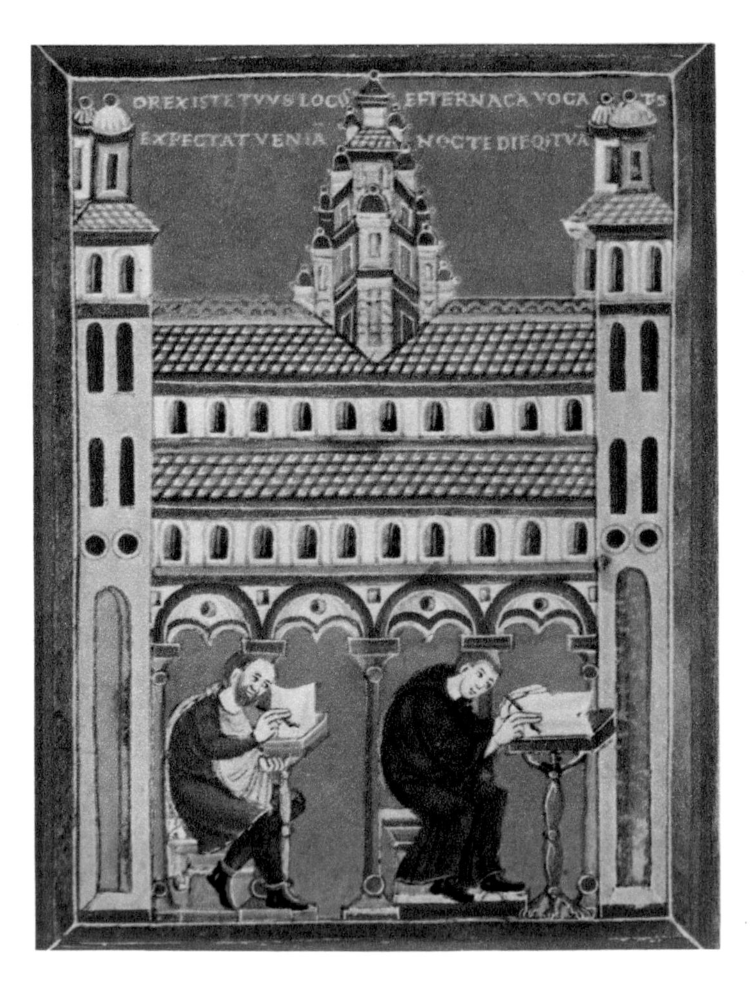

physicians studied at the newly established universities, and – of special importance – a large store of valuable manuscripts was accumulated in the libraries of the local chapter-houses and monasteries.

The first Basle personalities to become versed in law appear on the scene with academic degrees towards the end of the 13th century: "doctor legum" Berthold, Master Peter, and Master Rudolph of Rheinfelden. The earliest Basle physician on record was Canon Kuno (1187). He was followed by priest-physicians who held master's titles, showing that they had been educated at universities. Somewhat later lay physicians are also referred to in documents, figures such as "Master Symon medicus" (1288) or "Master John of Rheinfelden" (1320).

The mendicant orders of the Franciscans and Dominicans had chapters in Basle. The monastery of the Discalced Friars near the Spalen Gate and the Dominican monastery near the Kreuz Gate were erected in the 13th century. At the beginning of the 15th century the Carthusians also established themselves in Basle.

As early as the 14th century, the Dominican monastery possessed works by Avicenna, Averroes' commentaries on Aristotle, Latin translations of Galen, and medical works of the Parisian professors Albert the Great and Arnald of Villanova. In 1440 John Stoikovič of Ragusa, who took part in the Church Council, presented the local Dominicans with Greek and Latin manuscripts which later served the humanist Erasmus of Rotterdam as source references. A lending list from the year 1527 shows that, among other things, the library also contained the "Summa Theologica" of Thomas Aquinas. The library of the University of Basle still preserves valuable scientific manuscripts received by the Dominican monastery in 1559, among them the encyclopaedia "De Proprietatibus Rerum" of Bartholomew the Englishman and writings by Jean Buridan and Nicole Oresme.

Of even greater worth was the library of the Carthusians, upon whom the rules of their order im-

"St. Catherine and Mary Magdalene", painted c. 1445 by Konrad Witz of Basle, gives us a glimpse of a street scene in the late Middle Ages (detail right). It is probably a view on the Minster Square. Exterior panel of an altar wing. Musée des Beaux Arts, Strasbourg. Photo by Robert Spreng, Basle.

posed the duty of transcription. The works of the scholastics Alexander of Hales, Thomas Aquinas, and Duns Scotus, as well as Latin translations of Aristotle and Galen, were among the many manuscripts which the library contained. The libraries of the cathedral chapter-house and of the Discalced Friars' monastery, too, were richly endowed repositories.

Manuscripts were not only collected for their own sake, however. Alongside Paris and Frankfurt, Basle was a centre of the trade in copies. Whilst the scriptoria of the monasteries and chapter-houses transcribed manuscripts for their own needs, copyists in the non-ecclesiastical institutions did the same work for their living.

The gilds, as has been mentioned, were formed in the 12th and 13th centuries, almost at the same time as the universities. The first presage of what were to develop into corporations of artisans came in mandates issued by Charlemagne, the capitularies or statutes governing the administration of the royal manors, where the crafts are classified according to vocational groups. These documents prefigured the non-religious gilds, laying the groundwork for the formation of societies based on professional status, the merging of the artisan classes into the market economy, and making it possible for them to have their own supervisors with the competence to administer justice. Yet more than 300 years passed before the gilds actually came into being: only in 1140 was the corporation of "tick weavers" constituted in Cologne.

The gilds had a threefold origin: in the brotherhoods, in the episcopate, and in the magistracy. Basle furnished fitting examples of all three. And what is more, the German word for gild – "Zunft" – was coined in Basle, being derived from a Middle High German word which means about the same as the Latin "convenire", namely, to agree or come to an understanding or to bind oneself by contract. Ecclesiastical brotherhoods or "congregations" existed in Basle as early as the 11th and 12th centuries. Artisans joined together in order to help one another in need and sickness, and they held church services in common. Not until the 13th century, however, did such brotherhoods become gilds by dint of having a legal standing of their own. The brotherhood of furriers were the first to receive this privilege from Bishop Henry of Thun in 1226.

The oldest information concerning the Basle councils comes from a roll of fiefs of the 13th century. The administration of the episcopate had various offices to be filled: the baker's, the banker's, those of the smiths, coopers, and so on. From the office of the household retainers there developed the gild of the same name.

By 1200 the coucil of bakers had acquired a certain degree of self-administration. The bakers were presided over by their own Magister. The legal position of this magisterial office was noted down in a judicial document dated 1256.

The gilds had an extremely important bearing on the growth of the economy and society. From the system of a self-sufficient domestic economy, the different trades came to take on greater autonomy, and provision for household needs evolved into production for the market. For the first time in the history of mankind, as Rudolf Eberstadt writes, "a class of citizens which worked with its hands was given an honorable place in the life of the community".

Although the gilds may have acted as a drag on the development of the economy and technology in later times, when industrialization was nigh, in the high Middle Ages they were the nodes of progress in the crafts and trades.

Left: Pennon of the "Gold Star" gild, 15th century. As the shaving tool and ointment jar indicate, this gild was made up of the surgeons and barbers. The militia of the town was organized according to gilds. Wherever planted, within or without the city walls, the pennon was the standard around which members of the gilds assembled with their arms. Historical Museum, Basle.

Opposite: The tap-rooms of the gild houses were the meeting places of the craft brotherhoods. Glass pane of the tailors' gild in Basle, 1554. Historical Museum, Basle.

The universities and the gilds created the foundation upon which modern Western civilization was erected. The 13th century marked the beginning expansion of science and technology; the 17th century saw the beginning of their collaboration; while to us of the 20th century the "superstructure" of science, technology, and industrial organization has long since ceased to be a marvel, so self-evident does it appear.

In 1538 the Basle publisher Johann Walder printed the "Almagest", the chief work of the Alexandrian scholar Claudius Ptolemy, who lived in the second century A. D. At almost the same time, in 1543, there appeared in Nuremberg the "De Revolutionibus Orbium Coelestium" (On the Revolution of the Celestial Spheres) of Nicholas Copernicus. These two books expound two fundamentally different worlds. For Ptolemy, the earth is a fixed body around which the firmament revolves. Copernicus sees the earth as a planet, moving in two different ways; it turns on its own axis once every day and completes its journey around the sun once every year.

This almost simultaneous publication of works having to do with ancient and the latest science reveals two characteristic features of the Renaissance – the period which separates the Middle Ages from our Modern Age. They are the meticulous care given to cultivating and studying the works of the ancients, and the restless search and striving for new knowledge. Whereas philologists such as Thomas More, Erasmus of Rotterdam or Philipp Melanchthon devoted themselves painstakingly to the older Greek and Latin authors, the natural sciences, as experimental disciplines, were being helped to maturity by the pioneer labors of men like Leonardo da Vinci, Paracelsus, and Kepler.

These two traits – the cultivation of the heritage from antiquity and the quest for new, scientific knowledge – only appear to be opposed to and independent of one another. The broadening of intellectual horizons which began in the age of scholasticism and gathered speed with the advent of humanism had not unforeseeable results: the growth of the critical spirit and, concomitantly, a waning of the belief in authority. Thus in the first half of the 16th century the hoary authority of Ptolemy, which had prevailed for well-nigh fifteen centuries, crumbled and disappeared under the onslaught of Copernican ideas. The authority of Galen in anatomical science, almost as ancient as Ptolemy's in astronomy, went into decline at almost the same time, and Vesalius became the father of modern anatomy.

Basle in the age of humanism. Tinted pen-and-ink drawing by Conrad Morand, dated c. 1535. Historical Museum, Basle.

NICOLAI COPER-
NICI REVOLVTIONVM
LIBER PRIMVS.

Quòd mundus ſit ſphæricus. Cap. I.

RINCIPIO aduertendum nobis eſt, globoſum eſſe mundum, ſiue quòd ipſa forma perfectiſſima ſit omnium, nulla indigens compagine, tota integra: ſiue quòd ipſa capaciſsima ſit figurarum, quæ compræhenſurũ omnia, & conſeruaturũ maxime decet: ſiue etiam quòd abſolutiſsimæ quæq; mundi partes, Solem dico, Lunam & ſtellas, tali forma conſpiciantur: ſiue quòd hac uniuerſa appetãt terminari, quod in aquæ guttis cæteriſq; liquidis corporibus apparet, dum per ſe terminari cupiunt. Quo minus talem formam cœleſtibus corporibus attributam quiſquam dubitauerit.

Quòd terra quoq; ſphærica ſit. Cap. II.

Erram quoq; globoſam eſſe, quoniam ab omni parte centro ſuo innititur. Tametſi abſolutus orbis non ſtatim uideatur, in tanta montiũ excelſitate, deſcenſuq; uallium, quæ tamen uniuerſam terræ rotunditatem minime uariant. Quod ita manifeſtũ eſt. Nam ad Septentrionem undequaq; commeantibus, uertex ille diurnæ reuolutionis paulatim attollitur, altero tantundem ex aduerſo ſubeunte, pluresq; ſtellæ circum Septentriones uidentur nõ occidere, & in Auſtro quædam amplius non oriri. Ita Canopum non cernit Italia, Ægypto patentem. Et Italia poſtremam fluuij ſtellam uidet, quam regio noſtra plagæ rigentioris ignorat. E contrario in Auſtrum tranſeuntibus attolluntur illa, reſidentibus ijs, quæ nobis excelſa ſunt. Interea & ipſę polorum inclinationes ad emenſa terrarum ſpacia eandem ubiq; rationem habent, quod

a in

REVOLVTIONVM LIB. I. 11

declinatio Borea H ad Solem cõuerſa efficit. Quoniam decliuitas æquinoctialis ad A B lineam per reuolutionem diurnam detornat ſibi tropicum hyemalem parallelum ſecundum diſtantiam, quam ſub E A H angulus inclinationis compræhendit. Proficiſcatur modo centrum terræ in conſequentia, ac tantundem F maximæ declinationis terminus, in præcedẽtia: donec utriq; in B peregerint quadrantes circulorum. Manet interim E A I angu

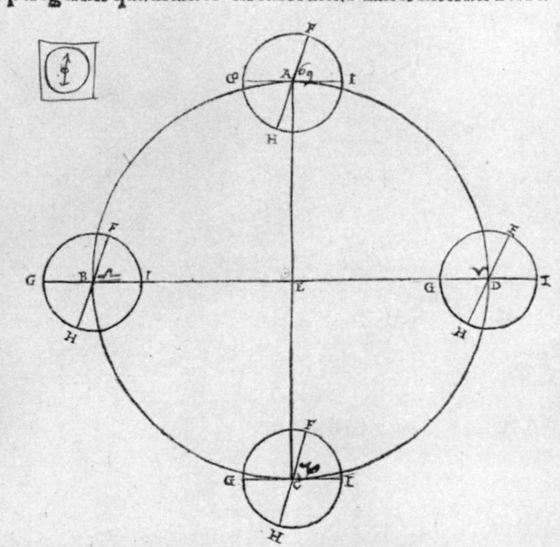

lus ſem per æqualis ipſi A E B, propter æqualitatem reuolutionum, & dimetientes ſemper ad inuicem F A H ad F B H, & G A I ad G B I, æquinoctialiſq; æquinoctiali parallelus. Quæ propter cauſam iam ſæpe dictam apparent eadem in immenſitate cæli. Igitur ex B Libræ principio, E ſub Ariete apparebit, conciderq; ſectio circulorum communis in unam lineam G B I E, ad quam diurna reuolutio nullam admittet declinationem, ſed omnis declinatio erit à lateribus. Itaq; Sol in æquinoctio uerno uidebitur. Pergat centrum terræ cum aſſumptis conditionibus, & per-

c iij acto

The changes which the age witnessed were, indeed, far-reaching and universal. Questions of faith were debated at reform councils, and with Martin Luther the reformed church entered the scene, rejecting the authority of the pope. In this age, too, the nation-state as we conceive of it was born. It is true that the Florentine politician Niccolo Machiavelli, in his celebrated work "Il Principe", claims absolute power for the prince, but – and here is the salient point – he places his power on an arguable footing. A breach has been made in the notion of the ruler as a wilful authoritarian.

With his book "On the Revolution of the Celestial Spheres", Copernicus substantiated the heliocentric view of the universe. Although the essential part of his hypothesis had been worked out in writing as early as 1507, Copernicus delayed publishing it until just shortly before his death. Left, the first page; and right, a portrayal of the earth's path around the sun from the work, published in 1543 by Johann Petrejus in Nuremberg.

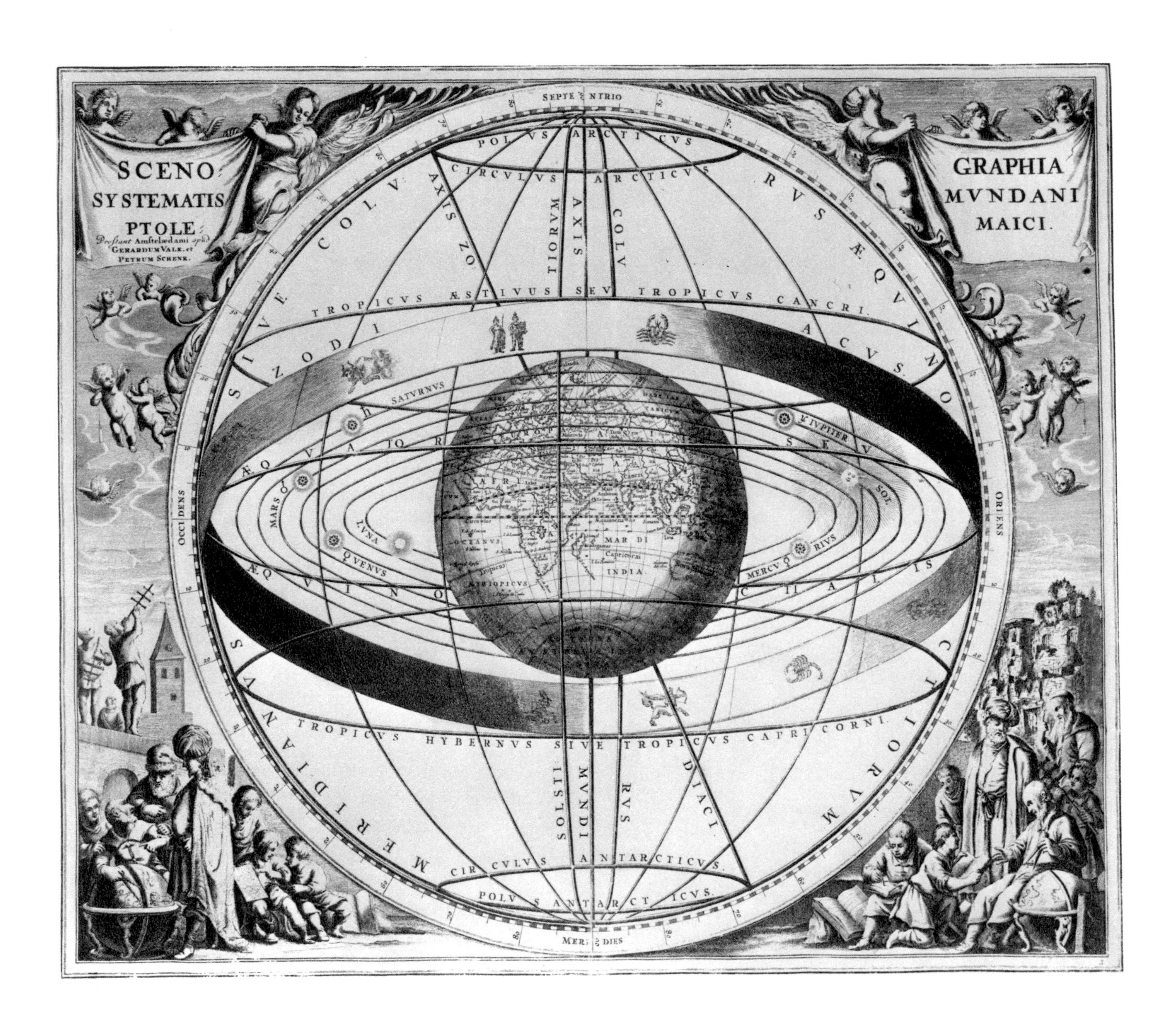

The geocentric universe of Ptolemy. In this system, which astronomers used from the 2nd to the 17th century, the centre of the stationary earth was the centre of the universe, a closed sphere. The whole system was carried from East to West about the earth once a day by the motion of the heavens.

Copper engraving from the "Harmonia Macrocosmica seu Atlas Universalis et Novus" of the Dutch mathematician and philologist, Andreas Cellarius. The first edition of this cartographical work appeared in Amsterdam in 1660. The above drawing is from the 1708 edition of plates.

The heliocentric universe of Copernicus. Although Copernicus' theory gained ground but slowly, by the end of the 17th century it had supplanted the ancient Aristotelean and Ptolemaic astronomy. Many of his observations were incorrect, but three 17th century scientists rectified them: Galileo with his astronomical telescope; Kepler, who adopted elliptical orbits; and Newton, who demonstrated that if heavenly bodies obeyed the same laws of motion as do those on earth, the modified Copernican system could be deduced from these laws.
Plate from the same work on "Macrocosmic Harmony" by Cellarius.

The rapid propagation of humanistic thought would not have been possible without the art of printing. Woodcuts had of course long been inserted as initial letters. From about 1400 onward, "block-books" or xylographica, in which each page was printed from a solid block of wood containing both picture and text, were also produced. But the technical perfection of type-printing was a triumph reserved to Johann Gensfleisch of Mainz – otherwise known as Gutenberg – in the forepart of the 15th century. Gutenberg did not succeed in keeping the invention of replica-casting secret, as had been his intention. Printing was already being done with his technique at Strasbourg in 1458, and by 1480 the art of printing according to Gutenberg was being practiced all over the continent.

In the printing of block-books wooden forms were used in which both text and illustrations were carved, giving a page-size unit. Gutenberg perfected the system of movable letters cast in metal, i.e. types.
Above: "The Children of Venus", a plate done in woodblock technique from the Basle Book of Planets, 1460. Bodmer Library, Geneva.
Left: Scene in a 16th century printer's shop. Woodcut from a chronicle of the Swiss Confederation by Johann Stumpf; Zurich, 1548.

In 1501 Basle, the richest community in old Switzerland, joined the Confederation. The gilds had wrested more and more rights from the patricians of the town, and their leaders had become monied aristocrats in their own right. The crafts, the arts, and commerce were thriving. The flowering of Basle doubtless is expressed most vividly in the "Heidnischwerk" ("heathen work") tapestries woven in the town which decorated the walls of its burghers' houses and the churches.
As the 15th century drew to a close, Basle became the town of humanism par excellence. The intellectual life which flourished within its walls radiated from two focal points: the printer's atelier and the university.

In the outgoing 15th century, the highly developed art of printing attracted artists as well as scholars to Basle. The young Dürer executed the title illustration of St. Jerome for Nicholas Kessler's "Epistolari Beati Hieronymi", published in Basle the year Columbus discovered America.
Left: Printing block with the artist's monogram on reverse side; right: a print from the block. Basle Art Gallery.

Wer artzeny ſich nyemet an
Vnd doch keyn preſten heylen kan
Der iſt eyn gůtter gouckelman

Von narrechter artzny.

Der gat wol heyn mit andern narrn
Wer eym dottkrancken bſycht den harn
Vnd ſpricht/wart/biß ich dir verkünd
Was ich jn mynen bůchern fynd

Page from the "Ship of Fools" by the Strasbourg humanist Sebastian Brant. This volume of moralizing poetry, printed in the Basle atelier of Johann Bergmann in 1494, was extremely popular, not least because of its illustrations. The work went through many new impressions and reprints. A large number of the woodcuts are by Dürer.

Around 1468, hardly three decades after Gutenberg's invention, the first printers set up shop in Basle. The art was introduced locally by Berthold Ruppel, probably a pupil of Gutenberg. A vigorous paper industry, the favorable location of the town for export traffic, and above all the aforementioned manuscript treasures in the monasteries probably helped to attract these early printers, who were men of high scholarly calibre.

By 1500 Basle printers were reaping the admiration of Christendom; the atelier of Froben, indeed, became the most prominent one in the world of that time. The first books printed in Basle were theological and morally uplifting works. Savonarola the Florentine used a Froben Bible printed in 1491, as did Martin Luther, who possessed a specimen dated 1509.

Characteristic of Basle printing at this time was the close collaboration between the printer and the humanist scholar. The designs and artwork, executed in woodcuts and metallic engravings, were done by artists like Urs Graf and the Holbein brothers, Hans and Ambrose. For his scrupulously printed edition of the holy fathers, ancient philosophers and contemporary poets, Johann Amerbach was counselled by his former teacher at the Sorbonne, Johann Heylin de Lapide. The first edition of the "Ship of Fools", the humanist Sebastian Brant's work which held a mirror up to the manners and morals of the age, was printed in 1494 by Johann Bergmann von Olpe and illustrated by the young Albrecht Dürer. A close association was formed between the best-known printer, Johannes Froben, and the man who was the very embodiment of humanism, Erasmus of Rotterdam. Among the many works of Erasmus printed in Froben's establishment, one achieved particular fame: the New Testament in the original Greek text, printed in 1516, a work which paved the way for biblical criticism. Greek and Hebrew scholars were charged with proofreading and correcting it, one of them being "Oecolampadius" (Johannes Heussgen), who later became a leader of the Reform in Basle.

Erasmus of Rotterdam spent many years in Basle, preparing his works for publication by Froben, who was his close friend.
Right: Page from the first edition of Erasmus' "Novum Instrumentum", printed by Froben in 1516. The work contains the critically edited Greek text of the New Testament, plus the Latin translation and annotations.
Below: One copy of "The Praise of Folly", a satirical work published in 1515, carried marginal drawings by Hans Holbein the Younger. On this page Erasmus directs the lash of his wit against sophistical theologians who presume that, just as Atlas bears the heavens upon his shoulders, the pillars of their logic support the Church. Basle Art Gallery.

190 ΕΠΙΣΤΟΛΗ EPISTOLA

tunicā, Ei uero qui pōt illos ſeruare a peccato imunes & ſtatuere in cōſpectu gloriæ ſuæ, incōtaminatos in exultatiōe, ſoli ſapienti deo ſeruatori noſtro, gloria & magnificētia, & imperiū & poteſtas, nūc & in omnia ſæcula. Amen.

Epiſtolæ Iudæ finis.

ΑΠΟΚΑΛΥΨΙΣ ΤΟΥ ΑΓΙΟΥ ΙΩΑΝΝΟΥ ΤΟΥ ΘΕΟΛΟΓΟΥ.

APOCALYPSIS BEATI IOANNIS THEOLOGI.

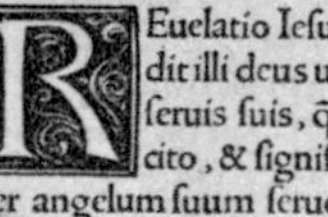

Euelatio Ieſu Chriſti quā dedit illi deus ut palam faceret ſeruis ſuis, q̄ oporteat fieri cito, & ſignificauit, mittens per angelum ſuum ſeruo ſuo Iohanni, qui teſtimonio perhibuit uerbo dei, & teſtimonium Ieſu Chriſti quæcumq; uidit. Beatus qui legit & audit uerba prophetiæ & ſeruat ea, quæ in ea ſcripta ſunt. Tempus enim prope eſt. Ioannes ſeptem eccleſijs quæ ſunt in Aſia. Gratia uobis & pax ab eo qui eſt, & qui erat, & q uenturus eſt, & a ſeptem ſpiritibus qui in conſpectu throni eius ſunt, & a Ieſu Chriſto qui eſt teſtis fidelis primogenitus mortuorum & princeps regum terræ. Qui dilexit nos & lauit nos a peccatis noſtris in ſanguine ſuo, & fecit nos reges & ſacerdotes deo & patri ſuo.

ΜΩΡΙΑΣ ΕΓΚΩΜΙΟΝ

ter, ſimile eſt illis, ... illotis pedib', & illotis manibus. Vt Euāgeliū aut Paulinas epiſtolas.) Ex hoc loco palam eſt, nō reprehendi theologos doctos & pios, ſed eos qui totā uitā, in hmōi conſumunt quæſtiunculis, cū in primis oportet theologum ipſos imbibiſſe fōtes, & in lege domini, noctes ac dies meditatū eſſe, ut aſſiduitas uertat in naturam, ut nō ſolum intelligat humano more, ſed etiam afficiatur & rapiat. Nemo ꝑe itelligit Chriſtū, niſi tract' a Chriſto. Tantum abeſt, ut ab his compreheēdatur, q impij ꝑpter ſophiſticas nænias, nihil omnino uel ſciūt, uel legunt. Noui permultos theologos, doctores, ut uocāt, q ante quinquageſimū annū, nondū euoluerant omnes epiſtolas Pauli, ut ꝑ familiaritatem mihi fatebantur. Iſti quoties ad interpretandum ſacras literas accedunt, Dij boni, q̄ frigent, q̄ ſordent omnia, q̄ nihil adferunt Chriſto dignum. Formant ac reformant. Notat eos, qui non accōmodant ſuas ſententias ad mentē ſcripturarum, ſed ſcripturas ad ſuā mentē trahunt, quod uocant fundare, ueluti cum duos Petri gladios trahunt ad duplicem poteſtatē, cum is locus prorſus eo ſpectet, ne pugnemus Chriſtiani. Cenſores orbis). Cenſores Romæ, morum magiſtri, & iudices erāt, hi ciues ſic notabant, ut qui ſenator eſſet, e ſenatu eijceretur, qui eques Romanus, equū publicum perderet, qui plæbeius in centum tabulas referretur, & ærarius fieret. Palinodiam canere.) Græci prouerbio dicunt, ..., pro eo, quod eſt, prius

diſpūtare, tam arrogāter, definire, ac diuine theologiæ maieſtatē, tam frigidis, imo ſordidis uerbis ſimul & ſententijs, conſpurcare. At interim ipſi feliciſſime ſibi placent, imo plaudunt, adeo ut his ſuauiſſimis nænijs, nocte dieq; occupatis, ne tantulum quidem ocij ſuperſit, ut euangeliū, aut Paulinas epiſtolas, uel ſemel liceat euoluere. Atq; interim dum hæc nugantur in ſcholis, exiſtimant ſeſe uniuerſam eccleſiam, alioqui ruituram, non aliter ſyllogiſmorum fulcire tibicinibus, q̄ Atlas cœlū hūeris ſuſtinet apud Poetas. Iam illud quantæ felicitatis eſſe putatis, dum arcanas literas, pinde quaſi cereæ ſint, pro libidine formant ac reformant, dum cōcluſiones ſuas, quibus iā aliquot ſcholaſtici ſubſcripſerūt, pluſq̄ Solonis leges, uideri poſtulant, & uel pontificijs decretis, anteponendas, dumq; ueluti cenſores orbis ad palinodiam trahunt.

Overleaf: Figured tapestry with fabulous animals, done in Basle c. 1490. So-called "heathen work" of this sort adorned both the homes of affluent burghers and the interiors of the churches. Color scheme from the well-preserved reverse side. Historical Museum, Basle.

don
ich bringt himels lon

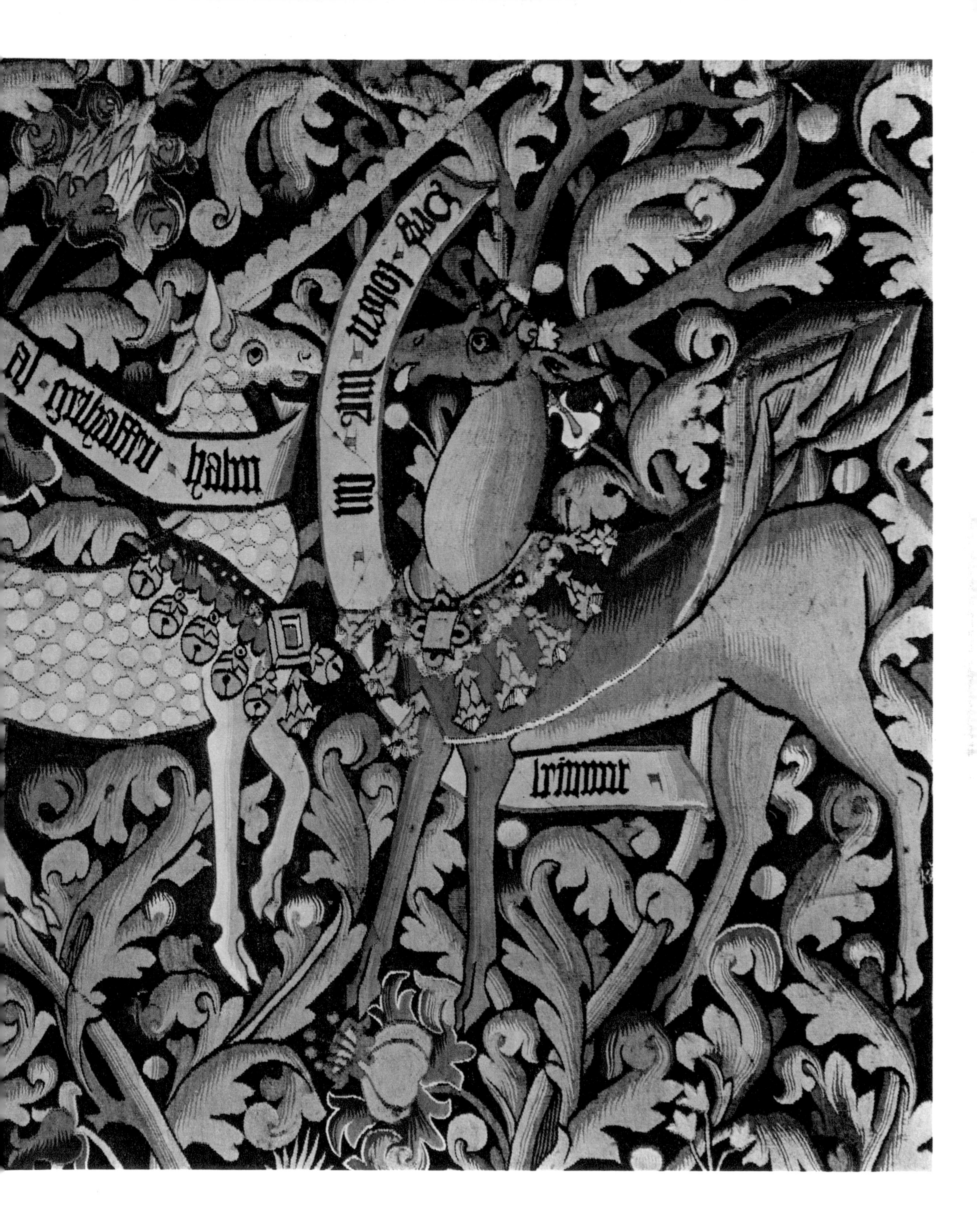

HIPPOCRA-
TIS COI MEDICORVM OMNIVM
longe principis, opera: quibus maxima ex parte
annorũ circiter duo millia Latina caruit lingua:
Græci uero & Arabes, & priſci noſtri Medici,
plurimis tamen utilibus prætermiſſis, ſcripta ſua
illuſtrarunt: nunc tandem per M. Fabiũ Rhauen
natem, Gulielmum Copum Baſilienſem, Ni
colaum Leonicenũ, & Andream Bren
tium, uiros doctiſſimos Latini-
tate donata, ac iamprimũ in
lucem ædita: quo re-
uera humano gene
ri nihil fieri po
tuit ſalu-
brius.

BASILEAE IN OFFICINA AN-
DREAE CRATANDRI, AN-
NO M. D. XXVI.

Elenchum librorum hoc opere contentorum,
in calce ſequentis Indicis reperies.

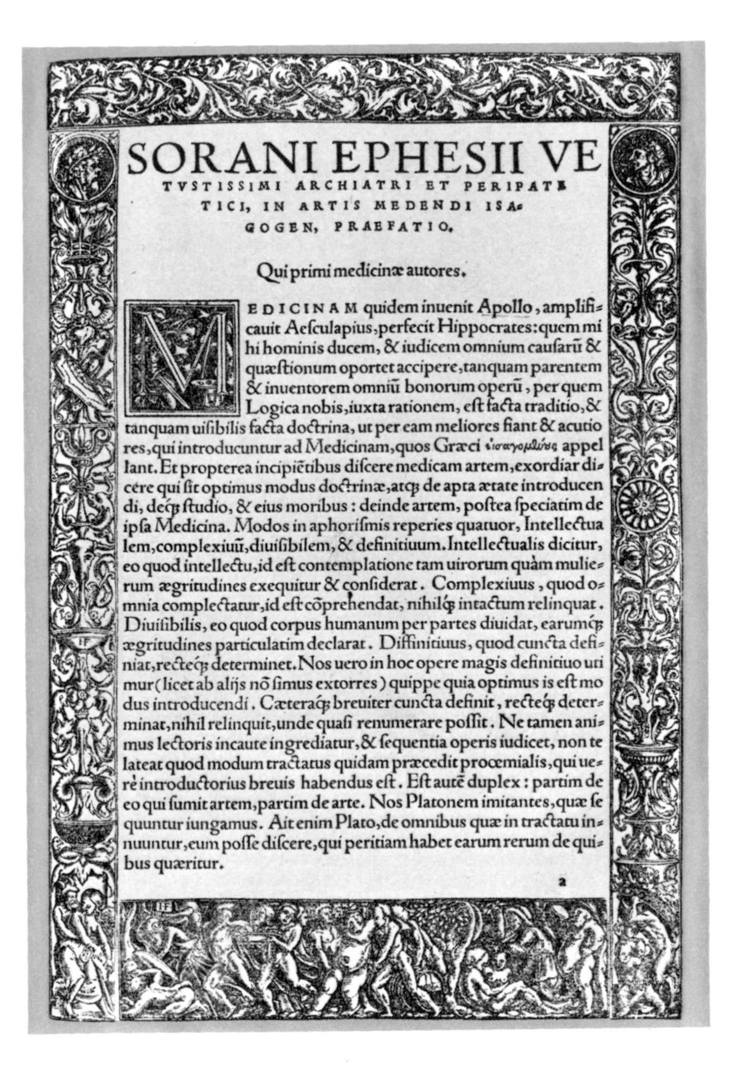

SORANI EPHESII VE
TVSTISSIMI ARCHIATRI ET PERIPATE
TICI, IN ARTIS MEDENDI ISA-
GOGEN, PRAEFATIO.

Qui primi medicinæ autores.

MEDICINAM quidem inuenit Apollo, amplifi-
cauit Aeſculapius, perfecit Hippocrates: quem mi
hi hominis ducem, & iudicem omnium cauſarũ &
quæſtionum oportet accipere, tanquam parentem
& inuentorem omniũ bonorum operũ, per quem
Logica nobis, iuxta rationem, eſt facta traditio, &
tanquam uiſibilis facta doctrina, ut per eam meliores fiant & acutio
res, qui introducuntur ad Medicinam, quos Græci εἰσαγομένους appel
lant. Et propterea incipiẽtibus diſcere medicam artem, exordiar di-
cere qui ſit optimus modus doctrinæ, atq; de apta ætate introducen
di, deq; ſtudio, & eius moribus: deinde artem, poſtea ſpeciatim de
ipſa Medicina. Modos in aphoriſmis reperies quatuor, Intellectua
lem, complexiuũ, diuiſibilem, & definitiuum. Intellectualis dicitur,
eo quod intellectu, id eſt contemplatione tam uirorum quàm mulie-
rum ægritudines exequitur & conſiderat. Complexiuus, quod o-
mnia complectatur, id eſt cõprehendat, nihilq; intactum relinquat.
Diuiſibilis, eo quod corpus humanum per partes diuidat, earumq;
ægritudines particulatim declarat. Diffinitiuus, quod cuncta defi-
niat, recteq; determinet. Nos uero in hoc opere magis definitiuo uti
mur (licet ab alijs nõ ſimus extorres) quippe quia optimus is eſt mo
dus introducendi. Cæteraq; breuiter cuncta definit, recteq; deter-
minat, nihil relinquit, unde quaſi renumerare poſſit. Ne tamen ani-
mus lectoris incaute ingrediatur, & ſequentia operis iudicet, non te
lateat quod modum tractatus quidam præcedit procemialis, qui ue-
rè introductorius breuis habendus eſt. Eſt autẽ duplex: partim de
eo qui ſumit artem, partim de arte. Nos Platonem imitantes, quæ ſe
quuntur iungamus. Ait enim Plato, de omnibus quæ in tractatu in-
nuuntur, eum poſſe diſcere, qui peritiam habet earum rerum de quibus quæritur.

a

In addition to theological volumes, Basle printers began publishing works of medical and natural science in the second quarter of the 16th century. These, too, in their punctilious philological editing, bore the stamp of the town of humanism. To mention but two of the many celebrated publications in this category which came off the Basle presses, there were the "Opera Omnia" of Hippocrates in 1526 and, three years later, the "Tardanum Passionum Libriquinque", a work on acute and chronic diseases by the second century gynecologist, Soranus of Ephesus.

Left: Title page of the Basle edition of Hippocrates' works. Hippocrates, a Greek physician who lived in the 5th century B.C., is regarded as the father of medicine. The first printed edition of his collected writings in Latin translation appeared in Rome in 1525. The following year Andreas Cratander published a revised edition in Basle.
Above: Page from an apocryphal work of Soranus of Ephesus in the 1528 edition of his collected writings prepared by Albanus Torinus, professor of medicine in Basle.

In the printing works of Basle we may also witness the turn from the old anatomy to the new. The carefully revised edition of Galen's collected works, the undisputed medical authority ever since the second century A. D., was printed in Basle in 1538. Five years later Vesalius' "Fabrica" was published in the atelier of Oporin, and with it the new era in anatomy had arrived.

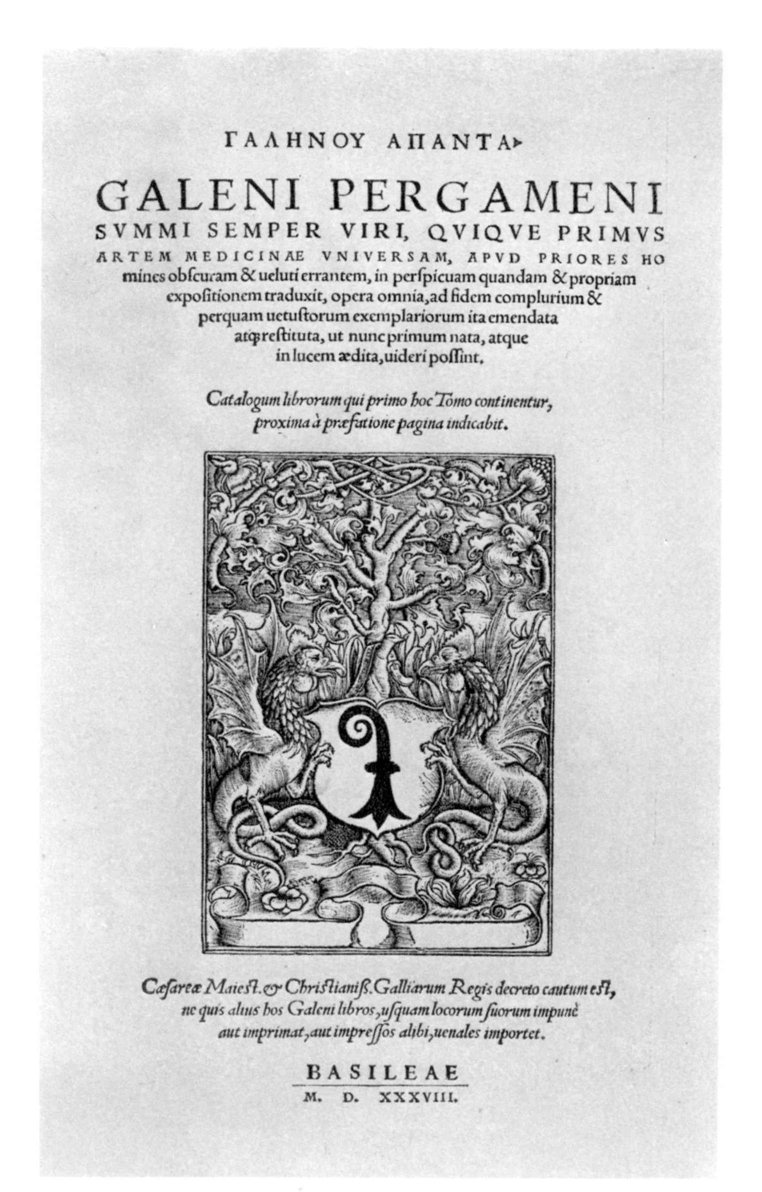

ΓΑΛΗΝΟΥ ΑΠΑΝΤΑ

GALENI PERGAMENI

SVMMI SEMPER VIRI, QVIQVE PRIMVS ARTEM MEDICINAE VNIVERSAM, APVD PRIORES HOmines obſcuram & ueluti errantem, in perſpicuam quandam & propriam expoſitionem traduxit, opera omnia, ad fidem complurium & perquam uetuſtorum exemplariorum ita emendata atq; reſtituta, ut nunc primum nata, atque in lucem ædita, uideri poſſint.

Catalogum librorum qui primo hoc Tomo continentur, proxima à præfatione pagina indicabit.

Cæſareæ Maieſt. & Chriſtianiſſ. Galliarum Regis decreto cautum eſt, ne quis alius hos Galeni libros, uſquam locorum ſuorum impunè aut imprimat, aut impreſſos alibi, uenales importet.

BASILEAE

M. D. XXXVIII.

Volumes emanating from the printers of Basle register the transition from Galenic to modern anatomy.
Left: Title page of the 1538 edition of Galen in Greek, produced by a society of five Basle printers (A. Cratander, J. Bebel, J. Herwagen, J. E. Froben, M. Isengrin). Note the familiar bishop's staff and boatman's pike.
Above: With his magnum opus, "De Humani Corporis Fabrica", Vesalius introduced naturalistic anatomy. This is the frontispiece of the 1543 first edition, published in Basle by Johannes Oporin.

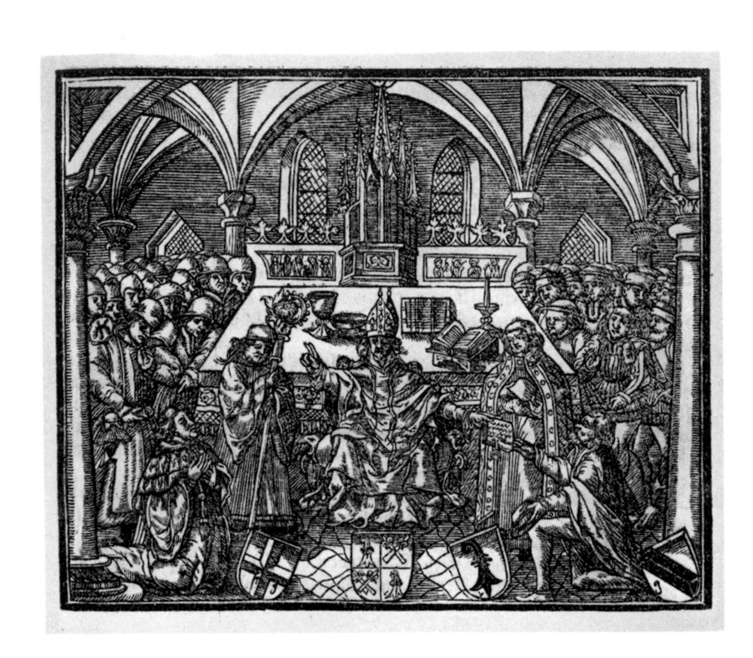

Left: The inauguration of the university on April 4th, 1460 in the Basle Minster. The bishop hands over the bull of foundation issued by Pope Pius II to an official representing the Town Council (right). Woodcut from the "Basle Chronicle" of Christian Wurstisen, after a colored pen-and-ink drawing in the first volume of the university rolls.
Below: A leaf from the Basle university rolls with entries from 1585/1586. Didacus Lainus, an American Indian (fourth from top), figures among the students listed. Of the others from many lands, even a Scotsman – one Wilhelmus Louius (Lowie) – is present. From Volume 2 of the rector's rolls; University Library, Basle.

Christophorus Stabel Lifcelensis 6. ß
Sebastianus Rex Valonensis 6. ß
Jacobus Muchimius Rhotus 6. ß
Didacus Lainus Americus Indus pp 0.
Georgius Graseckius Argentinen. 8. ß
Carolus Corthesius Gallus 5. ß
Joannes Zollerus Dorlicensis 10. ß
Sebastianus Welling a Vehingen nob. 15. ß
Casparus Feirler Glogouiensis 6. ß
Wilhelmus Louius Scotus pp 0.
Jo. Rodolph. Bullinger. Archiater Bernensis gratis
Franciscus Gerardus Gallus 6. ß
Anthemius A Streitberst Brunsuic. nob.
Hermannus eius frater germanus
Fridericus Dasydius Vestphal. Precept. 1. lb. 10. ß
Novemb. Antonius Heron Campanus. 6. ß
Petrus Roth Argentinensis 10. ß
Joannes Abesius Tyrolensis pp. 0.
Joannes Casparus
Leonhardus
Joan. Jacobus Egs à Rhinfelden FF. 2. lb.
Joannes Pfenningsack Helmstadien. — 10. ß
Jacobus Bongaretius Gallus 10. ß
Joannes de Saccarlarre Gallo nob. 15. ß
Henricus Schuartzius Schaffusianus 10. ß
Michael Herco Turingus 6. ß
Decemb. Petrus Etcendorpius Iuliacensis. 10. ß
Joannes Molitor Tigurinus pp 0.
Elias Rusnerus Leorinus Silesius 10. ß
1586.
Jan. Jo. Henricus Wildius Arouiensis 6. ß
M. Georgius Zecchius Coburgens. 10. ß
Joan. Fabricius Winshemius pp 0.

The "renaissance of botany", too, was reflected in the products of the Basle presses. In 1541 Oporin printed the Greek text of the botanical work by Theophrastus of Eresos, dating from the third century before Christ. In the following year the atelier of Isengrin brought out the Latin and the German first edition of the Book of Herbs by Leonhard Fuchs. Fuchs, together with his contemporaries Otto Brunfels and Jerome Bock, is regarded as one of the "fathers of botany".

The University of Basle traces its origins back to the universal Church Council. From 1431 to 1448 the spiritual élite of Christendom gathered in the Rhine town – as they had previously done in Pisa, Constance and Siena – bent on effecting a regeneration of the Church. With the adjournment of the meeting, the intellectual and economic prosperity of the synod town came to an end. For reasons mainly economic in nature, the city fathers decided to petition Pope Pius II for the right to establish a "school of higher learning". The Pope – who, as Enea Silvio Piccolomini, had taken part in the Council and had become a friend of Basle – granted his permission. On April 4th,

Two pages, dated 1493, from the university rolls with an entry by the Rector, Wilhelm Grieb, and his coat of arms. The idiosyncrasies which constitute the artistic signature of this "Basle Master of 1493", a maverick pupil of Martin Schongauer, can be seen in local contemporary woodcuts as well.

1460, twelve years after the conclusion of the Council, the university was solemnly inaugurated. Modelled on Bologna and Paris, the Basle institution was organized into four faculties: theology, jurisprudence, medicine, and the arts.

The first decades of its existence saw the lively growth of the theology, jurisprudence, and arts faculties. Medicine had to wait until the 16th century for its impetus, augured by the cometic career of a man whose thought and example were to lead science a big step farther in the direction of rationalism: Paracelsus. Oecolampadius the reformer and Froben succeeded in carrying through his nomination as municipal physician and professor with the town council in 1526. One year later Theophrastus Bombastus von Hohenheim, as Paracelsus had been styled at birth, in announcing his lectures averred that his teaching would not be based upon the ancient authors Galen and Avicenna, but rather upon his own writings.

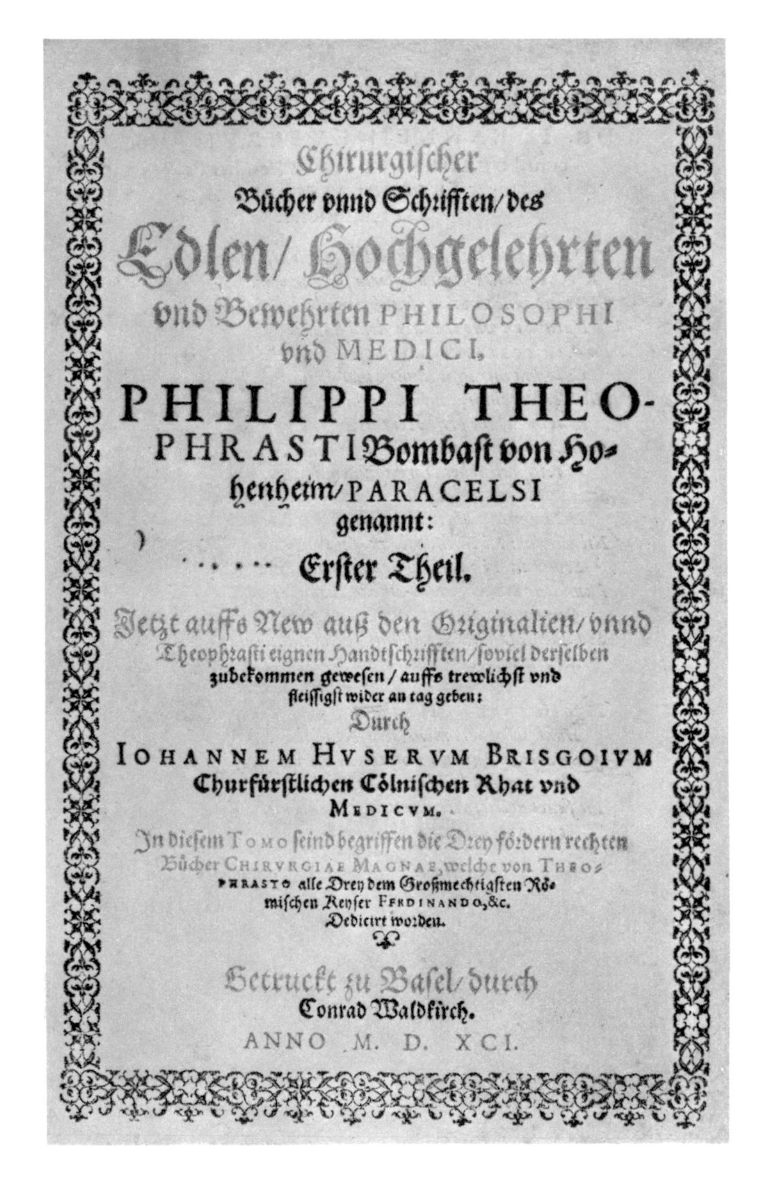

Chirurgischer
Bücher vnnd Schrifften/des
Edlen/Hochgelehrten
vnd Bewehrten PHILOSOPHI
vnd MEDICI,
PHILIPPI THEO-
PHRASTI Bombast von Ho-
henheim/PARACELSI
genannt:
Erster Theil.
Jetzt auffs New auß den Originalien/vnnd
Theophrasti eignen Handtschrifften/soviel derselben
zubekommen gewesen/auffs trewlichst vnd
fleissigst wider an tag geben:
Durch
IOHANNEM HVSERVM BRISGOIVM
Churfürstlichen Cölnischen Rhat vnd
MEDICVM.
In diesem TOMO seind begriffen die Drey fördern rechten
Bücher CHIRVRGIAE MAGNAE, welche von THEO-
PHRASTO alle Drey dem Großmechtigsten Rö-
mischen Keyser FERDINANDO, &c.
Dedicirt worden.
Getruckt zu Basel/durch
Conrad Waldkirch.
ANNO M. D. XCI.

According to Paracelsus, all substances contain three primary bodies: the active spiritual one, which he denotes as "mercury", the passive corporeal one, called "salt"; and the principle of soul which mediates between these two, namely "sulfur". The difference between the various material substances lies in the different quantities of these "hypostatical principles" which they contain. The human body, too, consists of the tria prima mercury-salt-sulfur, and if its natural equilibrium is upset, the imbalance manifests itself in the form of illness. In order to treat his patient, therefore, the physician must restore the natural balance by prescribing the appropriate drugs or chemicals.

With this line of reasoning Paracelsus brought illness and the effect of medication into some kind of rational relation for the first time. "Greater than Celsus", he deserves the epithet of "renewer of medicine" which has been ascribed to him.

With his theory of disease and of chemotherapy Paracelsus also brought about a change in the traditional aims of alchemy. Medicines (arcana), not gold, were the goal to be striven for. He himself introduced preparations containing compounds of metals such as iron, antimony, arsenic and so on into the pharmacopoeia.

His philosophy was as divided as his nature, boundlessly arrogant and touchingly eager to help at the same time. Side by side with his rational views which strike us as modern we find others, such as his doctrine of signatures, rooted deep in the mysticism of the Middle Ages.

Theophrastus von Hohenheim, the "renewer of medicine", had a brief career in Basle which ended with his flight in February, 1528. His influence on medical instruction in the town was lasting. The first of his many writings published in Basle appeared in 1562.
Above: Title page of the concluding volume in the 11-part collected edition of Paracelsus' works prepared by Huser. Published between 1589 and 1591, it is still the best edition.

Opposite: In a letter which he sent to Bonifacius Amerbach a few days after his departure from Basle, Paracelsus complains of the ignominy and lack of appreciation which had been his lot there. He does concede, however, that he may have been a bit free with his tongue in the presence of the magistrates and others. From that time until his death at Salzburg in 1541, he led an unsettled existence as a freelance practitioner. Fol. 317, MS. Ki. Ar. 18a; University Library, Basle.

S. Cum ad te nuper brevius scripsi Bonifaci Charis. eas cum
[illegible] accepisti [illegible] enim Basileam venit hic qui ipsas [illegible]
cum creditoribus quam aliquando pollicitus est, [illegible] adhuc prius
inquirenda mihi relinquentur, [illegible] vero in universum
negata sunt, idque tu [illegible] de toto
[illegible] pati aliquando vel non obviare aliquid omnino
non conveniat. Ita esto sunt dixerunt forte aliquid
[illegible] in [illegible] ad alios, quid tu [illegible]
[illegible] quicquid id est quod dixi re ipsa sic esse [illegible]
[illegible] nisi quod ad [illegible] verissime [illegible]
veritatem [illegible], Quod factum est [illegible]
[illegible] invidia [illegible], ubi
[illegible] tota hora amplius [illegible]
[illegible] id quod dici non potest, quod mi animo [illegible]
[illegible] si in [illegible] sunt, [illegible] id
[illegible] Calumnia in me [illegible] sufficerat
Ita [illegible] calumniis de me [illegible] magis
ac magis audio, [illegible]
[illegible] mihi
[illegible]
tibi libros [illegible] gratiarum actionem [illegible]
[illegible] Vale [illegible] Coluteria [illegible] 18
[illegible] Anno 28.

[illegible]
[illegible]
[illegible]

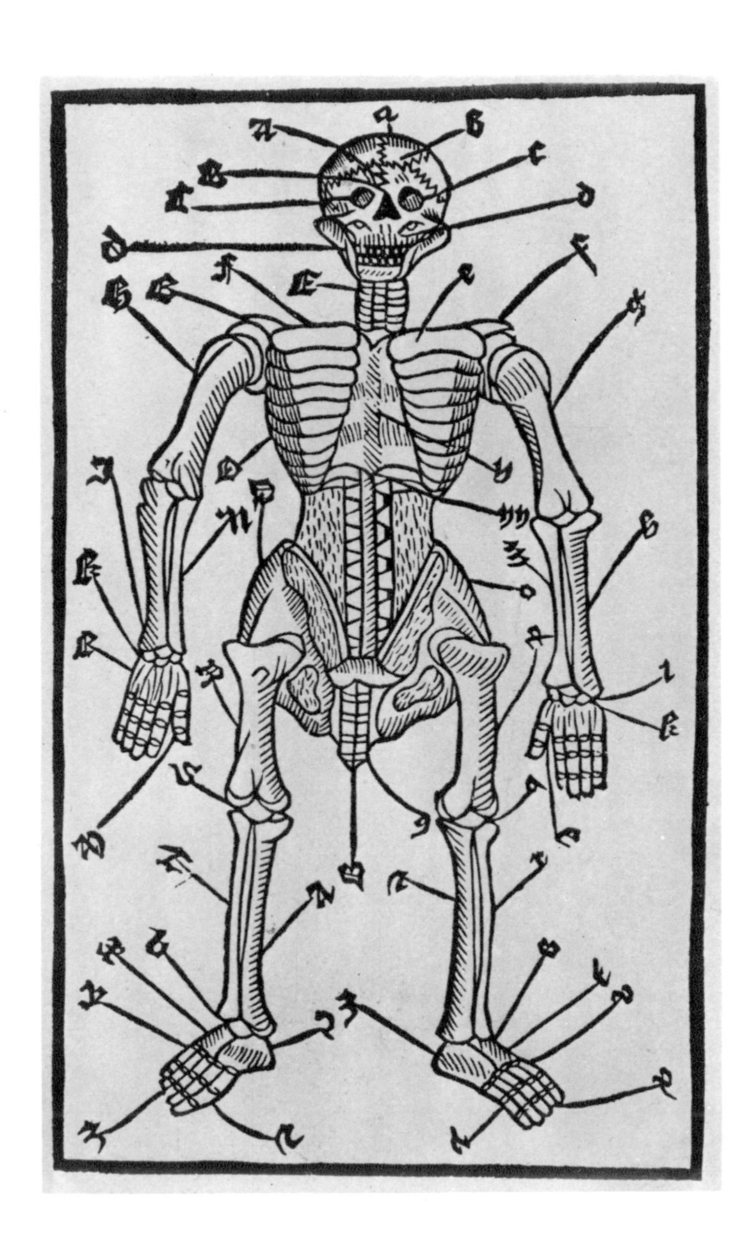

Human skeleton. Woodcut from the "Practica sive Philonium", a textbook of medicine and surgery by Valescus de Taranta. Lyons, 1500 edition.

As the incarnation of the enigmatic, questing and aspiring man, Paracelsus found his poetic memorials in Goethe's "Faust" and in the young Browning's "Paracelsus".

Quite as extraordinary as Paracelsus' ideas was his behavior. He was wont to deliver his lectures in the German language rather than in the Latin then universal. He refused the matriculation which the rules and regulations required and called down the envy and hate of many influential persons on his head. He came into conflict with the magistrates because of a fee he had been promised which was not paid and, in order to escape arrest for contempt of court, hurriedly left Basle in 1528.

Although Paracelsus' sojourn in Basle lasted scarcely a year, his ideas lived on in the town. Johannes Oporin, his assistant, and Basilius Amerbach copied down some of the master's lectures so accurately that it was possible to publish them. Adam von Bodenstein is another proof that the teaching of Paracelsus attracted loyal followers. He edited around thirty of Paracelsus' writings, and this fidelity to his former master cost him a professor's chair in 1564. One of the leading scholars at the university in the 16th century, Theodore Zwinger, the first of a dynasty of physicians and professors going down to the 18th century, gave a clear exposition of Paracelsian doctrine in his "Physiologia Medica" – more clearly than had Paracelsus himself.

A decade and a half after Paracelsus had blown through Basle, the town saw the "reformer of anatomy" inside its gates: Andreas Vesalius. He came from his crowded classroom at the University of Padua in 1543 in order to supervise the publication by Johannes Oporin of his "De Humani Corporis Fabrica Libri Septem", commonly known as the "Fabrica". The woodcuts illustrating this work are scientific and artistic masterpieces. The mechanics of the skeletal structure and the muscles are clearly depicted. These plates were used for over 200 years in illustrating anatomical works, for the last time in 1783.

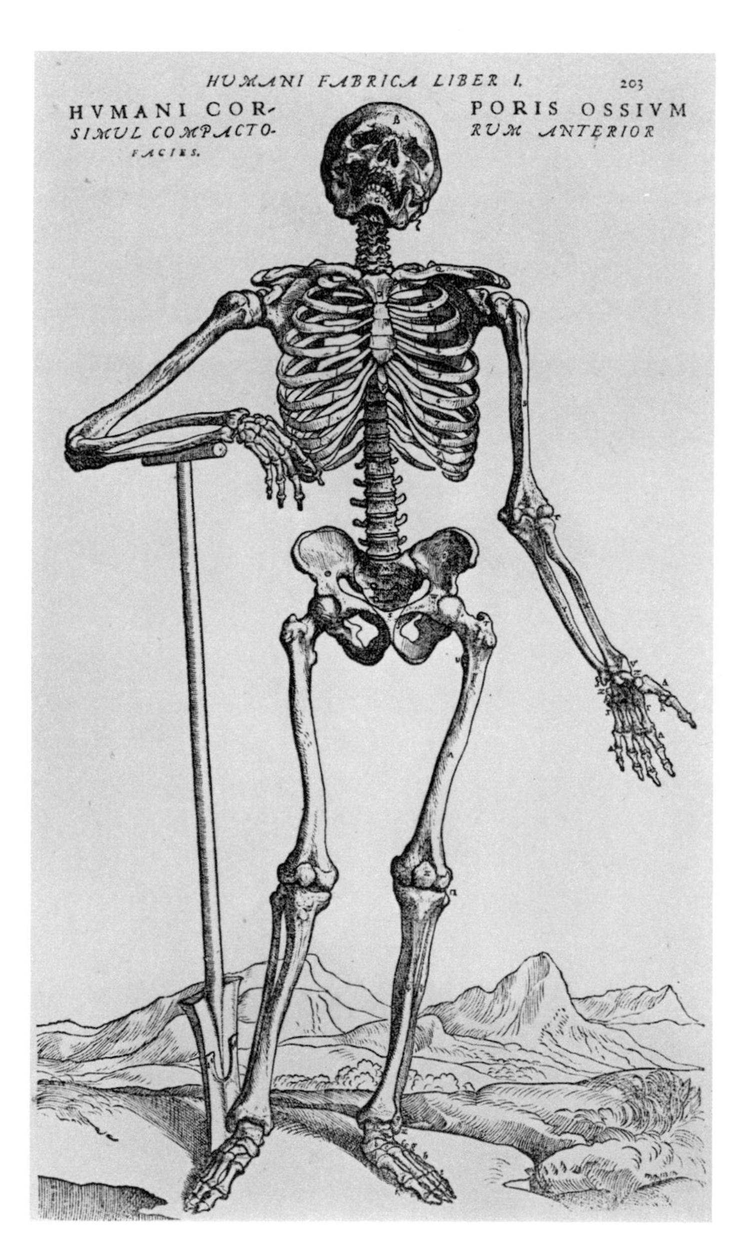

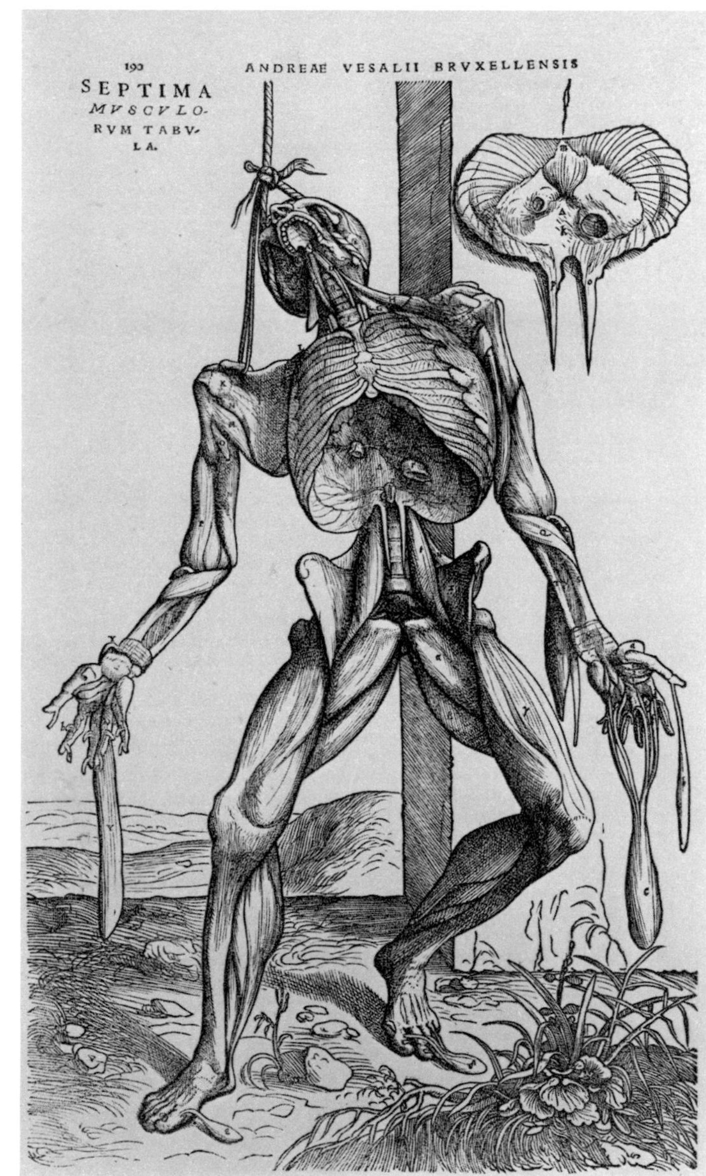

Galenic anatomy was a self-contained body of teaching which, in the opinion of learned men, called neither for extension nor change. The novel, lucid viewpoint of Vesalius sufficed to topple it, for he showed that many things would have to be explored anew and critically, from the very beginning. Here was where the development of modern anatomy set in.

The illustrations to Vesalius' "Fabrica" are both artistic and scientific masterpieces. These plates, done in woodcut technique under the supervision of the anatomist, are attributed to Jan Stephan van Calcar, a pupil of Titian. Left: the human skeleton; right: a plate from the volume depicting the muscular system.

Death and the Maiden. Oil-tempera on wood by Hans Baldung Grien dated 1517. Basle Art Gallery.

The Dance of Death was a favorite subject of pictorial art during the transitional 15th and 16th centuries. As the horror-consciousness of the late Middle Ages subsided, the dancing figure with all the features of a rotting corpse was gradually sublimated into the symbol of Death. The renowned "Dance of Death" in Basle, a series of murals in the old Dominican monastery, may have been painted shortly after the plague of 1439. Holbein's woodcuts on the theme were drawn and carved in Basle in the 1520s.

Even Vesalius, however, was not able to free himself completely of Galenic conceptions. Only in 1553 did his pupil Miguel Serveto discover the circulation of the blood through the lungs, and in 1616 William Harvey the circulation of blood throughout the body.

The title and first page of Felix Platter's work "On the Human Body", published in 1583. The "Dispositio", or table of contents, evinces this Basle physician's methodical way of thinking, a trait even more manifest in his "Praxeos" (1602–1608). In the latter work, he classifies diseases for the first time according to their symptoms, rather than by their "seat" in the organism.

In Basle Vesalius had himself entered on the university rolls and, in a public anatomy, demonstrated his method of dissection. His "Epitome", an abbreviated version of the "Fabrica" intended for non-medical people, was translated into German by Albanus Torinus, rector of the university.

Although Vesalius remained in Basle for a few months only, he bequeathed his influence on medical instruction. Felix Platter took him as a model, and Platter was the man who brought the medical faculty of Basle the esteem it later enjoyed.

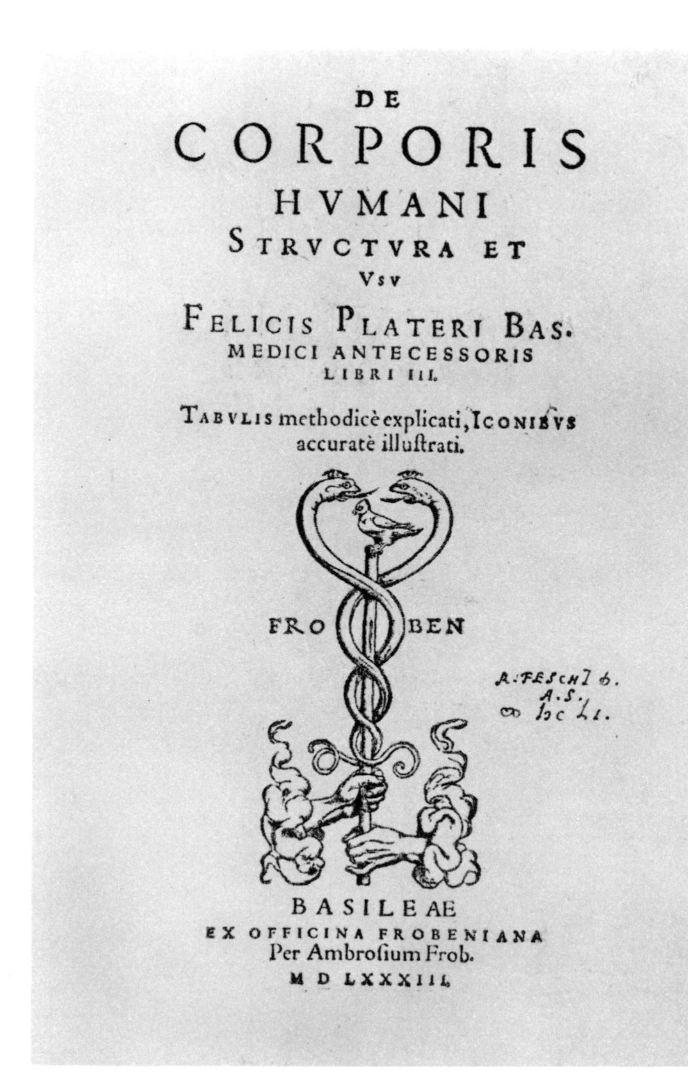

DE
CORPORIS
HVMANI
STRVCTVRA ET
VSV
FELICIS PLATERI BAS.
MEDICI ANTECESSORIS
LIBRI III.
TABVLIS methodicè explicati, ICONIBVS
accuratè illuſtrati.

FRO BEN

BASILEAE
EX OFFICINA FROBENIANA
Per Ambroſium Frob.
M D LXXXIII.

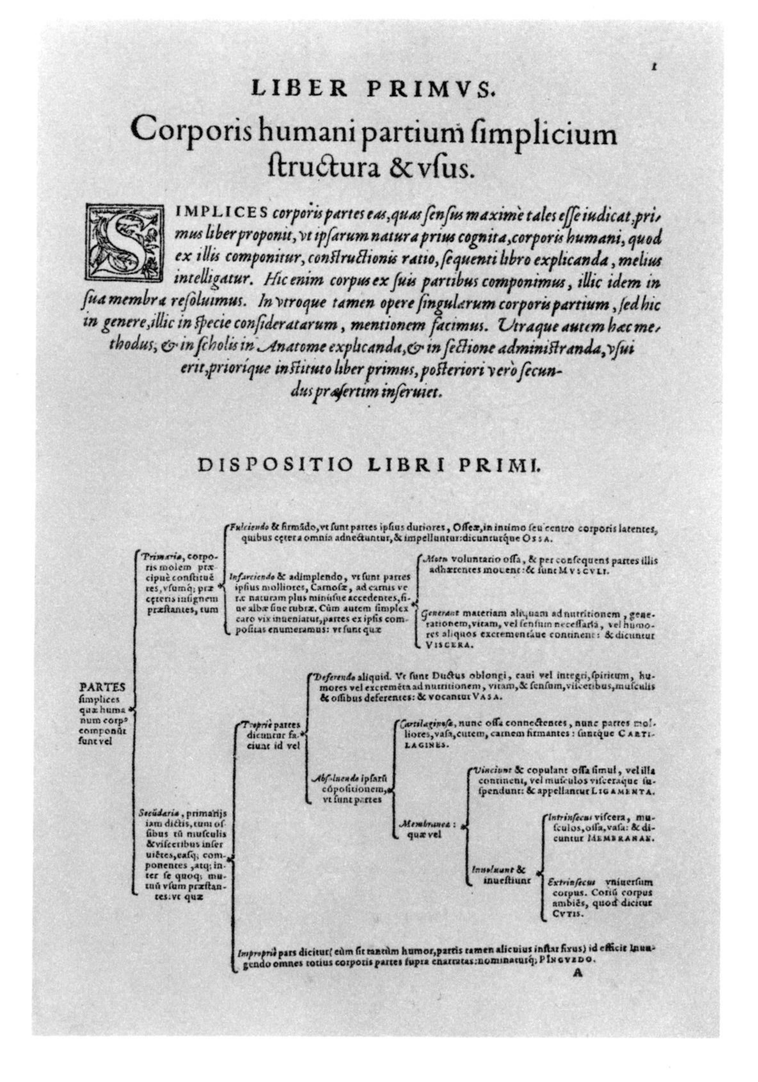

1

LIBER PRIMVS.

Corporis humani partium ſimplicium ſtructura & vſus.

SIMPLICES *corporis partes eas, quas ſenſus maximè tales eſſe iudicat, primus liber proponit, vt ipſarum natura prius cognita, corporis humani, quod ex illis componitur, conſtructionis ratio, ſequenti libro explicanda, melius intelligatur. Hic enim corpus ex ſuis partibus componimus, illic idem in ſua membra reſoluimus. In vtroque tamen opere ſingularum corporis partium, ſed hic in genere, illic in ſpecie conſideratarum, mentionem facimus. Utraque autem hæc methodus, & in ſcholis in Anatome explicanda, & in ſectione adminiſtranda, vſui erit, priorique inſtituto liber primus, poſteriori verò ſecundus præſertim inſeruiet.*

DISPOSITIO LIBRI PRIMI.

PARTES ſimplices quæ humanum corpꝰ componũt ſunt vel

- *Primaria*, corporis molem præcipuè conſtituẽtes, vſumq; præ cęteris inſignem præſtantes, tum
  - *Fulciendo* & firmãdo, vt ſunt partes ipſius duriores, Oſſeæ, in intimo ſeu centro corporis latentes, quibus cętera omnia adnectuntur, & impelluntur: dicunturque OSSA.
  - *Infarciendo* & adimplendo, vt ſunt partes ipſius molliores, Carnoſæ, ad carnis veræ naturam plus minúſue accedentes, ſiue albæ ſiue rubræ. Cùm autem ſimplex caro vix inueniatur, partes ex ipſis compoſitas enumeramus: vt ſunt quæ
    - *Motu* voluntario oſſa, & per conſequens partes illis adhærentes mouent: & ſunt MVSCVLI.
    - *Generant* materiam aliquam ad nutritionem, generationem, vitam, vel ſenſum neceſſariã, vel humores aliquos excrementáue continent: & dicuntur VISCERA.
- *Secũdaria*, primarijs iam dictis, tum oſſibus tũ muſculis & viſceribus inſeruiẽtes, eaſq; componentes, atq; inter ſe quoq; mutuũ vſum præſtantes: vt quæ
  - *Propriè* partes dicuntur faciunt id vel
    - *Deferendo* aliquid. Vt ſunt Ductus oblongi, caui vel integri, ſpiritum, humores vel excremẽta ad nutritionem, vitam, & ſenſum, viſceribus, muſculis & oſſibus deferentes: & vocantur VASA.
    - *Abſoluendo* ipſarũ cõpoſitionem, vt ſunt partes
      - *Cartilaginoſæ*, nunc oſſa connectentes, nunc partes molliores, vaſa, cutem, carnem firmantes: ſuntque CARTILAGINES.
      - *Membraneæ*: quæ vel
        - *Vinciunt* & copulant oſſa ſimul, vel illa continent, vel muſculos viſceraque ſuſpendunt: & appellantur LIGAMENTA.
        - *Inuoluunt* & inueſtiunt
          - *Intrinſecus* viſcera, muſculos, oſſa, vaſa: & dicuntur MEMBRANAE.
          - *Extrinſecus* vniuerſum corpus. Coriũ corpus ambiẽs, quod dicitur CVTIS.
  - *Impropriè* pars dicitur (cùm ſit tantùm humor, partis tamen alicuius inſtar fixus) id efficit Inungendo omnes totius corporis partes ſupra enarratas: nominaturq; PINGVEDO.

A

Specimen pages from the statistics Platter compiled on the epidemic which visited Basle from 1609 to 1611. University Library, Basle; MS. A λ III 5a.
At the age of 75 Platter, as town physician, drew up a report on the seven pestilences which he had lived through in Basle from 1539 to 1611. Data on the first six were taken from memory; the seventh he documented statistically. Street by street, he listed all habitations in both Greater and Lesser Basle, recording the number of those who fell ill, died, and recovered.

Platter, medical adviser to the Queen of France and the Dukes of Lorraine, Saxony, and Wuerttemberg, based himself to a large degree upon both the text and illustrations of Vesalius' "Fabrica" in his own work on anatomy which appeared in 1583. Platter was the first to classify mental diseases. Like Paracelsus, he attributed to them an importance equal to that of the bodily diseases and did not believe them caused by magic. His statistics on the epidemics of plague in Basle were far ahead of their time.

Im Kalten Keller Gesslin.

Zur obern müntz	Starb dem [illegible] Philip [illegible] sein sun.	1
	Kam auf er und sein sun.	2
In der undern müntz	Kam auf die frauw.	1
Zum kalten keller in [illegible] haus	Kamen auf ein par eevolck und dry kinder.	5

Im Todten Gesslin

Ins Philippen [illegible]	Starb [illegible]	1
Zu obern [illegible]	Starb der [illegible] Landvogt Iselin.	1
Zu undern [illegible]	Kam auf der [illegible] dochter und ein frauw die [illegible].	2
Im haus doran.	[illegible] schümacher Hans Hugel. j knecht [illegible] im spital ward er kranck.	—
Zum [illegible]	Starb Joh. Vualter Sprotaviensis Silesius Med. Stud.	1
	Ward kranck die magt. [illegible]	
Ins [illegible]	Starb j knab.	1
Am [illegible]	Starb der schnider der [illegible] dochterman. Christoffel [illegible]. Kam uf sy.	1 1 1

Auf dem Nodelberg.
Auf der [illegible] siten.

In des [illegible] hof.	0 · 0.	0
In der Druckery	Starb der meister zum [illegible] Hieronimus Gemuseus. 8 Sept.	1
Ins [illegible] hof.	0 · 0.	0
Ins [illegible] haus	0 · 0.	0
Ins [illegible]	Starb im ein döchterlin. 22 Aug.	1
Ins Wonnenfels haus	Starb er Hans Rudolf Wonnenfels 30. Oct.	1
	Kam auf sein frauw j sun und j döchterlin.	3
Ins Samuel Verzascha h.	Starb er her Samuel Verzasch 4 Octob. und sein frauw Dorothea [illegible] 11 Oct.	2
	Kam auf das döchterlin.	1
	Ward kranck j magt. starb [illegible].	—
In der [illegible] wittfrauw h.	Starb ir ein sun und j dochter.	2
	Kam auf der sun [illegible] und j dochter und sy selbs	3
In h. Lux Iselin hof.	Ward kranck j knecht und die magt. starb der knecht [illegible] die magt anderswo.	—

2

In des Jacob [illegible] h.	Starben 4 kinder. Item im sein brüder und sein schwester Maria. [illegible] frauw.	6
In Damian Irmi h.	Starb h. her Damian Irmi 11 Oct. und 2 sün	3
	Kam auf die frauw und j döchterlin.	2
	Ward kranck j magt starb anderswo.	—
Ins [illegible] h.	Starb er der Martin [illegible] und sein frauw und 2 kinder.	4
In Schniders haus.	Starb er der Oswald Spörlin und j knecht.	2

Auf der [illegible] siten

Ins Büchbinders [illegible]	Starb der büchbinder [illegible] 30 Oct. und 3 döchterlin.	4
	Kam auf der sun.	1
In der [illegible]	Starb D. Wolfgang [illegible] 23 Dec.	1
	Kam auf sein müter und schwester.	2
Ins [illegible] Philippen h.	0 0.	0
In h. Castillionai h.	0 0	0
Ins [illegible] h.	Starb sein frauw Maria Löffel 6 Nov. und ein döchterlin.	2
In seim andern h. [illegible]	Starb. D. Gulielmus Aragosius Med. Gallus [illegible] 97 [illegible]	1
Im andern [illegible]	0 0.	0
In D. Zwingers h.	Starb D. Jacobus Zwingerus 11 Octob. und sein frauw Judith Brandin [illegible] 2 kinder.	4
	Kamen auf zwei kinder.	2
	Ward auch kranck die magt. starb über Rhin.	—
Im haus bim brunnen an der [illegible]	Starb die wittwe Agatha [illegible]. Item im andern theil des haus Hans [illegible] frauw mit 4 kindern.	6
	Kam auf der Agatha dochter.	1
Im haus doran	Starb der [illegible] Marggräfer und seiner frauwen brüder [illegible]	
Ins schniders haus	Starb der schnider Rudolf [illegible] und 2 kinder	3
	Kam auf des schniders frauw.	1
Ins Armbrusters h.	Starb 1 sun und 3 döchteren.	4
Ins Damian [illegible] haus	Starb sein [illegible] Anna [illegible] und deren dochter kind.	2
	Kam auf die dochter.	

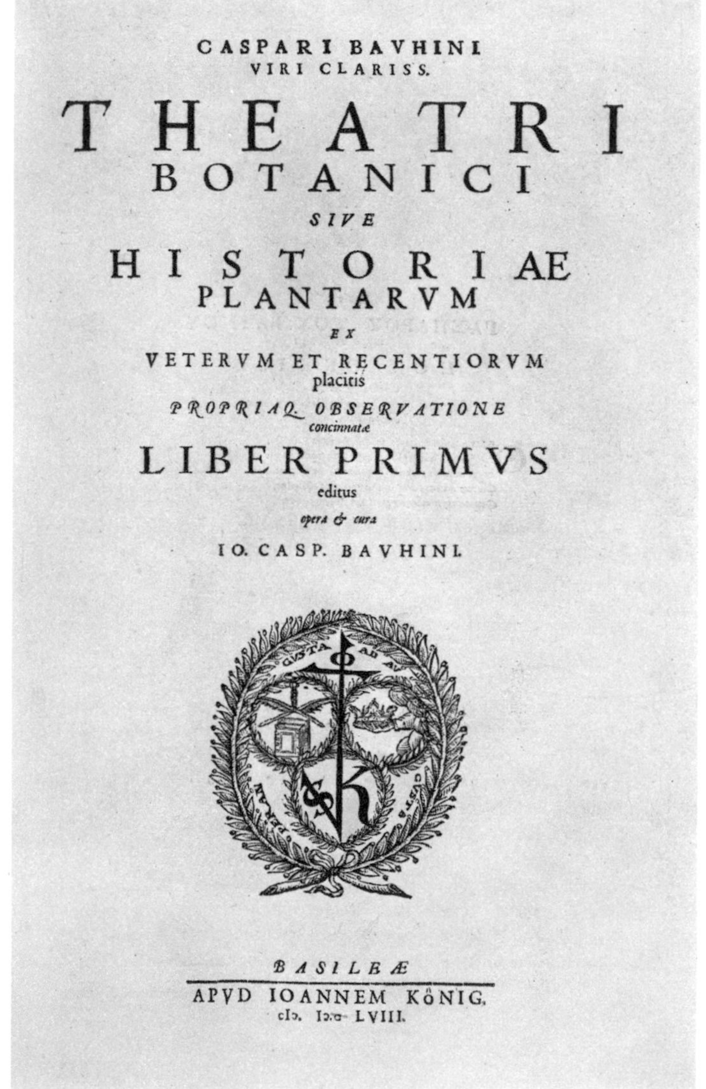

CASPARI BAVHINI
VIRI CLARISS.

THEATRI
BOTANICI
SIVE
HISTORIAE
PLANTARVM
EX
VETERVM ET RECENTIORVM
placitis
PROPRIAQ. OBSERVATIONE
concinnatæ
LIBER PRIMVS
editus
opera & cura
IO. CASP. BAVHINI.

BASILEÆ
APVD IOANNEM KÖNIG.
cIↄ. Iↄcc LVIII.

Still another university teacher of Basle played an important part in the development of the natural sciences: Caspar Bauhin. In 1589 he was appointed professor of anatomy and botany and in 1614 succeeded Platter in his offices as city physician and instructor in practical medicine. Some of Bauhin's terms for the muscles and plants are still employed today. He was the first to draw up a natural, if only external, classification of plants on the basis of exact observations.

Caspar Bauhin was preeminently a systematist. The herbarium which he started in the early 17th century is among the oldest plant collections still in existence.
Left: Page from an herbal with flower-bearing shoots and leaves of the foxglove. The writing is in Bauhin's hand. Botanical Institute of the University of Basle.
Right: Bauhin considered the writings which he himself edited as preliminary studies for a "History of Plants" that was to encompass several volumes. The first volume of the "Theatri Botanici", published posthumously, was intended as an introduction to this work. The manuscript of the remaining parts were lost.

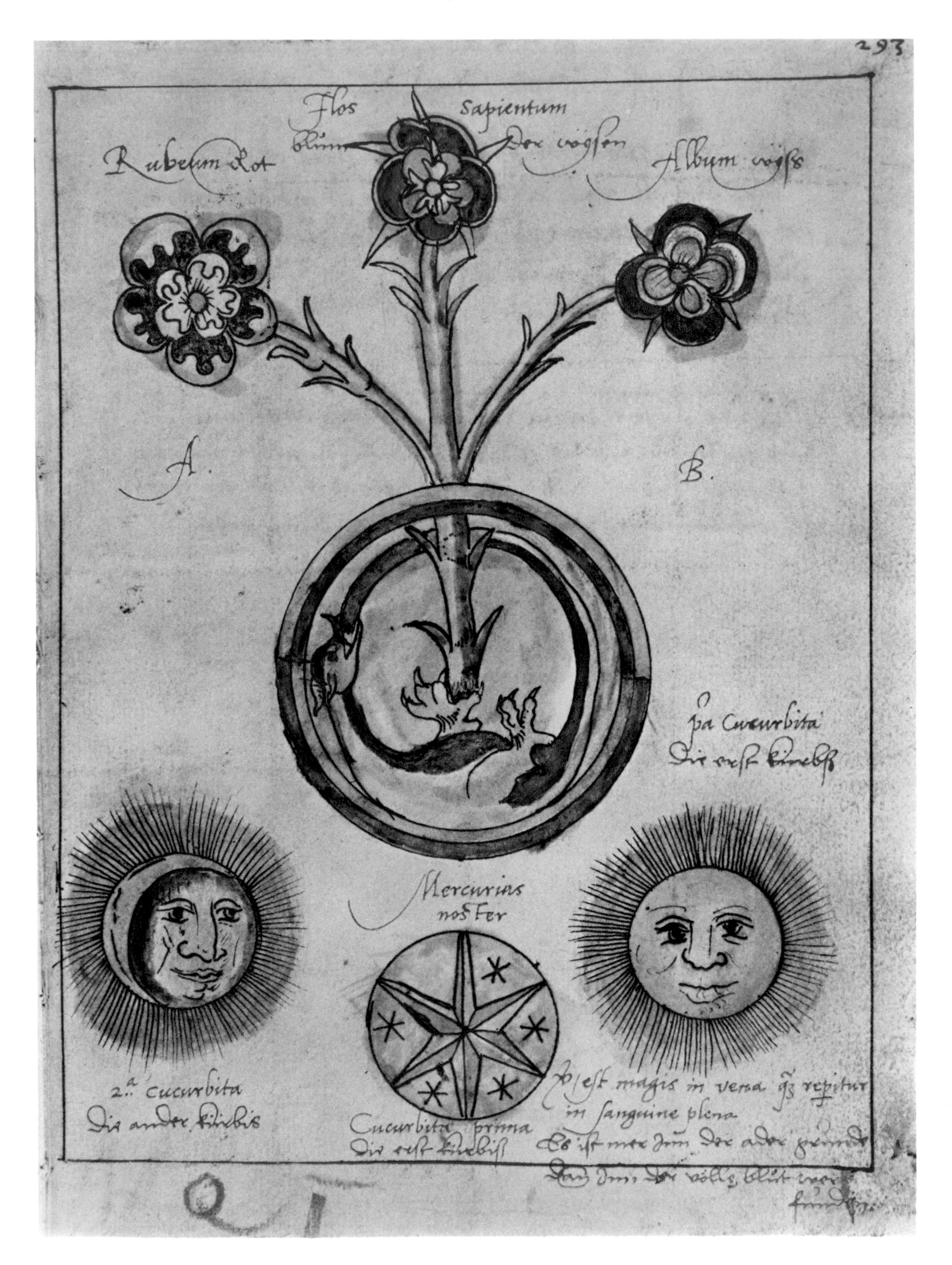
293
Flos sapientum
Rubeum Rot
Album weiss
A.
B.
pa Cucurbita
Mercurius noster
2.a Cucurbita
Die ander kürbis
Cucurbita prima
Die erst kürbiss
est magis in vena qz reperitur
in sanguine plena

The movement towards exact scientific techniques which led to our technological age can be charted by following the final phases of a science which actually was none because it lacked a rational foundation: alchemy. Alchemy in the Middle Ages was more than the mere "art of making gold". It was a view and a way of life, anchored in mysticism, which placed upon its adepts the task of seeking the elusive "Philosopher's Stone".

The Renaissance marked both the apogee and the beginning of the end of alchemy. We have already heard that Paracelsus declared medicines, not gold, to be the true aspiration of the alchemist, and with this formulation he made himself the founder of iatrochemistry. Yet at just about the same time, alchemistic frauds were using legerdemain to change iron into gold before the eyes of gullible princes. Their conjuring tricks clearly showed how much of the spiritual content of alchemy had been lost.

The scholasticism of the 13th century had prepared the way for the rational-scientific method of thinking. The Renaissance witnessed the first consequences. The interpretations of natural phenomena which had prevailed throughout the Middle Ages were abandoned and supplanted by new ones. The modern scientific conception of the world was beginning to emerge.

The 18th century brought to light yet another consequence of the evolution that had commenced hundreds of years earlier. The rational method of thinking pushed beyond the bounds of natural science and, in the "Age of Enlightment", came to permeate every facet of life.

Opposite: From a mid-16th century alchemical manuscript. Alchemy treated of matter and its transmutation in a two-fold manner – exoteric and esoteric – communicating its doctrines through a complex apparatus of symbols. Ouroboros, the serpent which bites its own tail, stands for the one which contains all, referring to the unity of all things. In this illustration the "Tail-Eater" symbolizes the Philosopher's Stone. The sun and moon are Babylonian emblems for gold and silver. University Library, Basle; MS. L IV 1.

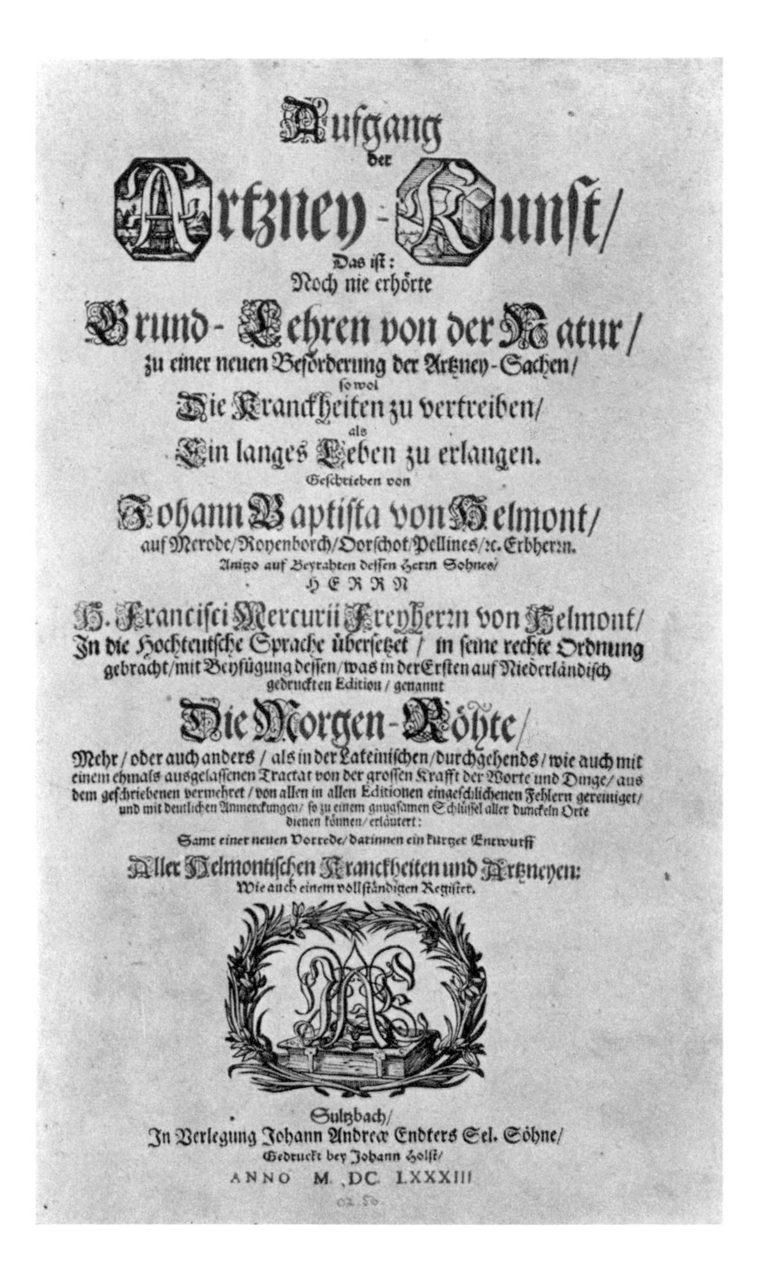

Aufgang
der
Artzney-Kunst/
Das ist:
Noch nie erhörte
Grund-Lehren von der Natur/
zu einer neuen Beförderung der Artzney-Sachen/
sowol
Die Kranckheiten zu vertreiben/
als
Ein langes Leben zu erlangen.
Geschrieben von
Johann Baptista von Helmont/
auf Merode/Royenborch/Oorschot/Pellines/2c. Erbherrn.
Anitzo auf Beyrahten dessen Herrn Sohnes/
HERRN
H. Francisci Mercurii Freyherrn von Helmont/
In die Hochteutsche Sprache übersetzet / in seine rechte Ordnung gebracht/mit Beyfügung dessen/was in der Ersten auf Niederländisch gedruckten Edition / genannt
Die Morgen-Röhte/
Mehr / oder auch anders / als in der Lateinischen/durchgehends / wie auch mit einem ehmals ausgelassenen Tractat von der grossen Krafft der Worte und Dinge/ aus dem geschriebenen vermehret / von allen in allen Editionen eingeschlichenen Fehlern gereiniget/ und mit deutlichen Anmerckungen/ so zu einem gnugsamen Schlüssel aller danckeln Orte dienen können/ erläutert:
Samt einer neuen Vorrede/ darinnen ein kurtzer Entwurff
Aller Helmontischen Kranckheiten und Artzneyen:
Wie auch einem vollständigen Register.

Sultzbach/
In Verlegung Johann Andreæ Endters Sel. Söhne/
Gedruckt bey Johann Holst/
ANNO M. DC. LXXXIII

Title page of a work on pharmaceutics by Jean Baptiste van Helmont, an important figure among the iatrochemists who also coined the term "gas". Although convinced that it was possible to transmute metals, van Helmont was an experimentalist who saw the finest task of alchemy to consist not in the obtaining of noble metals, but rather in the creation of medical remedies.

A considerable body of rational knowledge concerning nature had been accumulated by the scientists of the Renaissance. The philosophical formulation of rationalism, however, had to wait until the 17th century and René Descartes. In his "Discours de la méthode", which appeared in 1637, Descartes affirms that *"all things which we perceive very clearly and very distinctly are true"*. He bases this axiom – and in so doing betrays his roots in medieval philosophy – on the statement that our clear and distinct ideas are not subject to illusion because they originate in God. In the "Principia Philosophiae", his chef-d'œuvre dated 1644, Descartes avers that the corporeal world is determined by extension and motion, the primary qualities. The secondary qualities – color, for instance – exist only in the percipient being and therefore temporarily elude scientific observation. Only when such secondary qualities are converted into primary ones, as did happen later on to a greater and greater extent, will they become accessible to rational observation. As an example, the Dutch scientist Christiaan Huygens, in his "Traité de la lumière" of 1690, interpreted color as an undulatory motion of ether particles.

Ever since Descartes the task of science has consisted in the mathematical description of the form and motion of things. The first fully coherent mathematical-mechanistic explanation of inanimate nature was propounded by Sir Isaac Newton, on the basis of universal gravitation. In his "Philosophiae Naturalis Principia Mathematica" (usually referred to as the "Principles"), dated 1687, he derived all phenomena of motion from three theorems: the law of inertia, the law of motive force and change of momentum, and the hypothesis of universal gravitation (action and reaction). The first two axioms may be traced back to Galileo, but Newton was the first to incorporate them into a universal system. Nature, if it conforms so neatly to laws that it can be delineated with a few mathematical formulae, should also be amenable to control with the help of these

F. Sherwood Taylor has termed Newton's "Principles", completed in 1687, "perhaps the most powerful and original piece of scientific reasoning ever published". With this book he set forth a conception of absolute space and time which remained valid for over 200 years as the "Newtonian" universe. He defined the notions of mass, momentum, force, etc. and gave the first coherent mechanistic explanation of the world, inventing most of the mathematics to support it as well.

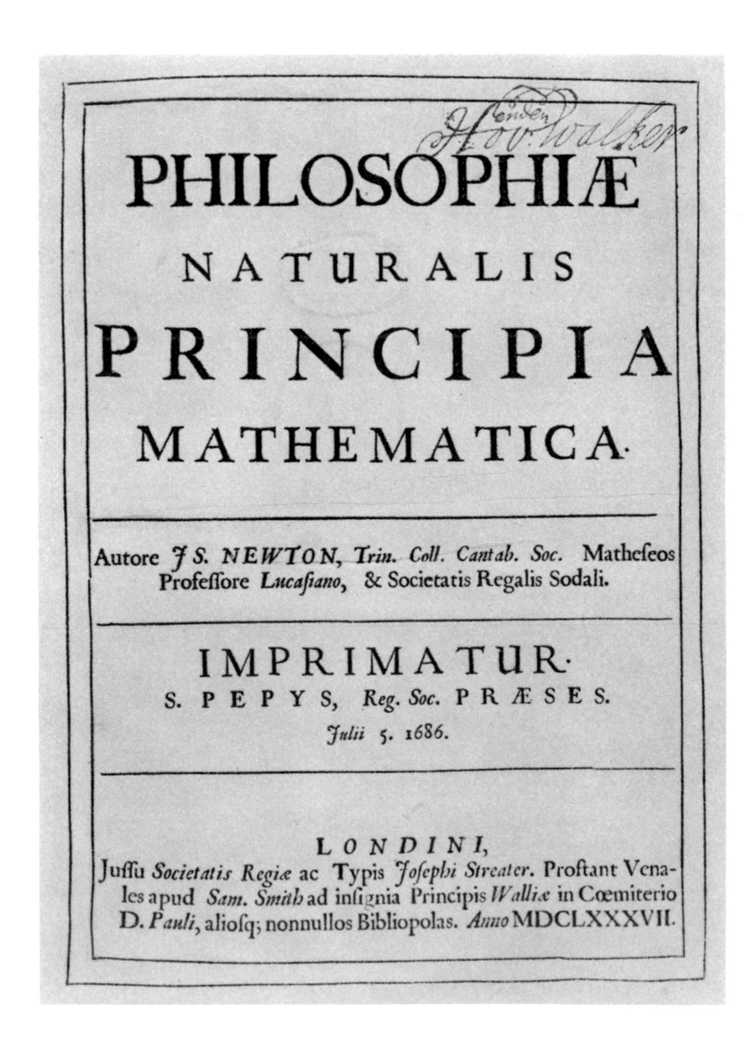

PHILOSOPHIÆ
NATURALIS
PRINCIPIA
MATHEMATICA.

Autore *J S. NEWTON*, *Trin. Coll. Cantab. Soc.* Mathefeos Profeffore *Lucafiano*, & Societatis Regalis Sodali.

IMPRIMATUR.
S. PEPYS, *Reg. Soc.* PRÆSES.
Julii 5. 1686.

LONDINI,
Juffu *Societatis Regiæ* ac Typis *Jofephi Streater*. Proftant Venales apud *Sam. Smith* ad infignia Principis *Walliæ* in Cœmiterio D. *Pauli*, aliofq; nonnullos Bibliopolas. *Anno* MDCLXXXVII.

Inaugural session of the "Institut de France" in the Louvre, April 4th, 1796. This official body absorbed the "Académie des Sciences" instituted by Colbert over a century before. Such learned societies aimed to promote and improve crafts and technology for the public weal. Copper engraving in the Bibliothèque Nationale, Paris.

formulae. Argument along these lines led to the establishment, in various European countries, of societies which had as their object the application of science to technology. In 1662 Charles II founded the "Royal Society of London for Improving Natural Knowledge"; Louis XIV set up the "Académie des Sciences" in 1666; and the Elector Frederick of Prussia the "Berlin Academy" in 1700.

The most important instrument for the study of extension and motion is mathematics – an instrument which required to be refined. The 17th century brought two crucial amplifications of this branch of knowledge: analytical geometry and the differential calculus. The principles of analytical geometry are given in Descartes' "La géometrie", published in 1638: all the geometrical properties of a curve can be exhibited by one single algebraic equation. Gottfried Wilhelm von Leibniz, who was a Cartesian, published his principles of the differential calculus in 1684; calculation with

297

LA

GEOMETRIE.

LIVRE PREMIER.

Des problesmes qu'on peut construire sans y employer que des cercles & des lignes droites.

Ous les Problesmes de Geometrie se peuuent facilement reduire a tels termes, qu'il n'est besoin par aprés que de connoistre la longeur de quelques lignes droites, pour les construire.

Et comme toute l'Arithmetique n'est composée, que de quatre ou cinq operations, qui sont l'Addition, la Soustraction, la Multiplication, la Diuision, & l'Extraction des racines, qu'on peut prendre pour vne espece de Diuision: Ainsi n'at'on autre chose a faire en Geometrie touchant les lignes qu'on cherche, pour les preparer a estre connuës, que leur en adiouster d'autres, ou en oster; Oubien en ayant vne, que ie nommeray l'vnité pour la rapporter d'autant mieux aux nombres, & qui peut ordinairement estre prise a discretion, puis en ayant encore deux autres, en trouuer vne quatriesme, qui soit à l'vne de ces deux, comme l'autre est a l'vnité, ce qui est le mesme que la Multiplication; oubien en trouuer vne quatriesme, qui soit a l'vne de ces deux, comme l'vnité

Commẽt le calcul d'Arithmetique se rapporte aux operations de Geometrie.

Pp est

MENSIS OCTOBRIS A. MDCLXXXIV. 467

NOVA METHODUS PRO MAXIMIS ET MI-nimis, itemque tangentibus, quæ nec fractas, nec irrationales quantitates moratur, & singulare pro illis calculi genus, per G. G. L.

SIt axis AX, & curvæ plures, ut VV, WW, YY, ZZ, quarum ordinatæ, ad axem normales, VX, WX, YX, ZX, quæ vocentur respective, v, vv, y, z; & ipsa AX abscissa ab axe, vocetur x. Tangentes sint VB, WC, YD, ZE axi occurrentes respective in punctis B, C, D, E. Jam recta aliqua pro arbitrio assumta vocetur dx, & recta quæ sit ad dx, ut v (vel vv, vel y, vel z) est ad VB (vel WC, vel YD, vel ZE) vocetur dv (vel dvv, vel dy vel dz) sive differentia ipsarum v (vel ipsarum vv, aut y, aut z) His positis calculi regulæ erunt tales:

TAB. XII.

Sit a quantitas data constans, erit da æqualis 0, & d ax erit æqu. a dx: si sit y æqu v (seu ordinata quævis curvæ YY, æqualis cuivis ordinatæ respondenti curvæ VV) erit dy æqu. dv. Jam *Additio & Subtractio*: si sit z -y † vv † x æqu. v, erit dz -y † vv † x seu dv, æqu. dz -dy † dvv † dx. *Multiplicatio*, dxv æqu. xdv † vdx, seu posito y æqu. xv, fiet dy æqu. xdv † vdx. In arbitrio enim est vel formulam, ut xv, vel compendio pro ea literam, ut y, adhibere. Notandum & x & dx eodem modo in hoc calculo tractari, ut y & dy, vel aliam literam indeterminatam cum sua differentiali. Notandum etiam non dari semper regressum a differentiali Æquatione, nisi cum quadam cautione, de quo alibi. Porro *Divisio*, d v/y vel (posito z æqu. v/y) dz æqu. † v dy † y dv / yy

Quoad *Signa* hoc probe notandum, cum in calculo pro litera substituitur simpliciter ejus differentialis, servari quidem eadem signa, & pro † z scribi † dz, pro -z scribi -dz, ut ex additione & subtractione paulo ante posita apparet; sed quando ad exegesin valorum venitur, seu cum consideratur ipsius z relatio ad x, tunc apparere, an valor ipsius dz sit quantitas affirmativa, an nihilo minor seu negativa: quod posterius cum fit, tunc tangens ZE ducitur a puncto Z non versus A, sed in partes contrarias seu infra X, id est tunc cum ipsæ ordinatæ

Nnn 3 z decre-

Two decisive advances extended the realm of mathematics in the 17th century.
Above: Descartes projected the outlines of analytical geometry in his "La geométrie"; Leiden, 1638.
Right: Leibniz introduced the differential calculus. Computation with infinitesimally small quantities enables mathematicians to manipulate constantly changing sequences of motion. This illustration shows the first page of Leibniz' paper on the new method in the "Acta Eruditorum", 1684.

infinitesimally small quantities is suited above all to the study of natural phenomena which are subject to constant change.

In the 17th and 18th centuries no city could boast of so intensive and so fruitful a cultivation of mathematics as Basle. This fact is due almost exclusively to one family of scholars, the Bernoullis.
In 1687 the University of Basle called Jacob Bernoulli, then thirty-three years of age, to the chair of mathematics. This appointment marked the beginning of the repute which the town came to enjoy in the field of exact science. Jacob Bernoulli had familiarized himself with Cartesian mathematics in Holland and also knew the differential calculus of Leibniz, who later became his friend. His mathematical achievements were prodigious: he devised new ways of solving differential equations and wrote textbooks on Cartesian geometry and on the probability theory. He was a successful teacher as well, counting his brother Johann and Leonard Euler among his famous pupils.
Euler was a native of the neighboring community of Riehen. If the Bernoullis were the Bachs of mathematics, Euler qualifies as the mathematician's mathematician. While still in his teens, he made his scholarly mark with a discourse comparing the Cartesian and Newtonian systems. He was responsible, among many achievements in the field of mechanics, for laying the groundwork of ballistics. His textbooks on mathematics and physics are pedagogical masterworks. His first St. Petersburg period – he had followed the younger Bernoullis there in 1727 – was ended by an invitation from Frederick the Great to come to Berlin, where Euler lived until 1766. By dint of his "Letters to a German Princess" he also became a proponent of Cartesian dualism, particularly with his view that only space as conceived in the mind, or subjectively, is accessible to exact scientific observation. This tenet was adopted by Kant and clearly formulated in his "Critique of Pure Reason" (1781).

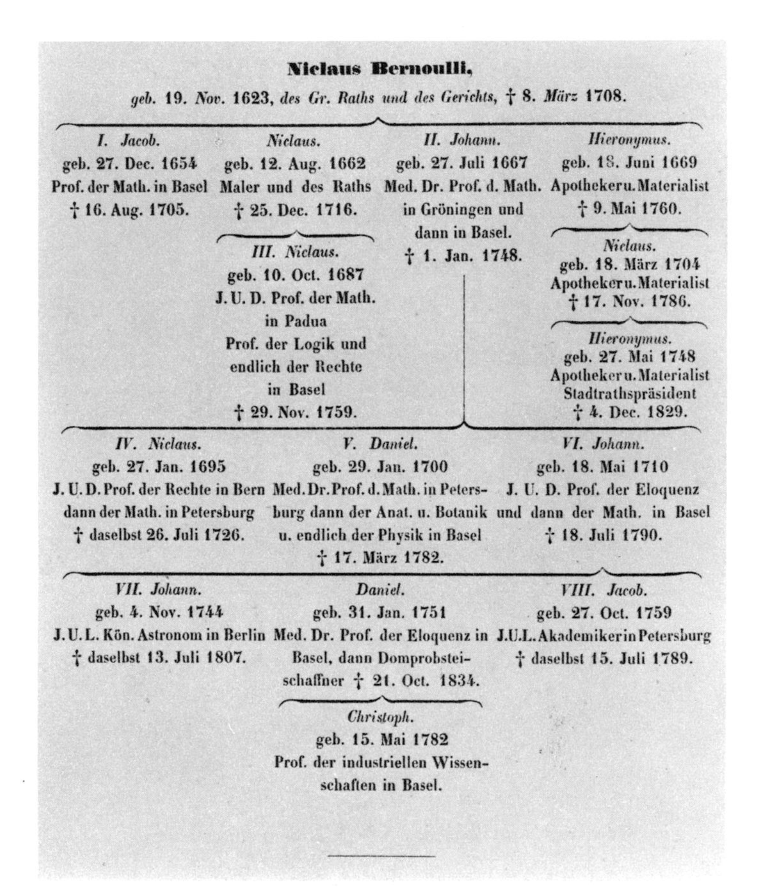

The family tree of the Bernoullis, a scholarly constellation which produced four generations of first-magnitude mathematicians and physicists. From "Die Mathematiker Bernoulli" by Peter Merian; Basle, 1860.

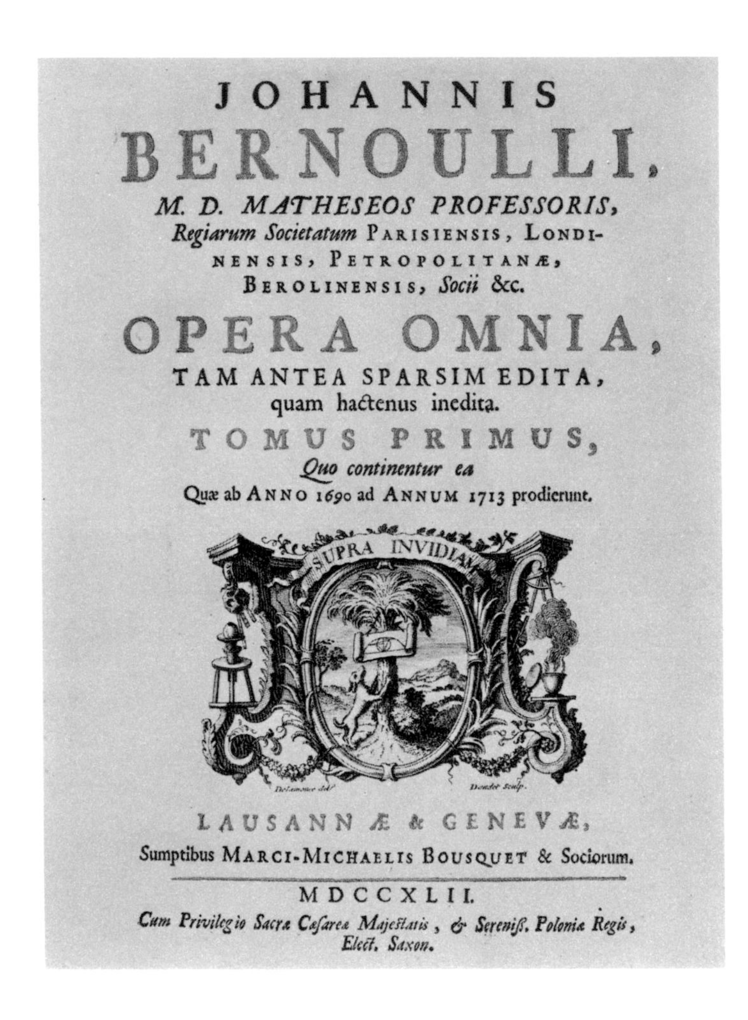

JOHANNIS
BERNOULLI,
M. D. MATHESEOS PROFESSORIS,
Regiarum Societatum PARISIENSIS, LONDINENSIS, PETROPOLITANÆ, BEROLINENSIS, *Socii* &c.
OPERA OMNIA,
TAM ANTEA SPARSIM EDITA,
quam hactenus inedita.
TOMUS PRIMUS,
Quo continentur ea
Quæ ab ANNO 1690 ad ANNUM 1713 prodierunt.

SUPRA INVIDIAM

LAUSANNÆ & GENEVÆ,
Sumptibus MARCI-MICHAELIS BOUSQUET & Sociorum.
MDCCXLII.
Cum Privilegio Sacræ Cæsareæ Majestatis, & Sereniss. Poloniæ Regis, Elect. Saxon.

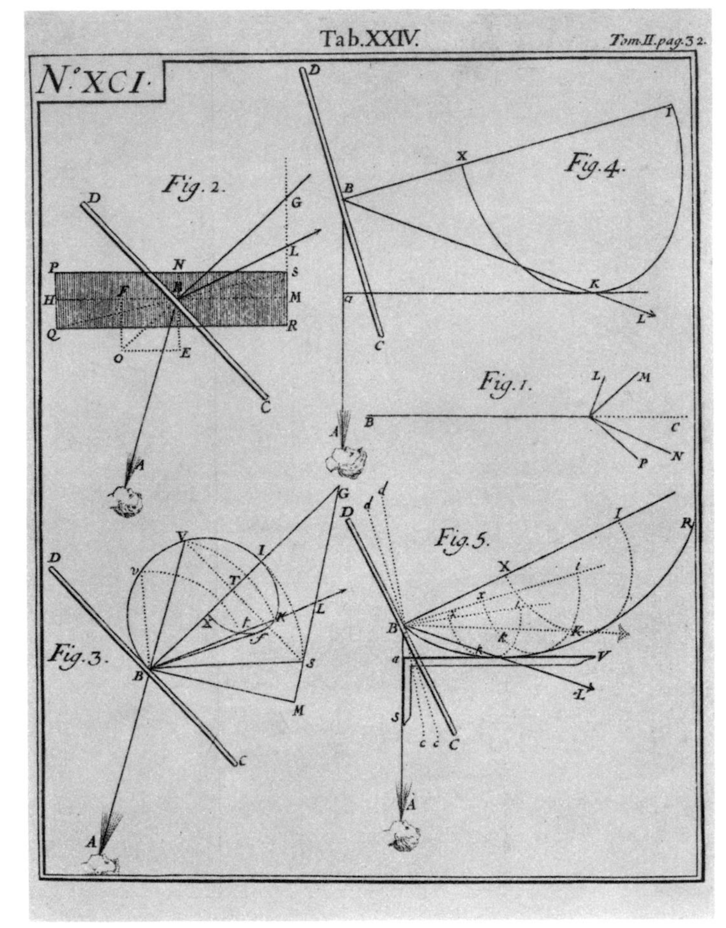

In contact with Leibniz, Jacob and Johann Bernoulli cultivated the differential calculus to the point where it became a utilizable instrument. They performed brilliant work on physical and astronomical, as well as strictly mathematical, problems. By applying the differential calculus and the theory of probability to technology and physiology, they contributed to the mechanization of men's outlook on life.
Left: Title page of Johann Bernoulli's Collected Works.
Right: In his "Manœuvre des vaisseaux", dated 1714, Johann Bernoulli used parallelograms of force to explain the motion of sailing vessels for the first time. Copper engraving from the Collected Works.

Johann Bernoulli succeeded to the Basle chair of mathematics upon Jacob Bernoulli's death in 1705. Johann was a pioneer in the field of pure and applied mathematics. To him we owe the first textbook on the differential calculus, which was published in 1696 by his pupil the Marquis de l'Hôpital. He coined the concepts of "integral calculus" and "function" and introduced into arithmetic the use of imaginary numbers. In his work on muscular power, "De Motu Musculorum", he applied mathematics to medical problems, while his "Manœuvre des vaisseaux" treated problems of navigation. In the 1730s the Académie des Sciences crowned Johann Bernoulli's works on planetary motion with high awards.

In 1738 Daniel Bernoulli published a work of fundamental importance for hydrodynamics and aerodynamics. Upon his law of energy for currents the mechanics of fluids and gases is based.

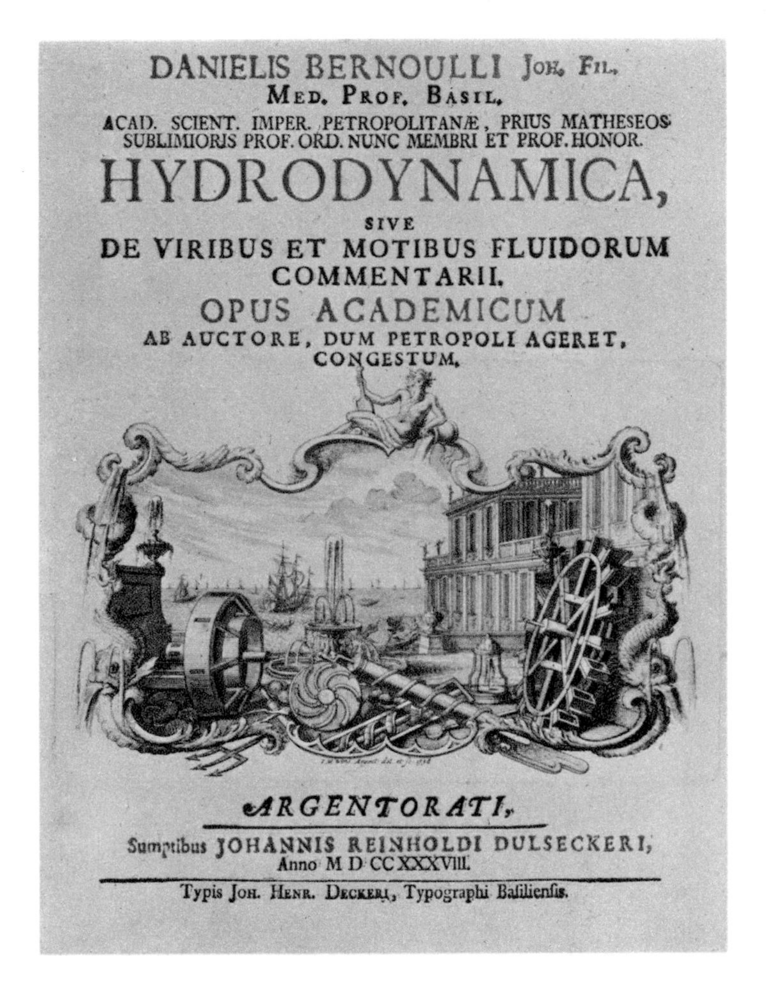
DANIELIS BERNOULLI JOH. FIL.
MED. PROF. BASIL.
ACAD. SCIENT. IMPER. PETROPOLITANÆ, PRIUS MATHESEOS SUBLIMIORIS PROF. ORD. NUNC MEMBRI ET PROF. HONOR.

HYDRODYNAMICA,
SIVE
DE VIRIBUS ET MOTIBUS FLUIDORUM COMMENTARII.
OPUS ACADEMICUM
AB AUCTORE, DUM PETROPOLI AGERET, CONGESTUM.

ARGENTORATI,
Sumptibus JOHANNIS REINHOLDI DULSECKERI,
Anno MDCCXXXVIII.
Typis JOH. HENR. DECKERI, Typographi Basiliensis.

The mathematical gift which ran in the Bernoulli family needs no special emphasis. All in all, nine of its members attained eminence. Nicholas Bernoulli, a nephew of Johann, became professor of logic and law, applying the probability theory to legal problems. In 1725 Johann's sons Daniel and Nicholas were called to the newly founded Academy of Sciences in St. Petersburg as professors of mathematics, followed two years later by Euler. Daniel returned to Basle in 1733 as a professor of anatomy and botany, and in 1750 he was appointed to the chair of "experimental and speculative philosophy". It was he who formulated the law of energy for currents, the fundamental principle of hydrodynamics and aerodynamics.

In his "Novum Organum", published in 1620, Francis Bacon had given an account of the scientific method. The plan he delineated erred not so much in its inductive bias as such, which experience has amply vindicated, as in its lack of discrimination with regard to the selection and handling of evidence.

Descartes helped to clarify scientific thinking by showing that phenomena in nature may be rationally comprehended if the actual process – the mechanics – is clearly conceived and can thus be formulated in mathematical terms. This mechanistic way of thinking did not stay limited to the natural sciences. It became a general one throughout the West and, applied to technology, it led to the Industrial Revolution.

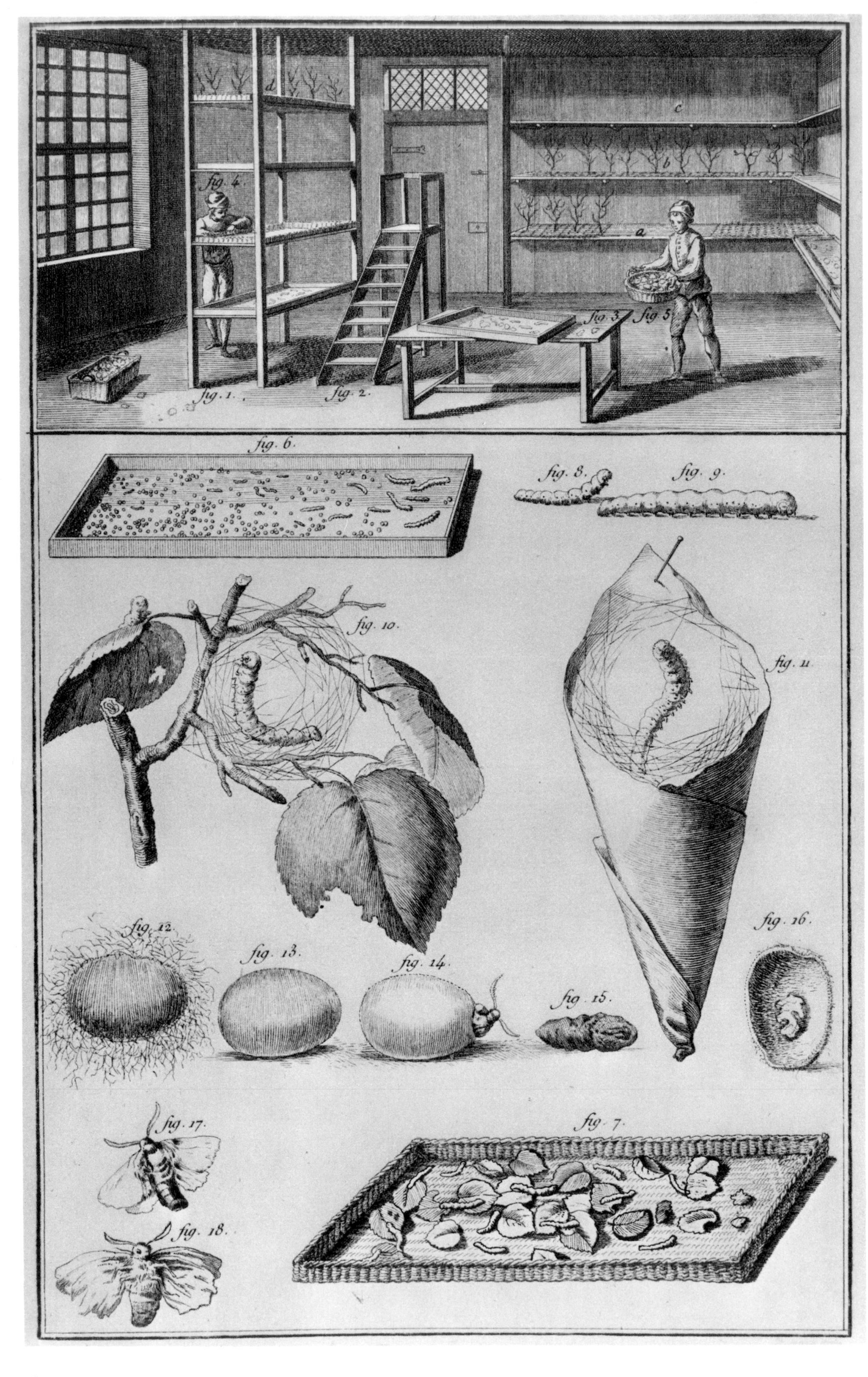
fig. 4.
d
c
b
a
fig. 3
fig 5
fig. 1.
fig. 2.
fig. 6.
fig. 8.
fig. 9.
fig. 10.
fig. 11.
fig. 12.
fig. 13.
fig. 14.
fig. 15.
fig. 16.
fig. 17.
fig. 7.
fig. 18.

Rationalism Triumphant: The Age of Enlightenment

In his "Traité de métaphysique" Voltaire wrote: "Unless we make use of the compasses of mathematics and the torch of experiment and physics, we shall certainly not be able to take a single step forward." In the first half of Voltaire's century, the 18th, Leibniz, Euler and the Bernoullis had made a polished instrument of mathematics. The painstaking acquisition and ordering of "experience" was the main concern of men of learning in the second half of the century.

Between 1751 and 1772 there appeared the twenty-eight volumes of the "Encyclopédie, ou Dictionnaire raisonné des sciences, des arts et des métiers". Into this compendium, expanded to 35 folio tomes by 1780, Denis Diderot and Jean Le Rond d'Alembert attempted to pack all experience relating to science, the crafts and the arts from ancient times to their own. Their work released a spate of other encyclopedias. Science and technology pervaded one another.

Rational methods were used to investigate the handicrafts and trades. In 1772, for example, the first sulfuric acid factory was put up near London, after the small-scale method of manufacturing this product had been replaced by the scientifically worked out lead chamber process. That factory marked the beginning of the development which led to a large-scale chemical industry in England. In France, Nicholas LeBlanc erected a plant for the manufacture of soda from common table salt in 1789; for the manufacturing procedure conducted along traditional craft lines which used plant ash as a starting material, he substituted a viable industrial method. This process of rationalization was not confined to chemical techniques, however. In 1786 Edmund Cartwright invented the mechanical loom,

Text and plates of the Encyclopedia compiled by Diderot and d'Alembert give an accurate and comprehensive panorama of the world as men saw it two centuries ago. This monumental work numbered champions of the Enlightenment such as Voltaire, Montesquieu, Rousseau, and Turgot among its contributors.

Opposite: Copperplate from one of the volumes of illustrations, showing silkworm cultivation in the "Rural Economy".

Below: Title page of Volume 16 of the Encyclopedia. Since publication of the work ran up against obstacles in various quarters, the Parisian publisher LeBreton had volumes 8 to 17 brought out under the cover of a firm in Neuchâtel, Switzerland.

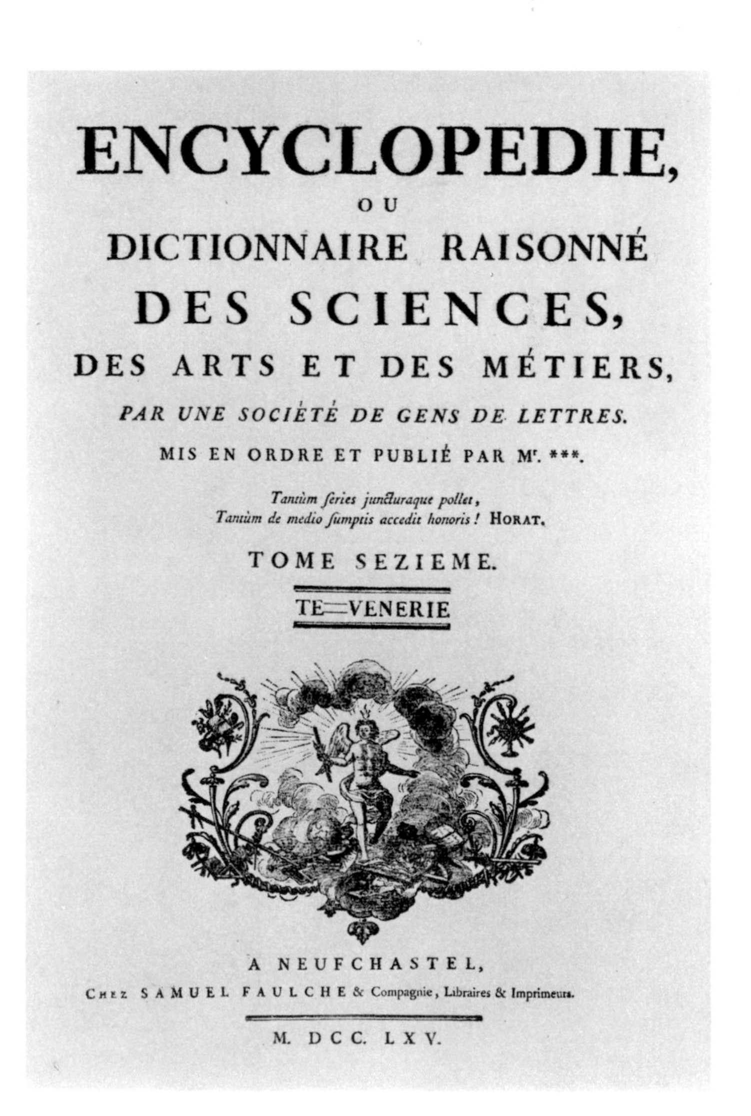

ENCYCLOPEDIE,
OU
DICTIONNAIRE RAISONNÉ
DES SCIENCES,
DES ARTS ET DES MÉTIERS,
PAR UNE SOCIÉTÉ DE GENS DE LETTRES.
MIS EN ORDRE ET PUBLIÉ PAR Mr. ***.

Tantùm series juncturaque pollet,
Tantùm de medio sumptis accedit honoris! HORAT.

TOME SEZIEME.
TE=VENERIE

A NEUFCHASTEL,
CHEZ SAMUEL FAULCHE & Compagnie, Libraires & Imprimeurs.
M. DCC. LXV.

During the Age of Enlightenment many trades, the manufacture of soda being one example, passed from manual to industrial methods. Below: Old-time preparation of potash by extraction from beech-wood ash. Copper engraving from "Ars Vitraria Experimentalis, or: The Compleat Art of Glassmaking" by Johann Kunckel; Frankfurt and Leipzig, 1689.
Right: Industrial production of soda by the LeBlanc process. Common salt is heated together with sulfuric acid and is transformed into Glauber's salt (sodium sulfate). The escaping hydrochloric acid gas which goes into solution with the water in the vessels marked E was used for making sal-ammoniac. In a further reaction the Glauber's salt is converted by heating with coal and calcium carbonate, in the form of chalk, to soda. Xylographs from Louis Figuier's "Marvels of Industry"; Paris, c. 1870.

while at almost the same time James Watt tapped a new source of energy with his rotative steam engine. Thanks to the "physiocrats", rationalism was also turned to the study of political economy. With his "Analyse du tableau économique", dated 1758, François Quesnay was the first to formulate the notion of the economic cycle. In 1776 the Scotsman Adam Smith

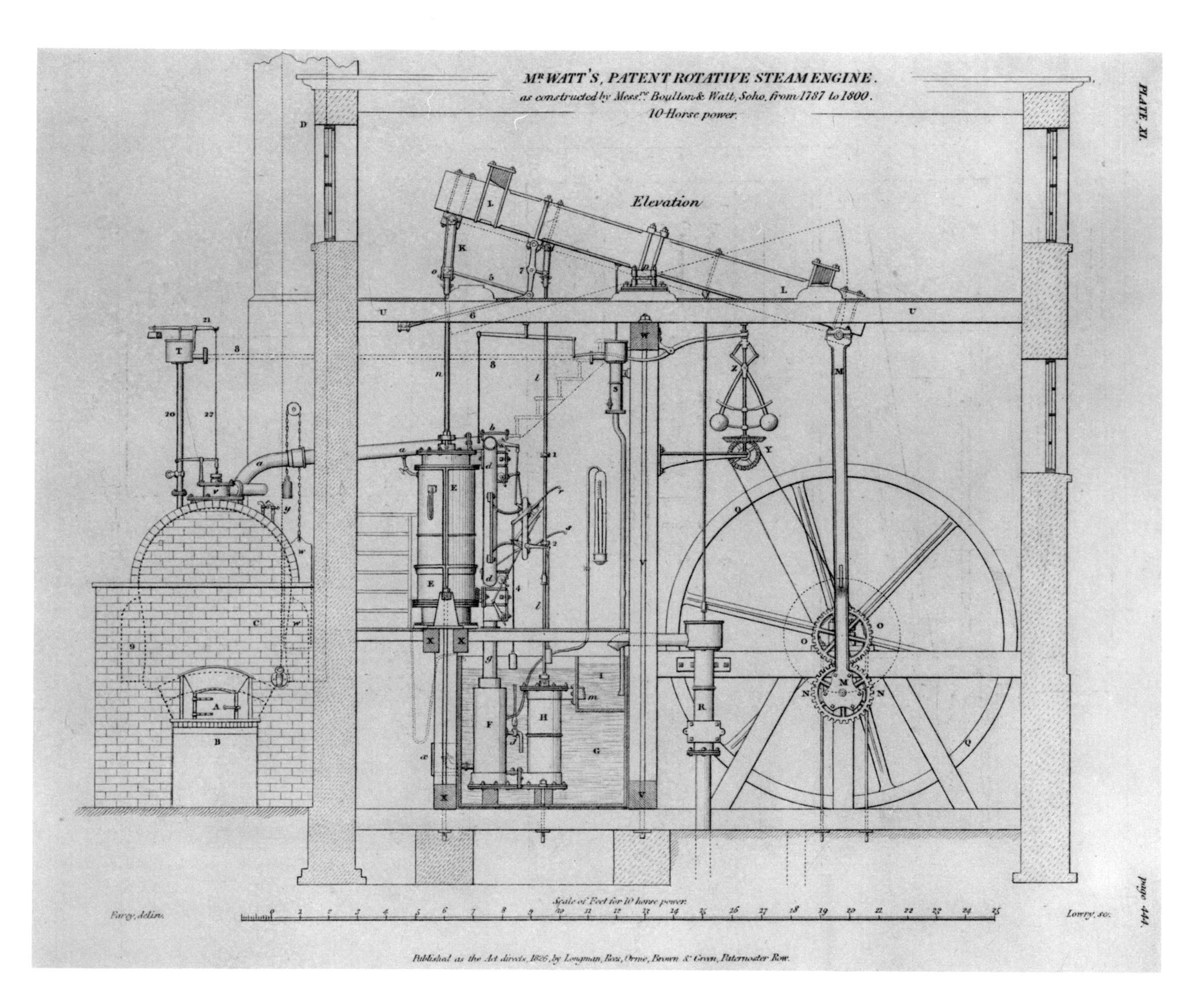

dealt with the laws determining the acquisition and distribution of worldly goods in "An Inquiry into the Nature and Causes of the Wealth of Nations". As the first great advocate of the view that state intervention in the workings of the economy should be kept to a minimum *(laissez faire)*, Smith is the father of economic liberalism.

Every schoolboy knows of the importance of James Watt's rotative steam engine in fomenting the "Industrial Revolution". The machine had the following structural features: (E) double-acting vertical cylinder; (F) condenser; (K) parallel motion bars (pantograph principle) connecting with (L) beam; (Z) centrifugal governor; and (MNO) sun-and-planet gear. Schematic diagram from "A Treatise on the Steam Engine" by John Farey; London, 1827.

DE L'ESPRIT
DES
LOIX,

OU DU RAPPORT QUE LES LOIX doivent avoir avec la Conſtitution de chaque Gouvernement, les Mœurs, le Climat, la Religion, le Commerce, &c.

A QUOI L'AUTEUR A AJOUTÉ

Des recherches nouvelles ſur les Loix Romaines touchant les ſucceſſions, ſur les Loix Françoiſes, & ſur les Loix féodales.

TOME PREMIER.

A GENEVE,
Chez BARILLOT, & FILS.

1748.

In the Age of Reason, another tag for the 18th century, the divine right of kings were being challenged by explorations in constitutional government.
Above: Montesquieu's "On the Spirit of the Laws" was published in Geneva in 1748. For this French aristocrat, laws, far from being divinely ordained, were organic growths, dependent upon customs, trends, economic necessity, and above all upon scientific knowledge. His advocacy of separately established legislative and executive powers helped to shape the constitutions of many modern democracies.

Below: Adam Smith's "Wealth of Nations" appeared in London the same year that the American colonies declared their independence. Panoramic in scope, Smith's inquiry subjects the entire economic process to detailed scrutiny with the aim of analyzing the mechanism of the market. His conclusion, that it is a cohesive, self-regulating system tending to become more and more productive, endeared Smith to 19th century liberals. Newly interpreted by Marx, his findings even had their impact on socialism.

AN
INQUIRY
INTO THE
NATURE AND CAUSES
OF THE
WEALTH OF NATIONS.

INTRODUCTION AND PLAN OF THE WORK.

THE annual labour of every nation is the fund which originally ſupplies it with all the neceſſaries and conveniencies of life which it annually conſumes, and which conſiſt always, either in the immediate produce of that labour, or in what is purchaſed with that produce from other nations.

ACCORDING therefore, as this produce, or what is purchaſed with it, bears a greater or ſmaller proportion to the number of thoſe who are to conſume it, the nation will be better or worſe ſupplied with all the neceſſaries and conveniencies for which it has occaſion.

BUT this proportion muſt in every nation be regulated by two different circumſtances; firſt, by the ſkill, dexterity and judgment
VOL. I. B with

Basle and the Rhine in the middle of the 18th century. Copperplate after a wash India ink drawing by Emanuel Büchel, engraved by Johann Martin Weis; Strasbourg, 1747.

The influence of rationalism on that area of experience now studied under the headings of political science and sociology was strongly marked. Charles-Louis de Montesquieu argued for a strict separation of the legislative and executive powers in government. His contemporary Jean-Jacques Rousseau had even more radical ideas to propound, among them the thesis that a state originally rests on the freely given consent of its members, an arrangement which he termed the "Contrat social".

All these 18th century currents circulated as far as Basle, too. Trade and industry began to win preponderance over the crafts. The end of patrician rule and the old Confederation was being prepared by the Enlightenment.

Back in the 16th century, when Stefano Pellizari proposed setting up a silk manufacturing plant employing 2000 workers, the City Council had turned down this project categorically. By the time another hundred years had passed Basle was a full-fledged commercial

From the first half of the 17th century on, ribbon weaving became an independent and ever more important branch of the Basle silk industry.
Left: Silk ribbon made in Basle, 1900. Private collection, Basle.
Above: Simple ribbon loom for apron-strings used in Canton Basle Country. The heddles were operated by pedal, the shuttle was inserted by hand. Swiss Museum for European Ethnology, Basle.
Opposite: Despite opposition from the gilds, the bar-loom on which several ribbons could be simultaneously woven eventually found acceptance in Basle. This ribbon-mill from the year 1764 was capable of handling 24 pieces. Swiss Museum for European Ethnology, Basle

and industrial centre. In 1670 tradespeople of the town owned 390 ships which carried textiles manufactured in Basle down the Rhine to Strasbourg and Frankfurt. And in 1682 the influential manufacturers and merchants banded together to form a "Directory of Tradesmen" for the protection of their interests.

Refugees from the Reformation and Counter-Reformation had transplanted luxury goods industries from their countries of origin, France and Italy, to Basle. They established factories for the manufacture of silk ribbons, trimmings embroidered with gold, and fine silken materials which became the bases of a thriving silk ribbon industry. Ribbon manufacture in Basle was notable for two peculiar traits: the use of the "ribbon-mill" as a machine, and the system of portioning out work to be done at home.

The ribbon-mill, or bar-loom, was introduced from Holland in the 1660s. On the so-called treadle-loom it

was possible to make one ribbon only, the shuttle being manually operated. With the new ribbon-mills sixteen or more ribbons could be woven simultaneously, thanks to the mechanical propulsion of several shuttles. Because of resistance from the gilds the invention made no headway in Germany and France.

The Emperor slept here – Francis of Austria in 1814. The front elevation of the "Blue House", built in the 1760s for the ribbon manufacturer Lukas Sarasin. Such elegant dwellings reflected the wealth which the silk ribbon industry had brought to Basle. Public Records Office.

The Basle Town Council proved more liberal, and the ribbon manufacturers were given the right to make use of the bar-loom in the late 17th century.

The system of dealing out work derived from official regulations concerning silk weaving. In 1612 the number of looms allowed was specified exactly. The "posamenters" or ribbon makers who lived outside of town were allowed to work for Basle entrepreneurs but were forbidden to sell their wares in the town. They worked in their own houses and with their own implements

for the Basle manufacturers and merchants. Their work was then fetched by their employers' runners in carts and passed on for export.

Just after the middle of the 18th century, at about the time the industrial revolution was getting underway in England and France, the Basle silk ribbon industry went into a phase of marked prosperity. The number of bar-looms rose from 1225 in 1753 to 2246 in 1785. This upswing was reflected in the wealth which accrued to the industrialists and merchants, most conspicuously in their splendid residences such as the "White House" and "Blue House" above the Rhine or the "Cherry Garden" on Elisabeth Street.

The political influence of the artisans, on the other hand, declined more and more, the ground they yielded being taken over by the "ribbon lords", the refugee patricians of the 18th century.

The Enlightenment was not without its impact on the educated class of Basle. The town clerk Isaak Iselin championed the physiocratic doctrines of Quesnay. In his "History of Mankind", published in 1776, Iselin asserted in good Benthamite fashion that the state must strive to bring about "the greatest happiness for the greatest number". In 1777 he founded the "Society for the Fostering of the Public Weal", an association which is still doing humanitarian work.

The most fervent advocate of the Enlightenment in Basle was Peter Ochs. In 1798, as the leader of the democratic party, he re-cast Basle in the mould of the French Revolution. That same year, as president of the Senate, he proclaimed the constitution of the Helvetic Republic, the director of which he became shortly thereafter. This stroke spelt the end of the old Confederation and of patrician Basle. The Enlightenment with its rational ideas had broken up the less strictly reasoned ties which had held the complicated structure of the old federation of cantons together. In the 19th century such ideas – this time in the guise of positivism and the creed of progress – were to become the driving forces of society.

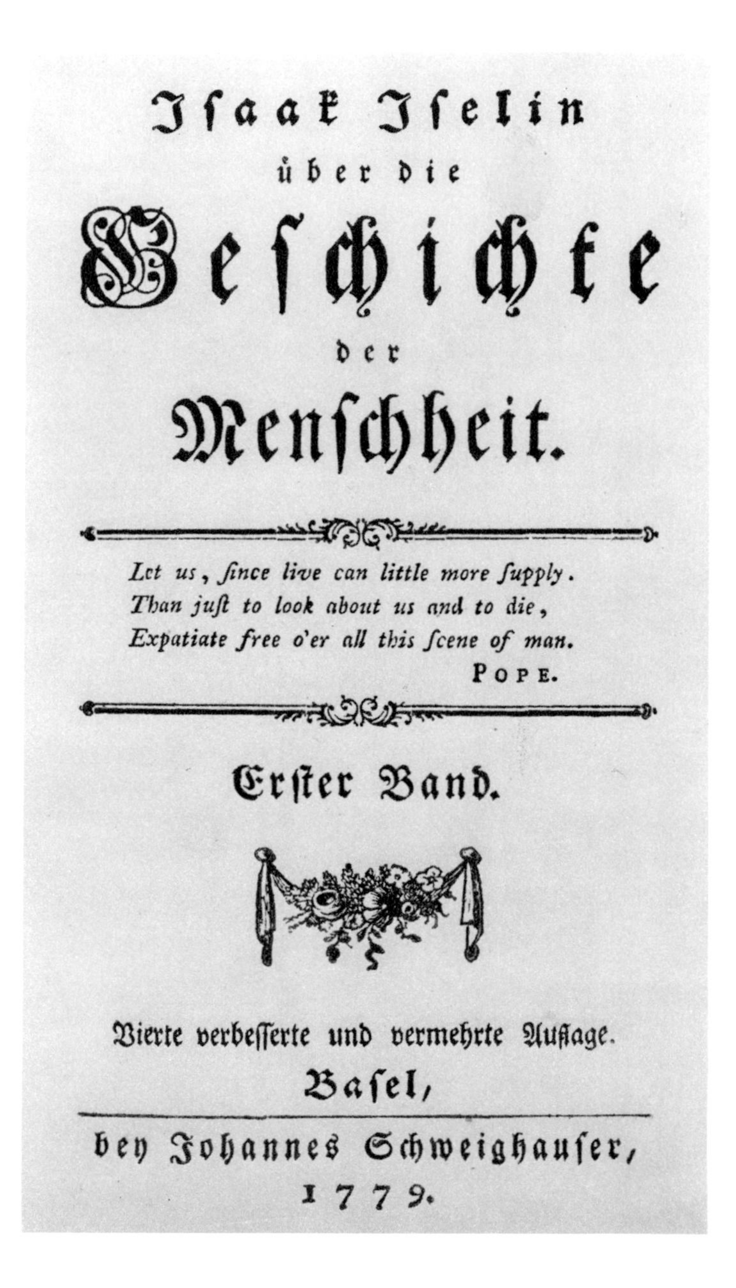

Isaak Iselin
über die
Geschichte
der
Menschheit.

Let us, since live can little more supply,
Than just to look about us and to die,
Expatiate free o'er all this scene of man.
POPE.

Erster Band.

Vierte verbesserte und vermehrte Auflage.
Basel,
bey Johannes Schweighauser,
1779.

Fitly enough, a quotation from Epistle I of Alexander Pope's "Essay on Man" keynotes Isaak Iselin's "History of Mankind". But the bit reproduced has stopped short of the punch line, which reads: "A mighty maze! but not without a plan." This was a thoroughly "enlightened" viewpoint, and the town clerk's espousal of it had a considerable influence on Peter Ochs, the impassioned revolutionary and democratic leader of Basle.

The Development of the Chemical Industry in Basle

The life-history of the chemical industry may be likened to the germination and growth of a tree. The bud must be vigorous, the soil fertile, and the climate salutary. In its crafts and trades Basle possessed robust buds, in its location and economic structure a soil that was fruitful, and in the disposition of its citizenry and officialdom a climate receptive to industry.

The Germs of the Chemical Industry

The primal cells from which industries arose were to be found in the crafts of the Middle Ages.
Throughout this pre-industrial period working methods, tools and know-how remained the same; technical skills in the old days were static. Their unchanging quality depended on a number of factors, among them the *Weltanschauung* of those times, social institutions such as the gilds, and not least on the fact that class and language separated artisans from scholars. Latin was long the tongue of the learned.
Men active in economic life took the lead in stimulating closer co-operation between the practical arts and natural science. In 1666 the French minister Colbert ordered the Academy of Sciences to investigate the handicrafts, particularly dyeing, with a view to rationalizing them. The ending of the divorce between craftsmen and scientists is pertinently expressed in Bischoff's "Essay on the History of the Art of Dyeing", written in 1780: "No longer shunning the dirt and foul smell of the workshops, or despising the workman for his simplicity, nowadays they [the men of learning] visit him at his work and discuss with him how and in what ways it may be improved."
With this step, the yoking together of artisans and scholars, modern technology began.
Formerly, as noted, working methods were static. Now they are subject to constant change: modern technology is pre-eminently dynamic. Applied and theoretical science help to further each other, since each break-through in knowledge opens up a possible new practical application, while each improvement in technique helps to amplify scientific research methods.

The chemical industry as it stands before us today assumes a bewildering variety of forms. Yet it grew from but a few germs – from the old-style trade in medicinal drugs and coloring matter, from the apothecary's laboratory, and from the gasworks that made its appearance around 1800.

Seal of the Plain and High-Color Dyers in Basle, dated 1725. Basle Public Records Office.

The Drugs Trade

Leafing through an old volume of botany – for example, the "New Compleat Book of Herbs" by the Basle professor Theodore Zwinger, Jr., published in 1696 – one is amazed by the plenitude of knowledge concerning the way drugs act which it contains. If we recall that the effects of drugs, whether used for medicinal or coloring purposes, elude direct observation and can only be disclosed through experience, then we are bound to ask just how this knowledge was amassed.

It is difficult to judge to what extent instinct, either that of ancient man or of the animals he watched, led to the discovery of drugs and their effects. One renowned authority in the field, Prof. Alexander Tschirch, relegates any attempt at explanation along these lines to the realm of fable. Certainly magical and mystical ideas were instrumental in the accumulation of lore relating to therapeutic and colorific agents.

In the magical view of things, certain properties peculiar to animal organs such as the heart, spleen or liver are transferred to him who benefits by incorporating them into his own body. Up to the 18th century, for instance, men believed in the efficacy of powdered narwhal tooth as an antidote. It was said to come from the fabulous and invincible "unicorn", which was as frequent a figure in old-time accounts of far journeys as the great sea serpent. Even as late as 1850 the monoceros myth had not yet died out and was still granted credence in serious works.

Bezoar stone from the entrails of ruminants such as the stag and goat, supposedly caused by a serpent's bite, was invested with the power to counteract snake venom and other poisons. The hunter who ate animal organs – the heart, spleen, liver, brain – might by so doing take on the special qualities of an animal. It is possible to trace a fairly straight line from such magic analogies in prehistoric times right up to the hormone extracts of the suprarenal cortex in our day, though conceptions have changed greatly en route to be sure.

Early 16th century dealer in drugs vending guaiacum wood, widely used at the time as a remedy against venereal disease. Woodcut illustrating the title page of Ulrich von Hutten's work, "Of the wood called Guaiacum, that healeth the French poxes"; Strasbourg, 1519.

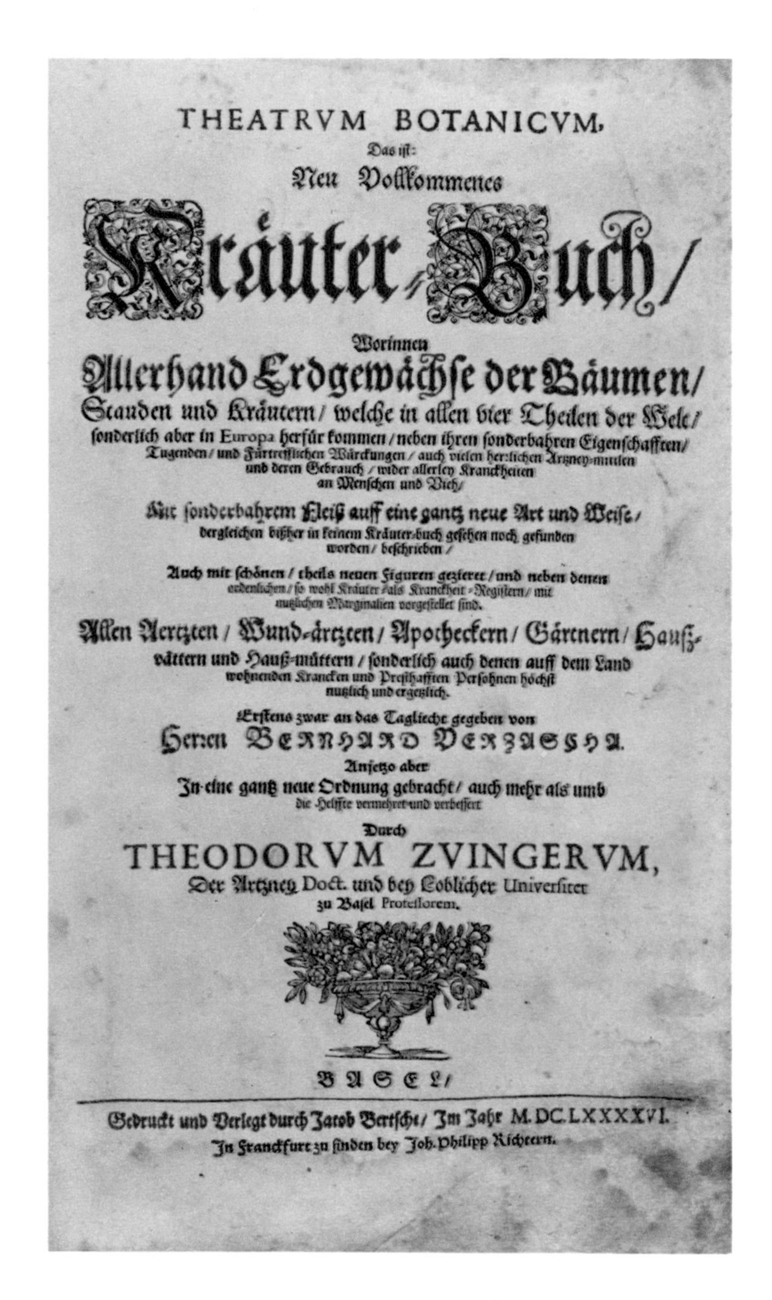

THEATRVM BOTANICVM,
Das ist:
Neu Vollkommenes
Kräuter-Buch/
Worinnen
Allerhand Erdgewächse der Bäumen/
Stauden und Kräutern/ welche in allen vier Theilen der Welt/
sonderlich aber in Europa herfür kommen / neben ihren sonderbahren Eigenschafften/
Tugenden / und Fürtrefflichen Würckungen / auch vielen herzlichen Artzney-mitteln
und deren Gebrauch / wider allerley Kranckheiten
an Menschen und Vieh/
Mit sonderbahrem Fleiß auff eine gantz neue Art und Weise/
dergleichen bißher in keinem Kräuter-buch gesehen noch gefunden
worden/ beschrieben /
Auch mit schönen / theils neuen Figuren gezieret / und neben denen
ordenlichen / so wohl Kräuter- als Kranckheit-Registern / mit
nutzlichen Marginalien vorgestellet sind.
Allen Aertzten / Wund-ärtzten / Apotheckern / Gärtnern / Hauß-
vättern und Hauß-müttern / sonderlich auch denen auff dem Land
wohnenden Krancken und Presthafften Persohnen höchst
nutzlich und ergetzlich.
Erstens zwar an das Tagliecht gegeben von
Herren BERNHARD VERZASCHA.
Anjetzo aber
In eine gantz neue Ordnung gebracht / auch mehr als umb
die Helffte vermehret und verbessert
Durch
THEODORVM ZVINGERVM,
Der Artzney Doct. und bey Loblicher Universitet
zu Basel Professorem.
BASEL /
Gedruckt und Verlegt durch Jacob Bertsch / Im Jahr M.DC.LXXXXVI.
In Franckfurt zu finden bey Joh. Philipp Richtern.

Title page of the Book of Herbs by Theodore Zwinger (1658–1724). Part of the stocks of the woodcuts contained in this work, dated 1696, had been used for a Latin commentary on Dioscorides (long-time authority on Materia Medica), which appeared in 1554. Zwinger's was one of the last typical herbals which illustrated, described, and discussed the medicinal properties of plants.

748 Kräuter-Buchs Achter und Letzter Theil/

Bezoar / Bezaar.

Ein Stein wider alles Gifft / Cap. 36.

Bezoar oder Bezaar und Bezahard / ist ein Name eines Steins / welcher eine behaltende Krafft deß Menschlichen Lebens hat / und eine außbündige Artzney wider alles Gifft ist / und kräfftiger in seiner Würckung / als alle andere Gifft-Artzneyen und Tyriac geachtet.

Es ist aber das Wort oder Namen Bezoar ein Arabischer und Persischer Name / und heißt auf unserer Sprach eine Behaltung deß Lebens / von seiner fürtrefflichen Krafft und Tugend wegen. Und um solcher seiner herzlichen Tugend willen / wird der Name dieses Steins auch andern Gifft-Arneyen zugeeignet / daß man daher Bezoar nennet eine jede Artzney / so dem Gifft und der Pestilentz widerstehet / und dem Menschen das Leben erhält. Also wird genennet und beschrieben Pulvis Bezoardicus, welches ein Pulver für die Pestilentz und Gifft ist / so doch in dasselbige Pulver der Stein Bezoar nicht gemischet wird / und ist also viel gesagt / als Pulvis Alexipharmacus seu Antidotarius, oder Pulvis contra venena, das ist / ein Gifft- und Pestilentz-Pulver / so denselbigen Widerstand thut.

Die Gestalt dieses Steins ist also / nemlich / es ist ein länglicher runder Stein / gleich einer Eycheln / darvon das Häublein abgezogen ist / außwendig glatt / und anzusehen wie ein poliertes Eysen / innwendig Aschenfarb / ist leicht / lässet sich schaben mit einem Messer / und so man das Pulver davon in Mund nimmt / solvirt es sich und zerschmiltzt / ist ohne allen Geschmack und ohne allen Geruch.

Dieser Stein Bezoar wird gefunden in Sicilien / Indien / und in Persien in Orient / von den Jägern / und wird in gar hohem Werth und Preiß geachtet und verkaufft.

Es schreiben die Araber / daß er wachse an den Augen der Hirtze / nemlich / wann die Hirtz alt werden / bekommen sie Würm in den Gedärmen im Leib / solche zu vertreiben und zu tödten / pflegen sie Schlangen zu suchen und zu essen / und damit sie von dem Gifft der Schlangen im Leib nicht beschädiget werden / gehen sie in ein frisch Wasser und tauchen sich biß an den Halß darein / daß man nur den Kopff herfür siehet gehen / und pflegen darinn etliche Tage / so lang biß sie empfinden / daß sie von dem Gifft erlediget seyn / zu verharren / alsdann trieffen ihnen zähe Thränen auß den Augen / wie ein Gummi / und werden an den Ecken der Augen hart / und groß wie Hasel-Nüß oder wie Eycheln / und seyn ihnen verhinderlich an dem Gesicht.

Wann sie nun auß dem Wasser wiedernm in ihre Lager kommen / und die Verhindernüß deß Gesichts mercken / gehen sie an die Bäume / und reiben sich mit dem Backen und Augen

Description of bezoar stone, once supposed to possess magic curative powers, particularly in counteracting poisons. Taken from the entrails of certain ruminants, this antidote was to be had from the European apothecary's shelf up to the middle of the 18th century. Page from the 1582 edition of the Book of Herbs by Adam Lonitzer, published in Frankfurt.

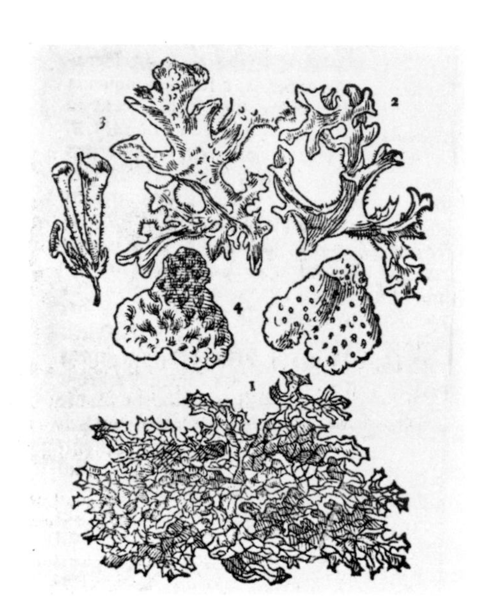

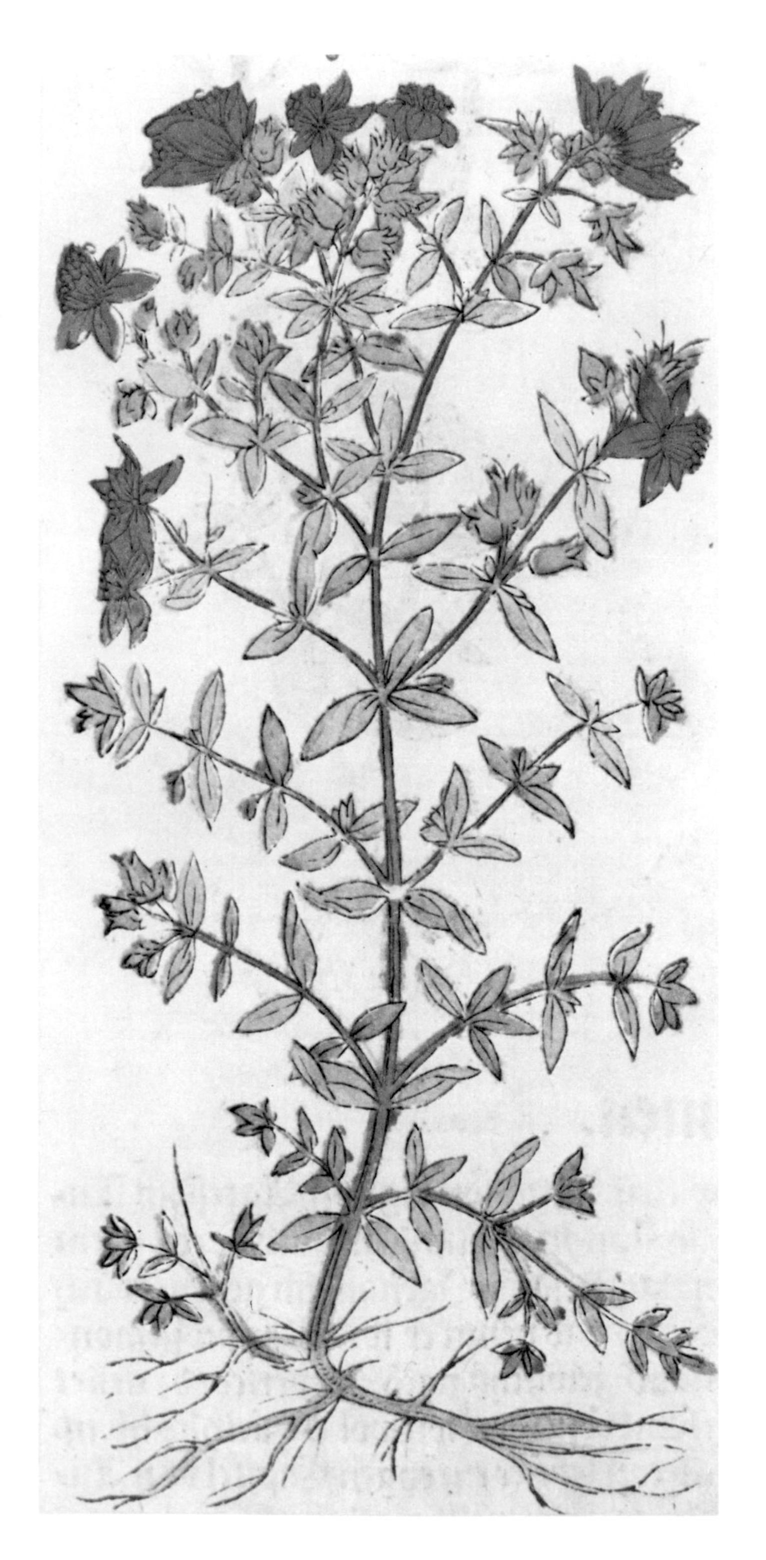

Woodcuts of three plants whose medicinal effect was indicated by their "signature".
Left: St. John's wort. Color plate from Hieronymus Bock's herbal; Strasbourg, 1577.
Above left: Saffron plant from Lonitzer's herbal; Frankfurt, 1557.
Above right: Lungwort from Zwinger's herbal.

The mystical view held that evidence of curative and colorific powers has been given by the Creator in the mark or "signature" that distinguishes a plant. It was the task of the initiate to interpret this sign, its name, form, and color. St. John's wort *(Hypericum perforatum* L.*)* has lanceolate leaves which appear to be perforated. The lance shape and perforation are indicative of curative power in case of external wounds. When squashed the receptacle gives off a red juice; this signals its use in internal hemorrhages. The use of lungwort *(Lobaria pulmonaria* [L.] Hoffm.*)* against pulmonary afflictions is betokened by its spotted leaves resembling the lungs. The dried stigmas of *Crocus sativus* L., dealt in under the market name of saffron, served not only as a yellow dyestuff and spice, but also as a medicament in jaundice.

Around 1800 there were about 30 coloring substances and several hundred healing drugs in use in Europe. Madder was the designation given the pulverized root of the *Rubia tinctorum* L., employed as a red dye. Until superseded by synthetic alizarin around the year 1870, madder was cultivated in huge amounts, mainly in the Low Countries, in the region of Avignon, and in Alsace. The hot, aqueous sediment of the finely crushed root produced shades ranging from red to violet on wool, cotton, and linen; red if the fibrous material was first steeped in an alum solution, violet if similarly treated in a solution of iron vitriol. By a long drawn-out process which Oriental dyers had brought to Europe around 1750, the famous, brilliant Turkey red was produced.

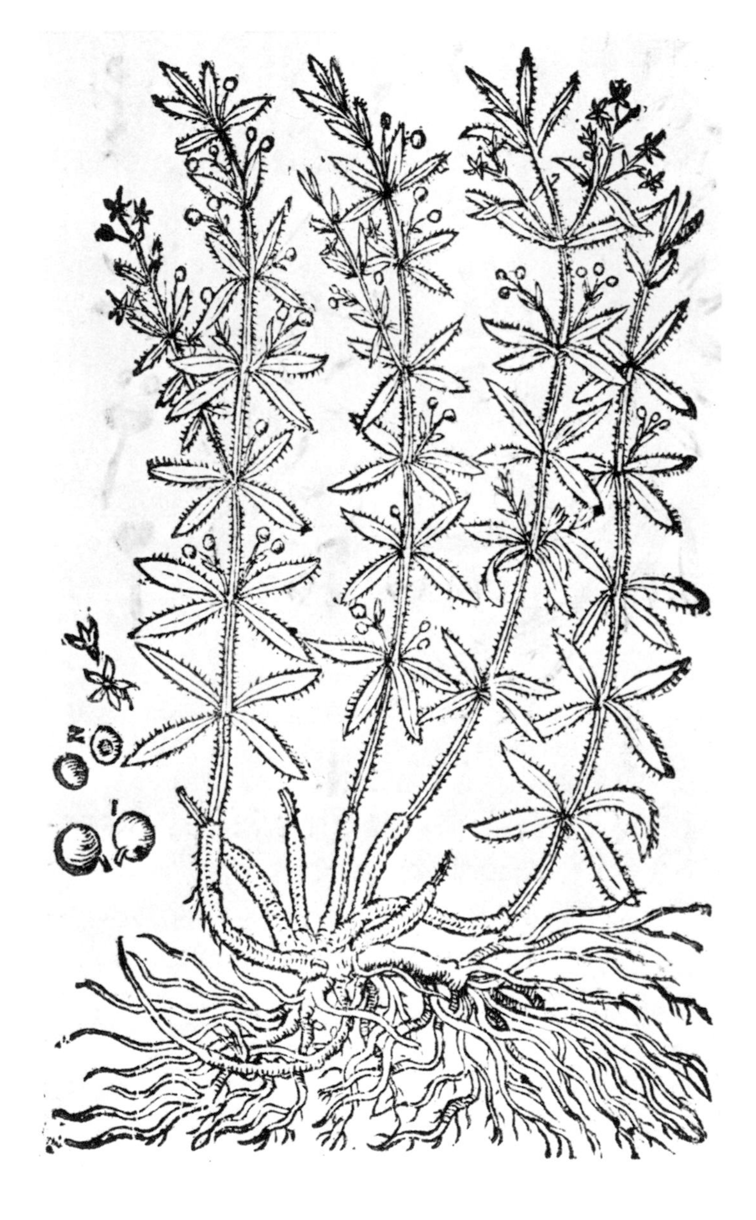

Madder root was once the main source of red dye.
Above: The madder plant as depicted in Zwinger's herbal.
Left: Lizari, the dried roots, a market form of madder (life-size).

In the Middle Ages woad was the most important blue coloring agent. This was a fermented preparation from the leaves of dyer's woad *(Isatis tinctoria* L.*)*, marketed in fist-sized balls. From the 13th to the 16th century the cultivation of this dye plant was the source of Thuringia's wealth. The hegemony that woad so long enjoyed was finally broken by the introduction of indigo from overseas.

Until supplanted by indigo from the lands of the "Indikos" in the 16th century, indigenous dyer's woad was the main blue coloring agent in Europe.
Right: Dyer's woad. From Lonitzer's herbal.
Below: Indigo dye as marketed after being obtained from any of several plants belonging to the indigofera genus.

The dried, unripe berries of the buckthorn were an important substance for yellow dyeings.
Above: Buckthorn. Woodcut from Zwinger's herbal.
Right: The yellow berries of the buckthorn (magnification x 2).

The dyer of old did not lack for plants yielding yellow colors. Weld or woald *(Reseda luteola* L.*)* was grown as a useful plant throughout Europe. The fruit of the buckthorn *(Rhamnus cathartica* L.*)*, the common sawwort *(Serratula tinctoria* L.*)*, and the desiccated sprigs of the dyer's broom or greenweed *(Genista tinctoria* L.*)* were found everywhere, as were bulb scales and the foliage of the birch and aspen. With the aqueous decoctions of these drugs the dyer illuminated all fibres yellow after pre-mordanting them with alum. Materials pre-boiled with ferrous and cuprous salts could be colored olive to brown. It is worthy of note that yellow-coloring saffron was extracted in the neighborhood of Basle in the 15th century; the "Saffron" gild of Basle merchants took its name from this substance.

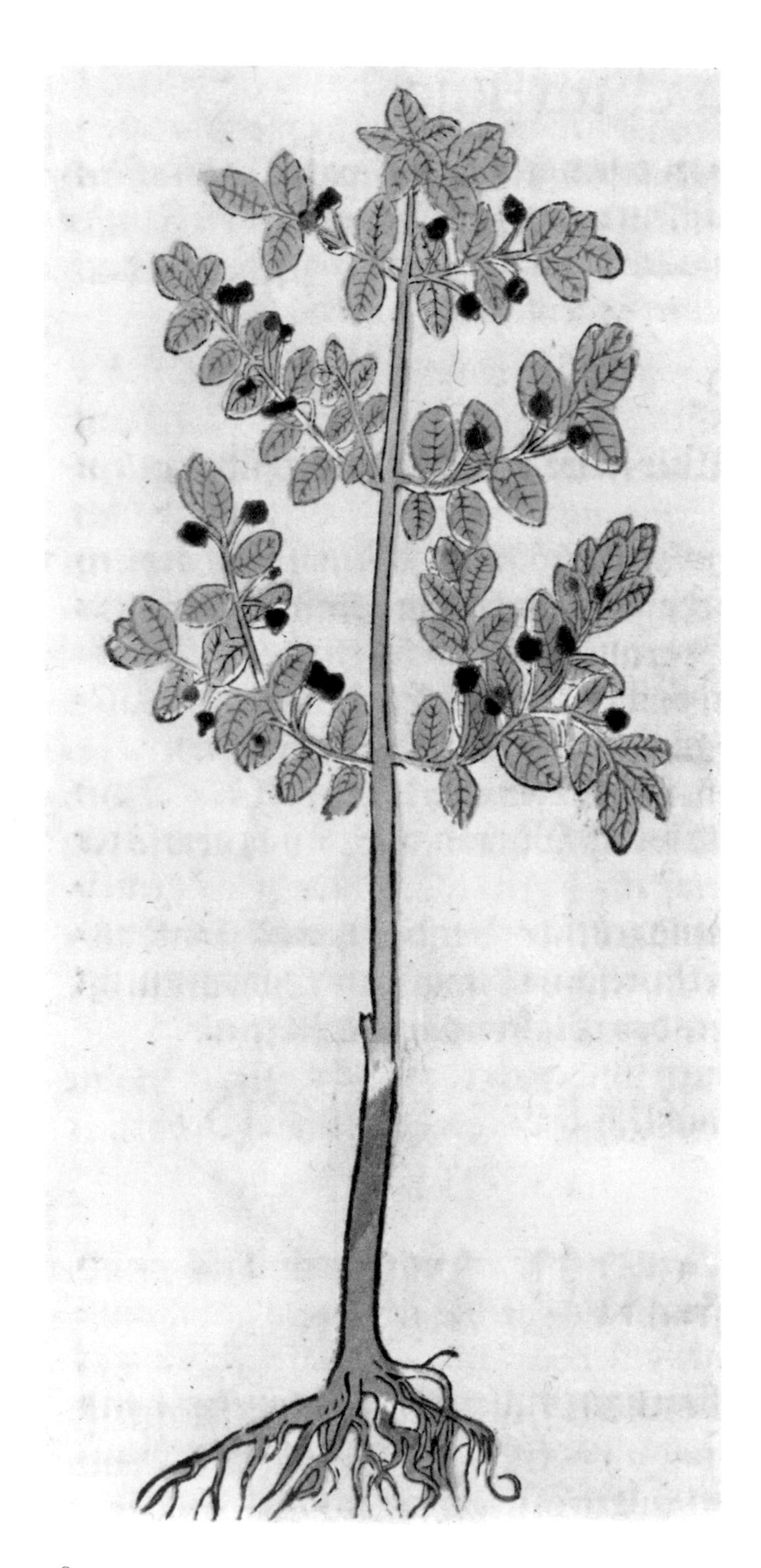

The discovery of America brought the dyer many new varieties of coloring matter. Dyewoods – various redwoods, fustics, and above all logwood – found their way to Europe in big quantities. On textile material treated with an alum bath, these woods, when grated, yielded colors which, although not specially durable, were cheap and bright.
From among the enormous amount of medicinal drugs let it suffice to mention but a few as examples which may help to illustrate the later development to industrial products.
The aqueous decoction of the dried bark of the black alder-tree *(Frangula alnus* Mill.*)* has been taken since ancient times as a purgative. The exact dosage is important, however, since excessive doses bring on cramps.

Decoctions of the bark of the alder buckthorn and of Rhamnus purshiana DC. are still used as purgatives.
Left: The alder buckthorn. Colored woodcut from Bock's herbal.
Below: The bark of Rhamnus purshiana.

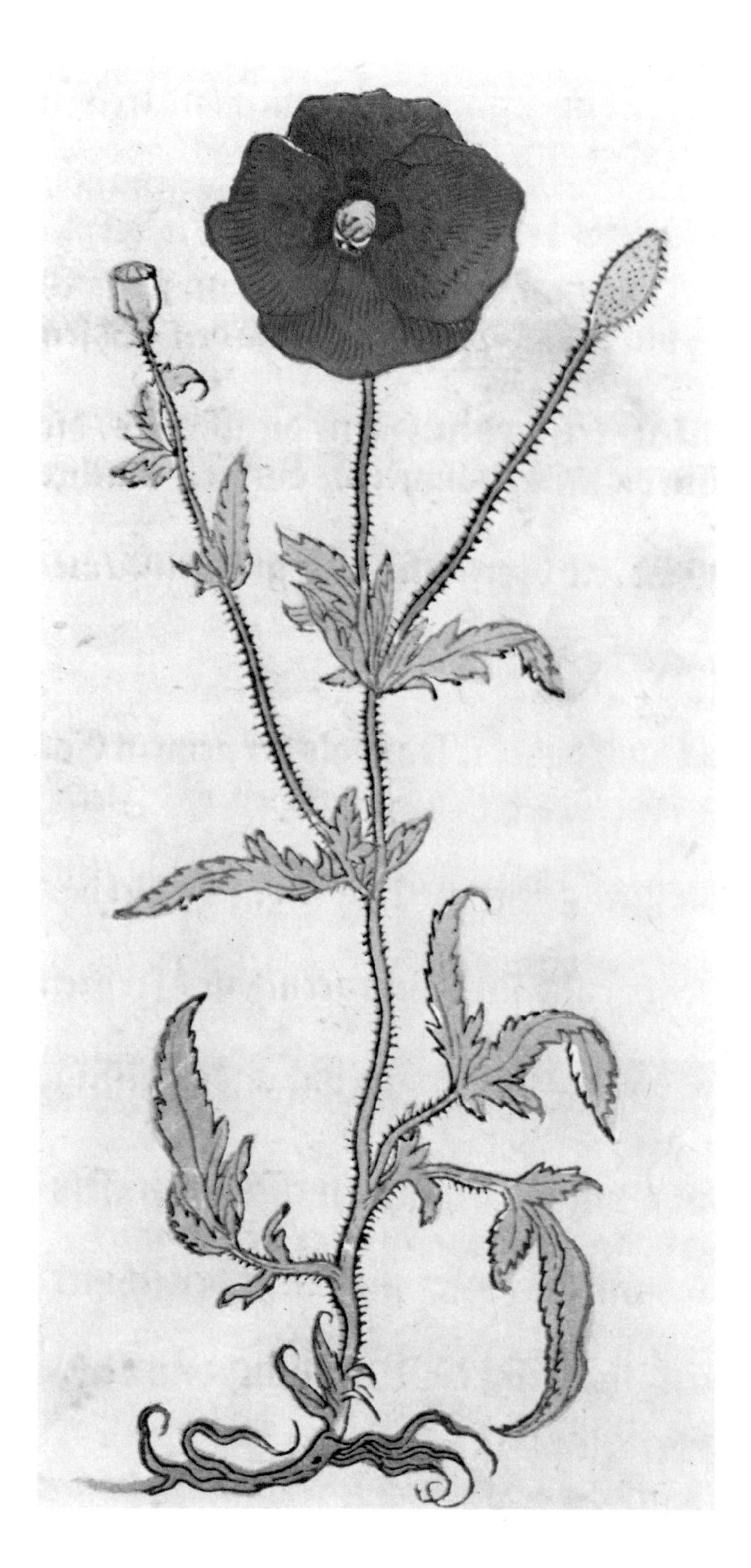

According to Theodore Zwinger, it is "on that account a potent peasant physic of which feeble natures should be ware".

The dried leaves of the foxglove *(Digitalis purpurea L.)* were recommended in England as early as the 11th century as a tea against "sluggishness of the blood". Remarkably enough, in the 16th century this stimulating effect on the circulatory system was no longer known to Leonhard Fuchs, Jerome Bock and Otto Brunfels, the aforementioned botanists. Only in 1775 did the English physician William Withering discover its coronary action anew.

The use of poppy sporocarps as a hypnotic goes very far back in time. Zwinger states that a syrup prepared from these drugs will bring back sleep to the insom-

In their capsules poppy plants contain sleep-inducing opium alkaloids.
Left: Corn poppy (Papaver rhoeas L.). Colored woodcut from Bock's herbal.
Below: Capsules of the opium poppy.

niac. The danger of taking too large doses was also known, however, for "one should not give more than three-quarters of an ounce of it to a fully grown person". Opium, the dried-up latex of the unripe cystocarp of the common poppy *(Papaver somniferum* L.*)*, contains sleep-inducing and pain-deadening substances to a still larger amount.

Peruvian bark *(Cinchona spp.)* was brought from South America to Europe around the middle of the 17th century and was dealt in as an expensive febrifuge. Up to the 20th century this drug was the sole effective remedy against malaria.

Old-style drugs are prepared for use by boiling out, or extracting. These aqueous extracts were employed thousands of years ago in the form of "decoctions" and "dyeliquors". But strangely enough, not until the beginning of the 19th century were the constituents of such extracts deemed to be worth separating off and

Cinchona bark contains quinine, which is a "febrifuge": it lowers fever.
Left: Branch of the cinchona tree. Copperplate accompanying the first exact description of this plant, "Sur l'arbre du quinquina", by Charles-Marie de La Condamine. Mémoires de l'Académie Royale des Sciences; Paris, 1740.
Below left: Cinchona bark (Cortex Chinae).
Below: Quinine crystals in dark field; magnification x 120.

investigating. In 1810 Chevreul separated the dyestuff of logwood (the heartwood of *Haematoxylon spp.*) from the aqueous extract; in 1815 Pelletier isolated santaline, the dyestuff from "red sandal wood" *(Pterocarpus santalinus* L. f.*)*, and four years later, together with Caventou, he obtained quinine from the decoction of Peruvian bark. Note how compressed is the chronology of these isolations: in 1817 Sertuerner extracted morphine from opium; in 1820 Runge isolated caffein from coffee; while in 1828 Lapier, Robiquet and Colin took out a patent for the extraction of the red dyestuff of the madder root.

The question arises why the separation of active principles from drugs did not arouse scientific interest sooner. The isolation of the substances contained in a decoction, and the use of a substance thus separated out in place of the drug as found in nature, must evidently be preceded by the insight that the curative or colorative action may be ascribed, not to the whole drug, but rather to its component substances. As obvious as this assumption may sound, it was not in fact self-evident at all.

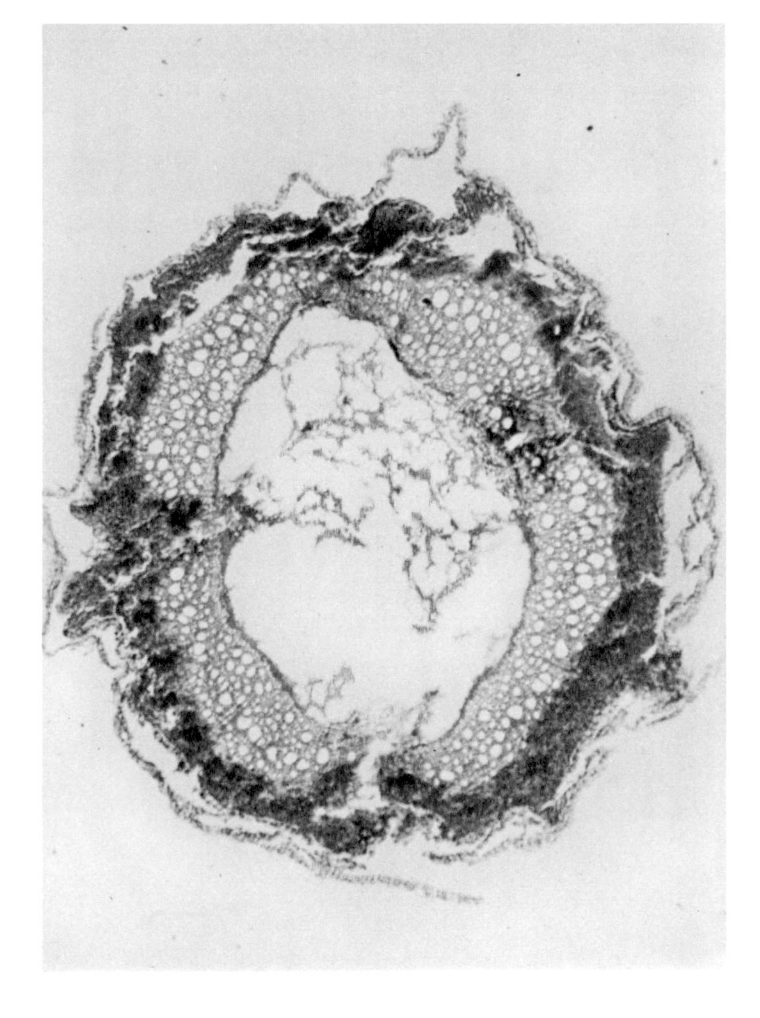

The madder root, besides other dyes, contains red-coloring alizarin.
Right: Madder root in cross-section; magnification x 10.
Below: Crystals of sublimated alizarin; magnification x 5.

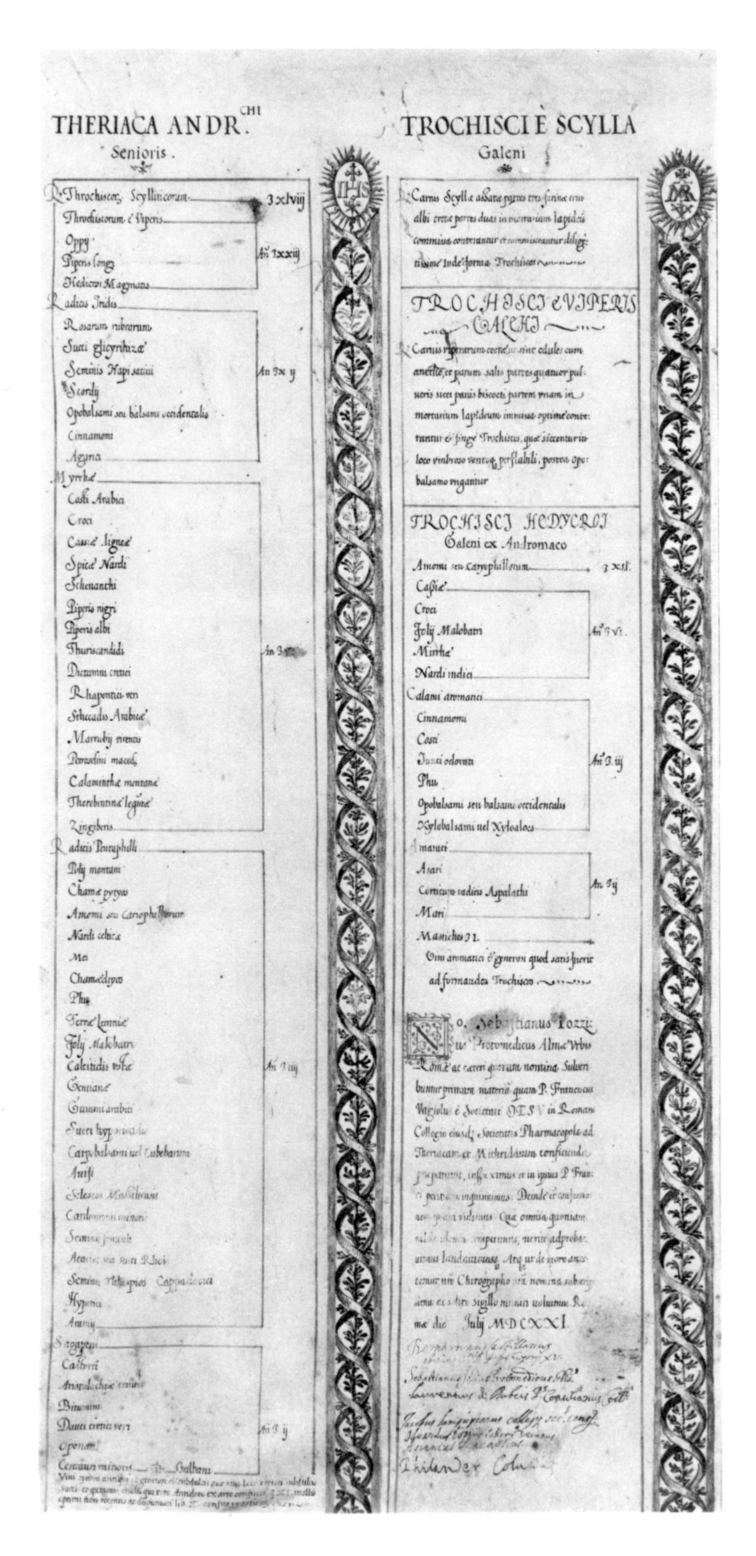

THERIACA ANDR.CHI
Senioris.

TROCHISCI E SCYLLA
Galeni

TROCHISCI E VIPERIS GALENI

TROCHISCI HEDYCROI
Galeni ex Andromaco

In former times, those skilled in medicine or dyeing looked on a drug as something whole and entire. Preparation was usually carried out according to ritual-like precepts. Polish kermes, a species of scale insect used as a red coloring matter for wool and silk, were gathered by the peasants on St. John's eve amidst solemn ceremonials. The hypnotic mandrake root *(Mandragora officinarum* L.*)* might only be pulled from the soil by a dog inside a magic circle. And the doctrine of signatures clearly indicates that the action of a drug was not to be sought in an "active principle", but rather in the drug as a whole.

Paracelsus' demand that the effective agent contained in a medicament should be recognized in its specific capacity and used separated for medicinal purposes has often been misunderstood. By the "effective agent" Paracelsus did not mean the active principle as we employ this term nowadays. He directed his fire against foolish and complicated universal recipes, like the one for the poison antidote theriaca, put together from dozens of drugs such as opium, pepper, cinnamon, myrrh, anise, viper's bugloss, St. John's wort, mummy, and so on.

The active principle, then, and not the whole drug – here lay the new angle. René Descartes planted the seed of this change in his "Discourse on Method" (1637). As has been touched on, he sees the world as a machine. In order to understand its mechanism, this machine must be split up into its parts, which can then be comprehended by measuring, counting, and weighing them. This mechanistic mode of thinking immediately pervaded physics. Not until the very end of the 18th century, however, with Lavoisier and Dalton did it come to prevail in chemistry, and in medicine it had to wait until Virchow later on in the 19th century.

Left: Recipes for theriaca from the Jesuit dispensary in Rome, 1621. Swiss Museum of Pharmaceutical History, Basle.
Opposite: How mandrake was plucked, with due attention to ritual. Illuminated page from a Latin translation of Dioscorides (fl. 1st century A.D.). 12th century codex, Harley MS. 5294, f. 43, British Museum.

aspargat ita ut sol mergat. manu dextra sic pcet. Dea sca tell' & cetera q
in libri capite scripta sunt. Herba basilisca illis locis nascit ubi fuerit ser-
pens basilisc' n eni unu .e. cor gen' s; genera st tria unu .e. olocrys' aliud
.e. stellat' capite auro & tciu .e. sanguineu ut mineu .i.e. capite aureo.
Hos omis herba basilisca optinet facile. Si qs ea secu habuerit serpentes
optinet nec uisa mala huic nocere possunt. Olocris' aute q dr crisens qd uidit
insufflat & incendit. Stellat' aute q .e. crisco cefal' asterias qs uiderit ul pcus-
serit defluens et totos sa p se remanebit. Omis uiolentias cor hec herba legitia
optinet. Si qs homo eam secu habuerit ab omib; generationib; serpentiu erit
tutus. Est herba tal' simil' salici foliis oblongioribus; radix ei pede ursi simil.
latte habens aurosu simile celidonie flore aute crissococcu q ea leget mud' sit
circu scribat eam auro argento cornu ceruino & ebure dente apro cornu tau-
rino & frugis mellitos i uestigio pones. Nomen herbe Mandragoras.

Hui' genera sunt .ii. mascul' & femina sed
mascul' folia albidiq ora habet & maiora
mala i magnitudi ne mali matiani
ntri q; uis una .e. Ad oclor' fervores
Hui' folia re- centia tu polenta
tinsa oclis sup posita psunt
ualidissime & uulneribus;
inferiore eade collec

tiones omisq;
duritias sol
uit & spargit.
Ad stigma
ta corpor'
Septe dieb;
uisales can
indib; h.

tenit insricta sine ulceratione deterget eade
clidos reseruata hanc rota cu medendi
Ad igne sacru. Radix ei cu aceto trita

DISCOURS

DE LA METHODE

Pour bien conduire ſa raiſon,& chercher
la verité dans les ſciences.

PLUS

LA DIOPTRIQVE.

LES METEORES.

ET

LA GEOMETRIE.

Qui ſont des eſſais de cete METHODE.

A LEYDE

De l'Imprimerie de IAN MAIRE.

CIↃ IↃ C XXXVII.

Auec Priuilege.

3

DISCOURS

DE LA METHODE

Pour bien conduire ſa raiſon,& chercher
la verité dans les ſciences.

Si ce diſcours ſemble trop long pour eſtre tout leu en vne fois, on le pourra diſtinguer en ſix parties. Et en la premiere on trouuera diuerſes conſiderations touchant les ſciences. En la ſeconde, les principales regles de la Methode que l'Autheur a cherchée. En la 3, quelques vnes de celles de la Morale qu'il a tirée de cete Methode. En la 4, les raiſons par leſquelles il prouue l'exiſtence de Dieu, & de l'ame humaine, qui ſont les fondemens de ſa Metaphyſique. En la 5, l'ordre des queſtions de Phyſique qu'il a cherchées, & particulierement l'explication du mouuement du cœur, & de quelques autres difficultez qui appartienent a la Medecine, puis auſſy la difference qui eſt entre noſtre ame & celle des beſtes. Et en la derniere, quelles choſes il croit eſtre requiſes pour aller plus auant en la recherche de la Nature qu'il n'a eſté, & quelles raiſons l'ont fait eſcrire.

LE bon ſens eſt la choſe du monde la mieux partagée: car chaſcun penſe en eſtre ſi bien pouruû, que ceux meſme qui ſont les plus difficiles a contenter en toute autre choſe, n'ont point couſtume d'en deſirer plus qu'ils en ont. En quoy il n'eſt pas vray ſemblable que tous ſe trõpent: Mais plutoſt cela teſmoigne que la puiſſance de bien iuger, & diſtinguer le vray d'auec le faux, qui eſt proprement ce qu'on nomme le bon ſens, ou la raiſon, eſt naturellement eſgale en tous les hommes; Et ainſi que la diuerſité de nos opinions ne vient pas de ce que les vns ſont plus raiſonnables que les

PREMIERE PARTIE.

a 2 autres,

Title page and the first page of text from the "Discourse" dated 1637, in which Descartes laid the groundwork of modern mathematical-scientific method.

A drug – to come back to our main subject – is therefore composed of carrier substances and active substances. The properties these substances (as distinguished from the whole drug) possess enable them to act upon the mechanism of the body's "economy" or, in the case of dyeing, to find their way into the textile material.

Enterprising dealers in drugs began supplying their customers with extracts in the 1820s. Between 1820 and 1822 the apothecary Joseph Pelletier established the first factory for extraction in Paris. He was followed in 1823 by Friedrich Ludwig Koch in Oppenheim. Both obtained quinine by extracting it from Peruvian bark.

Extracting plants now began shooting up like mushrooms. Three years after Pelletier's factory opened, official statistics recorded four of them in the Seine Departement alone with a yearly turnover of more than 400,000 francs. As a result the price of quinine dove from 13 to 2.5 florins the ounce within six years.

Among the many new establishments, two are particularly worthy of mention because big chemical enterprises grew from them: in 1827 the apothecaries H.E. Merck in Darmstadt and J.D. Riedel in Berlin began the large-scale production of quinine.
In the field of coloring substances we lack exact information on the beginning of industrial extraction. Alizarin, the dyestuff of the madder root, known in those days as garancin, was produced along factory lines for the first time by Thomas Frères in Avignon and placed on the market in large amounts from 1836 on. Here again developments were fast and furious: in 1843 there were a dozen garancin production plants operating in the neighborhood of Avignon alone. As dyewoods are more easily extracted, one is obliged to assume that the beginning of industrial dyewood extraction may be placed at an earlier date.

In its drugs trade Basle, too, harbored a germ of the chemical industry – a germ from which the present-day firm of J. R. Geigy developed. The founder, Johann Rudolf Geigy-Gemuseus, who had been in the trade since 1758, had himself officially registered as a "materialist", or dealer, in 1764. In 1857 the business, styled J. R. Geigy & U. Heusler at that time, acquired a good-sized manufacturing site in the vicinity of the then Baden Station, where they built their "extract" factory for the large-scale production of dyewood extracts of all kinds. Two years later the plant director, J. J. Mueller-Pack, risked the big jump to coal tar dye manufacture: the production of fuchsine was started up in 1859.

The Geigy extraction factory at the turn of the century. Works Archive, J. R. Geigy S.A., Basle

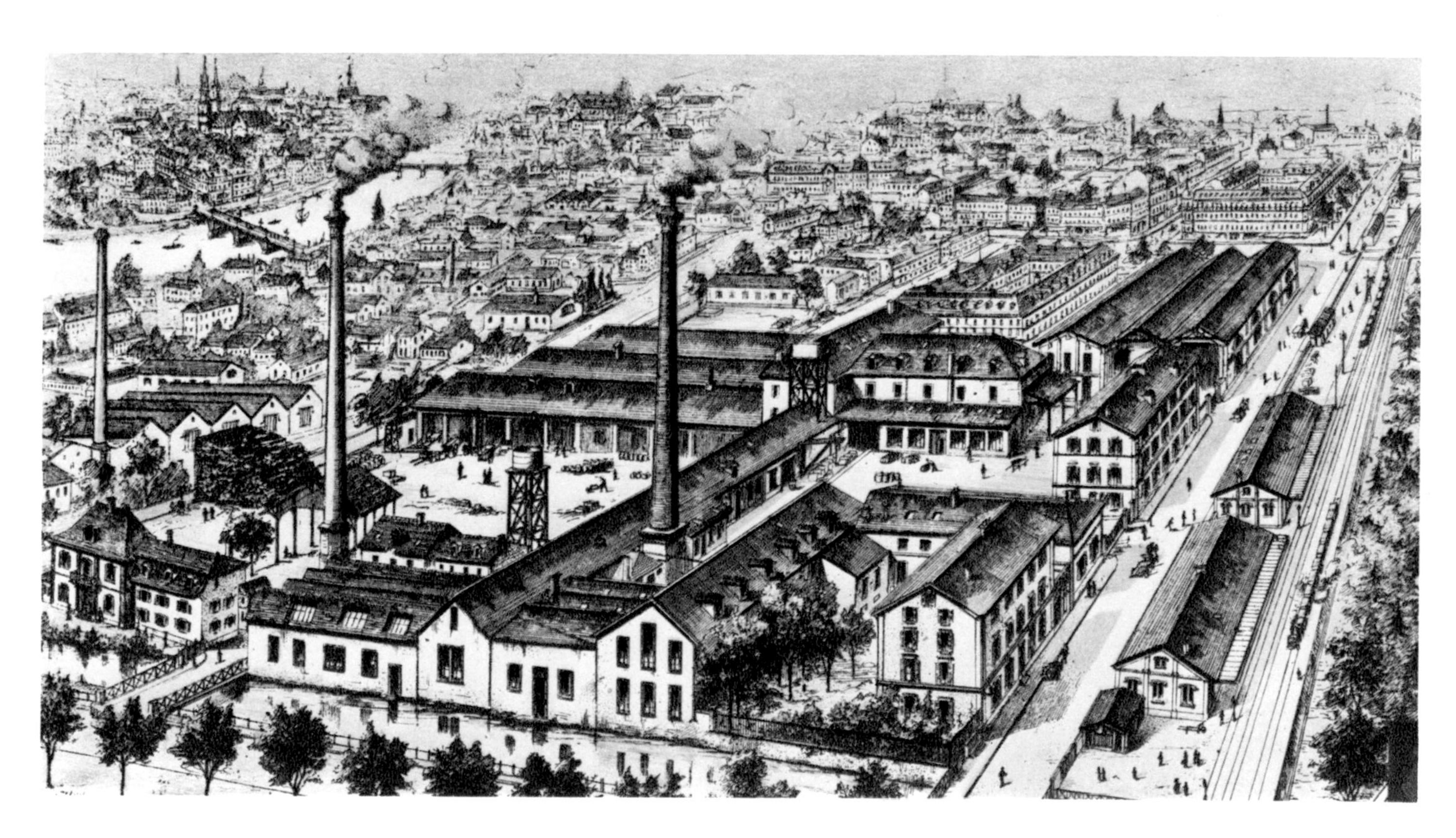

6

Pl. I.
Teinturier de Riviere, Attelier et différentes Opérations pour la Teinture des Soies.

A silk dyeworks in the latter part of the 18th century. Copper engraving from the voluminous Encyclopedia of Diderot and d'Alembert; Paris, 1772.

Dyeing

Up to the middle of the 19th century, vegetable and animal substances were the agents used for dyeing textile materials, the only exception being a few mineral colors. By far the largest part of these natural substances contain mordant dyestuffs, which require that the textile fibre be mordanted with metallic salts to

achieve fixation. These metallic compounds are deposited in the fibres as hydroxides; in the ensuing dyeing operation the dyestuffs react with them to produce insoluble complexes fast to washing.
Aluminium, copper, tin and chromium salts were employed as mordants. Wool and cotton were boiled for a number of hours, while silk was left to soak at room temperature overnight in the aqueous solution of the metallic salts, the mordant bath. To prepare the dyebath, the dyer placed the coloring matter in a linen sack and extracted it by boiling for a few hours. The sack was then taken out, and the dyeliquor was thus ready to take the mordanted textile material. As a rule dyeing was carried out for one hour in a hot liquor, with the material kept constantly in motion, the hanks being turned on their sticks and piece goods raked.
Tin mordants generally produced the clearest dyeings. Aluminium, chromium, copper and iron salts yielded duller and bluish shades. With a tin mordant, madder yields orange shades; on alum-mordanted material, red shades; and with chromium, copper, and iron salts, brown and violet shades.
The mordants, as well as other dyeing assistants such as soap and Turkey-red oil, were prepared in the dyeworks itself. Dyeing plants were thus well set up to carry out chemical operations. It is therefore not surprising that in the early period of color chemistry coal tar dyes, too, were prepared in the dyehouse. The bluish-red silk dye fuchsine, or magenta, named after the fuchsia flower, was discovered in 1859 by Verguin in the laboratory of the Renard Frères et Franc silk dyeworks, Lyons. This dyeworks afterwards grew into a coal tar dye factory, and, under the protection of the French patent laws, captured a monopoly position in the manufacture of fuchsine.
The Basle silk dyer Alexander Clavel was related to Renard. In 1859 he acquired the licence to manufacture fuchsine for 100,000 francs and immediately began production – the first to do so in Basle. For five years he manufactured this coal tar dye as well as its blue,

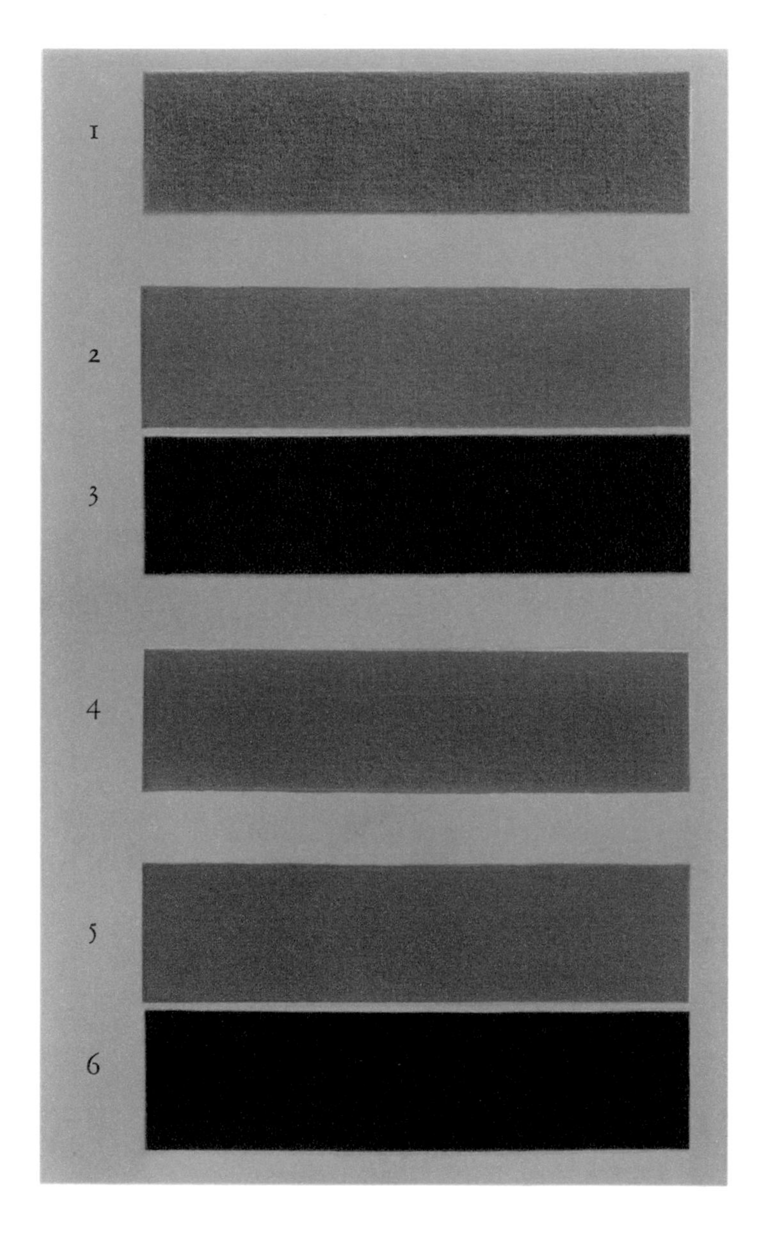

Finished dyeings of madder on cotton, pre-treated with various mordanting salts: (1) tin mordant, (2) weak and (3) strong aluminium mordant, (4) chrome mordant, (5) weak and (6) strong iron mordant.

violet, and green derivatives in a dyehouse laboratory near St. Clara's Square. Then in 1864 health regulations laid down by the authorities obliged him to build an aniline dye factory outside the city gates on Klybeck Street – the cell from which the organism that was to become CIBA Limited grew.

From an experts' report dated 1864 to the public health authorities of Basle, we learn that in addition to Clavel's, four other dyeworks were making coal tar dyes or using fuchsine which they bought to prepare blue, violet, and green. These four were Mueller-Hauser, Haering, Schetty, and Lotz. But unlike Clavel's factory, none of them developed into full-fledged chemical firms.

A noteworthy example of a dyeworks as the nucleus of a big chemical enterprise was that of Weskott in Barmen. From 1861 on Friedrich Bayer, working with Johann Friedrich Weskott, undertook experiments relating to the preparation of coal tar dyes in the Weskott "établissement". In the year 1863 it became a chemical factory, which developed into the present-day "Farbenfabriken Bayer Aktiengesellschaft" (Bayer Dyeworks Limited).

Opposite: In the second half of the 19th century Alexander Clavel operated a silk dyeworks near the old Blaesi Gate. From its laboratories came the first aniline dyes to be produced in Basle. Watercolor by A. Winterlin, dated 1865. Municipal and Minster Museum, Basle.
Below: CIBA c. 1893 as seen from a balloon. Photograph by E. Spelterini. Höflinger Archive, Basle.
Overleaf: One of the property deeds, dated 1864, which preluded Alexander Clavel's transferral of aniline dye manufacture to Klybeck Street, present-day site of the CIBA home office.

Zu wissen sei hiermit, daß zwischen

Herrn **Jakob Bolliger** Zimmermeister
von Rued, Gemeinde Schiltwald Canton Aargau
hier niedergelassen, mit Einwilligung seiner
rechtlich verbeiständeten Ehegattin, Frau Elisabeth
geborene Walter, als Verkäufer.

Herrn **Alexander Clavel-Linder**
als Käufer, Bürger von Basel, folgender Verkauf
und Kauf ist abgeschlossen worden.

Es verkauft nämlich Herr Jakob Bolliger
an Herrn Alexander Clavel-Linder eine
Parzelle Land in Section A. No 729, nun mit
No 797 bezeichnet, im mindern Stadtbann an der
äußern Klybeckstraße, enthaltend 117 Ruthen
10 Quadratfuß. Anwänder: Stadtwärts Herr
Mössinger No 646, östlich Verkäufer No 798, nördlich
Käufer No 777, westlich der Rhein.

Mit Inbegriff aller Zugehörde und Gerechtigkeit

Diese Liegenschaft ist aller Beschwerden und
Beladenschaften frei, ledig und eigen.

Hierauf ist dieser Verkauf und Kauf zugegangen
und geschlossen worden, um die Summe von Frs 2,342.

Zwei

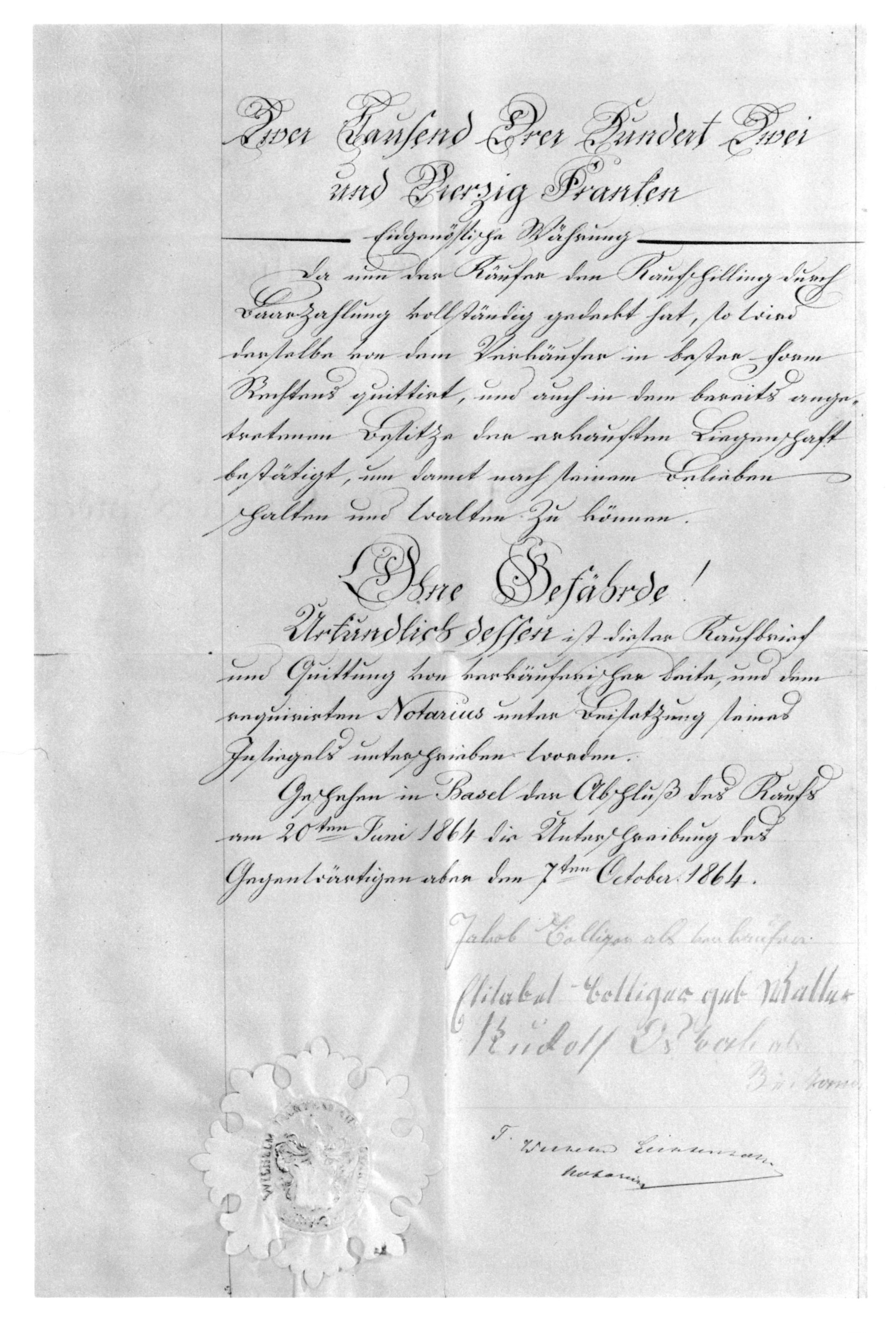

Zwei Tausend Drei Hundert Zwei und Vierzig Franken

Eidgenössische Währung

Da nun der Käufer den Kaufschilling durch Baarzahlung vollständig getilgt hat, so wird derselbe von dem Verkäufer in bester Form Rechtens quittirt, und auch in dem bereits angetretenen Besitze der erkauften Liegenschaft bestätigt, um damit nach seinem Belieben schalten und walten zu können.

Ohne Gefährde!

Urkundlich dessen ist dieser Kaufbrief und Quittung von verkäuferischer Seite, und dem requirirten Notarius unter Beisetzung seines Insiegels unterschrieben worden.

Geschehen in Basel der Abschluß des Kaufs am 20ten Juni 1864 die Unterschreibung des Gegenwärtigen aber den 7ten October 1864.

Jakob Tolliger als Verkäufer

Elisabet Tolliger geb. Walter

Rudolf [illegible] als Beistand

[illegible] Notarius

The Apothecary's Laboratory and Small-Scale Chemical Trade

In the last quarter of the 18th century, just before the onset of the industrial age, chemical products – acids, alkalis and salts – were still being produced in the small workshops.

The technical equipment for chemical operations, such as distillation apparatus, smelting furnaces, and filtering units, could be found in the laboratories of the mine forges, the chemists' shops, and the alchemists' laboratories. In the forge ores and metals were assayed; at the chemist's medicines were prepared; and the alchemist sought the "Quinta essentia", the "Philosopher's Stone" which would bestow eternal life and inexhaustible wealth upon the adept. Of these three institutions, only the apothecary's laboratory proved fertile soil for the growth of modern chemical industries.

The goal of the alchemist – the "fifth essence" – was pegged at quite a more lofty level than soda or salt-

Above: 14th century Italian chemist's shop. Miniature from the "Tacuinum Sanitatis in Medicina", a work formerly in the possession of the Cerutti family, nobles of Verona, and ascribed to the Arabian physician Abulcasis. MS. ser. no. 2644, Austrian National Library, Vienna.
Right: Analytical checking of saltpetre manufacture. In the 16th century practical chemistry was helped along greatly by experience gained in the assaying laboratories attached to mine forges. Woodcut from Lazarus Ercker's "Treatise describing the foremost kinds of Metallic Ores and Minerals"; 1580 edition, Frankfurt.

petre. His method was rooted in mysticism rather than in a soberly rational comprehension of nature. The testing rooms of the mine foundries served as auxiliary installations in the obtaining of metals, and important chemical relationships were discovered in such laboratories. In 1550 the Sienese mining engineer Vannoccio Biringuccio published his "Pirotechnia", a full compendium of the chemical knowledge of his time. With his "Treatise describing the foremost kinds of Metallic Ores and Minerals" (1574 – translated into English a hundred years later by Sir John Pettres), Lazarus Ercker, chief imperial surveyor of mines in Bohemia, helped to broaden knowledge of analytical chemistry. Even more famous as a foundry expert was George Agricola, whose works on practical mining, richly illustrated with woodcuts, were printed in Basle.

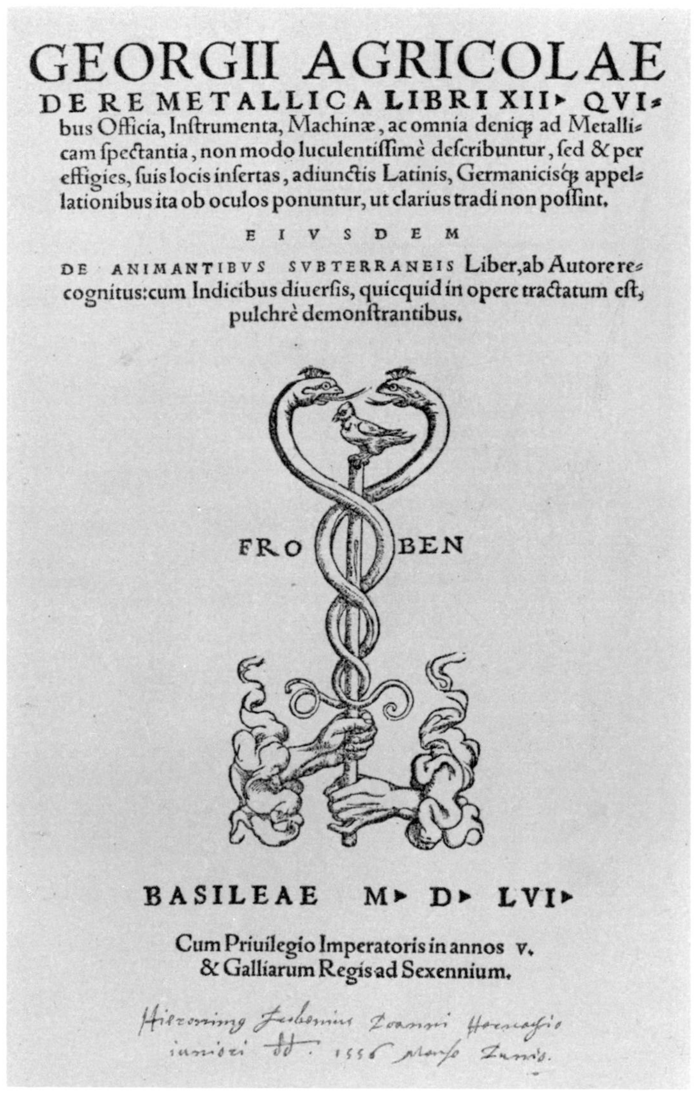

GEORGII AGRICOLAE

DE RE METALLICA LIBRI XII. QVIbus Officia, Instrumenta, Machinæ, ac omnia denique ad Metallicam spectantia, non modo luculentissimè describuntur, sed & per effigies, suis locis insertas, adiunctis Latinis, Germanicisque appellationibus ita ob oculos ponuntur, ut clarius tradi non possint.

EIVSDEM

DE ANIMANTIBVS SVBTERRANEIS Liber, ab Autore recognitus: cum Indicibus diuersis, quicquid in opere tractatum est, pulchrè demonstrantibus.

FRO BEN

BASILEAE M. D. LVI.

Cum Priuilegio Imperatoris in annos V. & Galliarum Regis ad Sexennium.

George Bauer of Saxony, usually known as Agricola, wrote his "De Re Metallica" at the time when the mining industry was expanding anew.
Above: This copy of the first edition, dated 1556, carried a dedication by the printer Hieronymus Froben of Basle.
Left: Woodcut from Agricola's work showing how nitric acid was prepared.

Below: 16th century laboratory for working gold and silver. From Ercker's "Treatise".
Right: Title page of the first journal for pharmaceutical and industrial chemistry, founded by Johann Trommsdorff. Quite in keeping with the character of this periodical is the portrait of Paracelsus on its cover.

Journal
der
Pharmacie
für
Aerzte und Apotheker
von
Johann Bartholmä Trommsdorff
Apotheker zu Erfurt, der churfürstlich-maynzischen Akademie der Wissenschaften ordentliches Mitglied.

Ersten Bandes, erstes Stück.

Leipzig 1793.
bey Siegfried Lebrecht Crusius.

From the apothecary's shop many chemical factories grew, whether as extraction plants serving the drugs trade or as producers of fine chemicals above and beyond their own needs. The first chemical plant, described by the poet Goethe and still in existence today, was established in 1788 by the apothecary Wolfgang Caspar Fikentscher at Marktredwitz in Thuringia. The most important of the pioniers from the ranks of the dispensing chemists was Johann Bartholmae Trommsdorff. In 1813 he established a chemical factory for inorganic preparations in Teuditz near Luetzen. As a professor of chemistry in Erfurt he wrote textbooks for pharmacists and dyers, helping to join together the main original branches of the chemical industry: the apothecary's laboratory, the drugs trade, and the dyeworks. Trommsdorff furthered industrial chemistry in

other important ways too, for his school produced no fewer than 32 founders of factories. Moreover, with "Trommsdorff's Journal" he created the first periodical devoted to industrial chemistry.
The workshops originally attached to the chemists' shops were separated from them as time went on, and in this way the first autonomous small-scale chemical trade came into being.

The Amsterdam laboratory of the dispensing chemist Anthoni d'Ailly, where quinine was being extracted on a factory scale in the 1820s. Oil painting by Johannes Jelgerhuis, 1818. Rijksmuseum, Amsterdam.

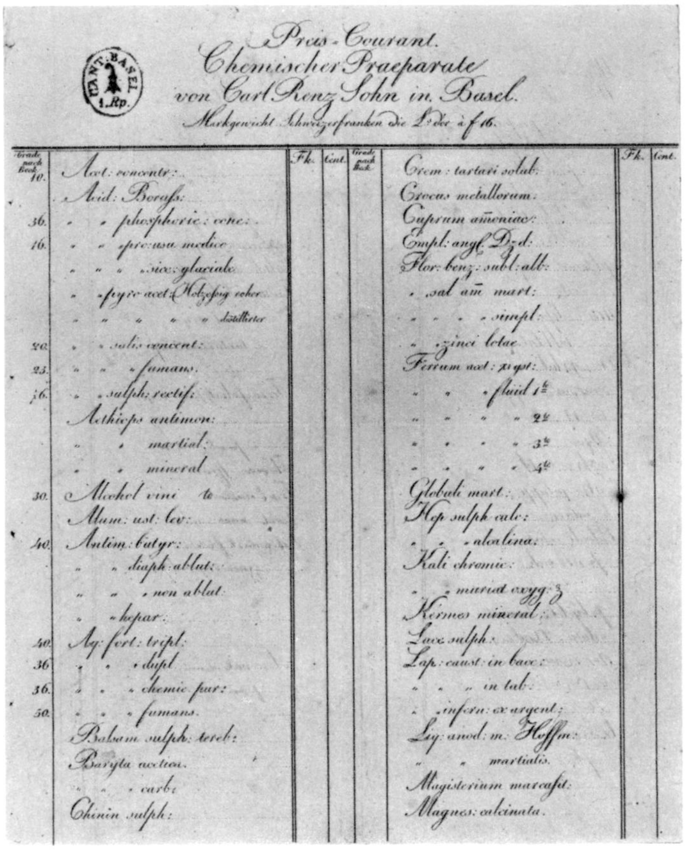

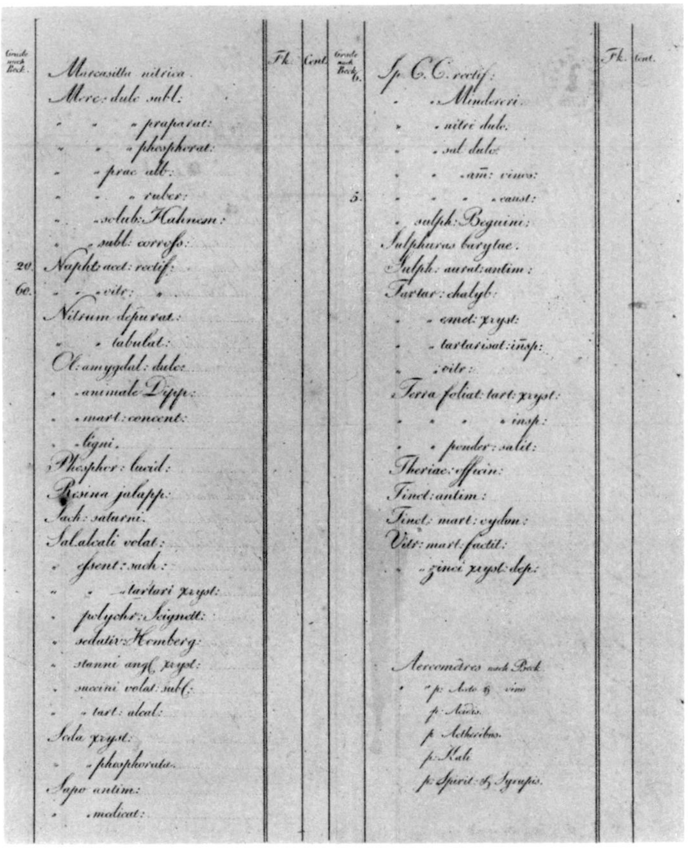

In Basle chemical factories were established at almost the same time as those in Germany. In 1812 Johann Jakob Schaeffer, who came from the Bavarian Palatinate, and Carl Friedrich Renz, a native of Wuerttemberg, set up shop before the Riehen Gate and began the manufacture of chemicals for dyeing and cloth printing. One of their employees became a competitor when, in 1819, Johann Christoph Assal founded a plant nearby for the manufacture of the same materials. In 1826 Carl Renz, Jr., opened the third chemical factory on Basle soil at Grenzacher Street. Promising though they seemed in their beginnings, all these undertakings fell by the wayside: the firm of Renz, Sr. in 1839, then the business founded by Assal in 1863, while the Renz, Jr. business was taken off the commercial register at the request of the proprietor in 1909.

A list of goods marketed by Carl Renz Jr. in 1834. This business was typical of small chemical undertakings in Basle. Basle Public Records Office.

The Gasworks

When coal is heated combustible gases are released. Although this phenomenon was known as far back as the first half of the 16th century, not until 1781 did Professor Minkelaers use such gas to illuminate his laboratory in Loewen. Thanks to the researches of the Scotsman William Murdoch, gas manufacture became technically feasible in the first years of the 19th century. In 1802, in the Soho district of London, gaslight burned publicly for the first time as a bright accompaniment to the Peace of Amiens. The first street-lighting with gas was set up in 1813 on Westminster Bridge. On the Continent, Paris followed in 1819, Basle did not get gaslight until 1852.

In the dry distillation of coal, the process used to manufacture gas, tar and ammonia escape from the reaction chamber, as well as the actual illuminating gas. These by-products have to be removed; the coal tar is condensed by cooling and the ammonia washed out with water. Coke is left in the reaction chamber.
Coke was a coveted raw material for the smelting of iron ore. Liebig taught the utilization of ammonia salts as valuable fertilizers. Only coal tar was a bothersome waste product, and nobody was interested in it. Nobody, that is, except a few chemists who isolated pure substances from this unsightly mass: naphtalene, anthracene, phenol, toluene, benzene. As was to be expected, these newly discovered substances prompted a number of chemical investigations. In 1834, for instance, Eilhard Mitscherlich, a professor at the University of Berlin, succeeded in converting benzene into nitrobenzene with nitrating acid, a mixture of salpetre and sulfuric acid. By a simple reduction the Russian Nicholas Zinin obtained aniline from this nitrobenzene in 1841. The name "aniline" was a coinage of Carl Julius Fritzsche in St. Petersburg, who distilled the same oily fluid from indigo, the natural dyestuff of *Indigofera anil* L.

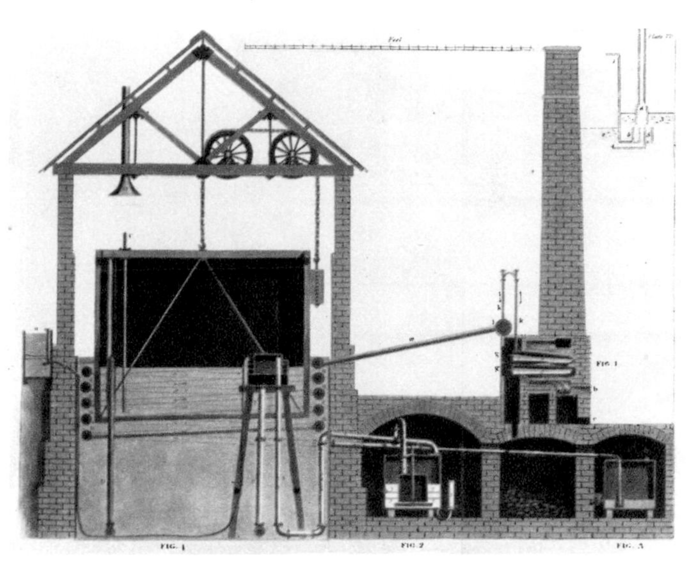

Early installations for making illuminating gas, constructed by Samuel Clegg. Lithographs from the first textbook on illuminating gas, "A Practical Treatise on Gas-Light" by Fredrick Accum (3rd ed., London, 1816).
Above: Small plant built in 1812 for the publisher R. Ackermann in London.
Below: Plant for manufacturing gas to light the streets, put up in 1814 for the Chartered Gas Light & Coke Company in London.

The St. Johann city gasworks (left) and the Durand & Huguenin aniline dyes factory; in background, a part of the Sandoz factory area. Balloon view taken by Spelterini in 1893. Photo archive of the Basle Gas & Waterworks.

Aniline suddenly became of great industrial importance, for "aniline purple", the first synthetic dyestuff, was shortly obtained from it. In 1856 the English chemistry student William Henry Perkin attempted to produce quinine synthetically. To his surprise, however, he found in the reaction mixture a dyestuff which colored silk bluish-red. This was later named mauveine, after the French word for the flower of the mallow. Perkin proceeded to exploit his discovery industrially, building the first coal tar dye factory in England in 1857. Since that time the gasworks has supplied the starting materials for coal tar factories, which also explains why it early became the nucleus of the chemical industry. In 1850 Jean-Gaspard Dollfus of Mulhouse applied for a concession from the Basle Town Council for the building of a gasworks, and in 1852 began manufacturing illuminating gas in a plant before the Steinen Gate. In 1860 the city gasworks was transferred to a site near the St. Johann Gate on the Rhine.

In the same year Dollfus established a plant nearby for the processing of coal tar, and in 1862 he commenced manufacture of synthetic dyestuffs. This plant developed into the present-day dyes factory of Durand & Huguenin.

In 1862, i.e. three years after the discovery of fuchsine, there were three factories in Basle manufacturing coal tar dyes: the Clavel silk dyeworks, the J. J. Mueller extraction factory, and the Dollfus plant next to the gasworks.
As noted, the Clavel establishment developed into CIBA. After manufacturing installations had been transferred to Klybeck Street, the factory was purchased by Bindschedler & Busch in 1873. It was newly named the "Society of Chemical Industry in Basle" in 1884. Since 1945 the abbreviation "CIBA" has been the official style of the company.
The J. J. Mueller & Co. extraction factory was absorbed by the present-day J. R. Geigy S. A., while the Dollfus plant gave rise, as just noted, to Durand & Huguenin Limited. It is not difficult to establish connections between these first undertakings and the dyestuff factories which arrived later on the Basle scene. The Mulhouse chemist Armand Gerber set up dyes manufacturing as plant manager at Dollfus. In 1864 he went into business for himself. With Wilhelm Uhlmann, a businessman, he founded his own aniline dye factory on Klybeck Street, next to Clavel's plant. This enterprise merged with the Society of Chemical Industry in 1898. Alfred Kern, chief chemist at Bindschedler & Busch, and Edouard Sandoz, employed in a commercial capacity at Durand & Huguenin, opened a dyes factory in 1886 from which the firm of Sandoz Limited developed.

In 1892 Robert Bindschedler, having left the Society of Chemical Industry, began manufacturing dyestuffs and special pharmaceutical preparations in nearby Kleinhueningen. His firm, known as the "Bindschedler Chemical Factory, Basle", expanded in 1904 by acquiring a plant at Monthey in the Canton of Valais and fused with the Society four years later.
The story of the youngest among the chemical enterprises in Basle, F. Hoffmann-La Roche & Co., differs from the others. It was spontaneously generated and not affiliated, even through personal ties, with any of the older firms. In 1894 Fritz Hoffmann-La Roche joined the M. C. Traub chemical firm, which had been established two years previously, as a partner. His aim, which was to create his own pharmaceutical specialities, he carried into effect upon founding a business in 1896.
The development of the Basle chemical industries, with the personal and contractual associations which characterized their operations in the beginnings, are briefly surveyed in the chart that follows.

Photo of the Hoffmann-La Roche chemical works taken a few years after its establishment. Works Archive, F. Hoffmann-La Roche & Co.
Overleaf: 100 years of industrial chemistry in Basle. A survey of the five leading firms and their relationships.

CIBA Limited

1859 Alexander Clavel begins manufacture of fuchsine in the laboratory of his silk dyeworks at Lower Rebgasse 4/6

1864 Dyes production transferred to Klybeck Street

1873 Clavel's firm sold to Bindschedler & Busch

1883 Bindschedler, Busch & Co.

1884 Firm re-incorporated as Society for Chemical Industry in Basle

1889 Manufacture of pharmaceutical specialities taken up

1898 Absorption of the Aniline Dyeworks, formerly A. Gerber & Co., through merger

1908 Absorption of the Basle Chemical Factory, with its Kleinhueningen and Monthey works, through merger

1928 Production of textile auxiliaries and finishing agents begun

1933 Manufacture of plastics begun

1945 CIBA Limited

1954 Manufacture of insecticides begun

1958 Color photo-chemistry and large-screen color television projection programs initiated

A. Gerber

1864 Establishment of the A. Gerber & Uhlmann Aniline Dyes Factory on Klybeck Street

1885 A. Gerber & Co.

1896 Aniline Dyeworks, formerly A. Gerber & Co.

R. Bindschedler

L. Durand

A. Kern

R. Bindschedler

1893 Establishment of the Bindschedler Chemical Factory, Basle, in Kleinhueningen

1898 Basle Chemical Factory

1904 Purchase of the Société des Usines de Produits Chimiques de Monthey (Valais)

Sandoz Limited

1886 Establishment of the Kern & Sandoz chemical factory for the manufacture of aniline dyes on Gas Street

1893 Sandoz & Co.

1895 Chemical Factory, formerly Sandoz

1916 Manufacture of textile auxiliaries and finishing agents begun

1921 Production of pharmaceutical specialities taken up

1937 Production of insecticides begun

1939 Sandoz Limited

1918 Community of Interests Agreement between CIBA, Sandoz, and Geigy (Basle C.I.)

1929 Merger of Basle C.I. with German I.G. Farben (2-party cartel); inclusion of French dyes manufacturers (3-party cartel)

1932 Inclusion of I.C.I., England (4-party cartel)

1934 Establishment of "Interpharma" for maintaining common interests (Further member: A. Wander Limited, Berne)

1939 International Dyestuffs Cartel dissolved upon outbreak of war

1950 Basle C.I. terminated at year's end

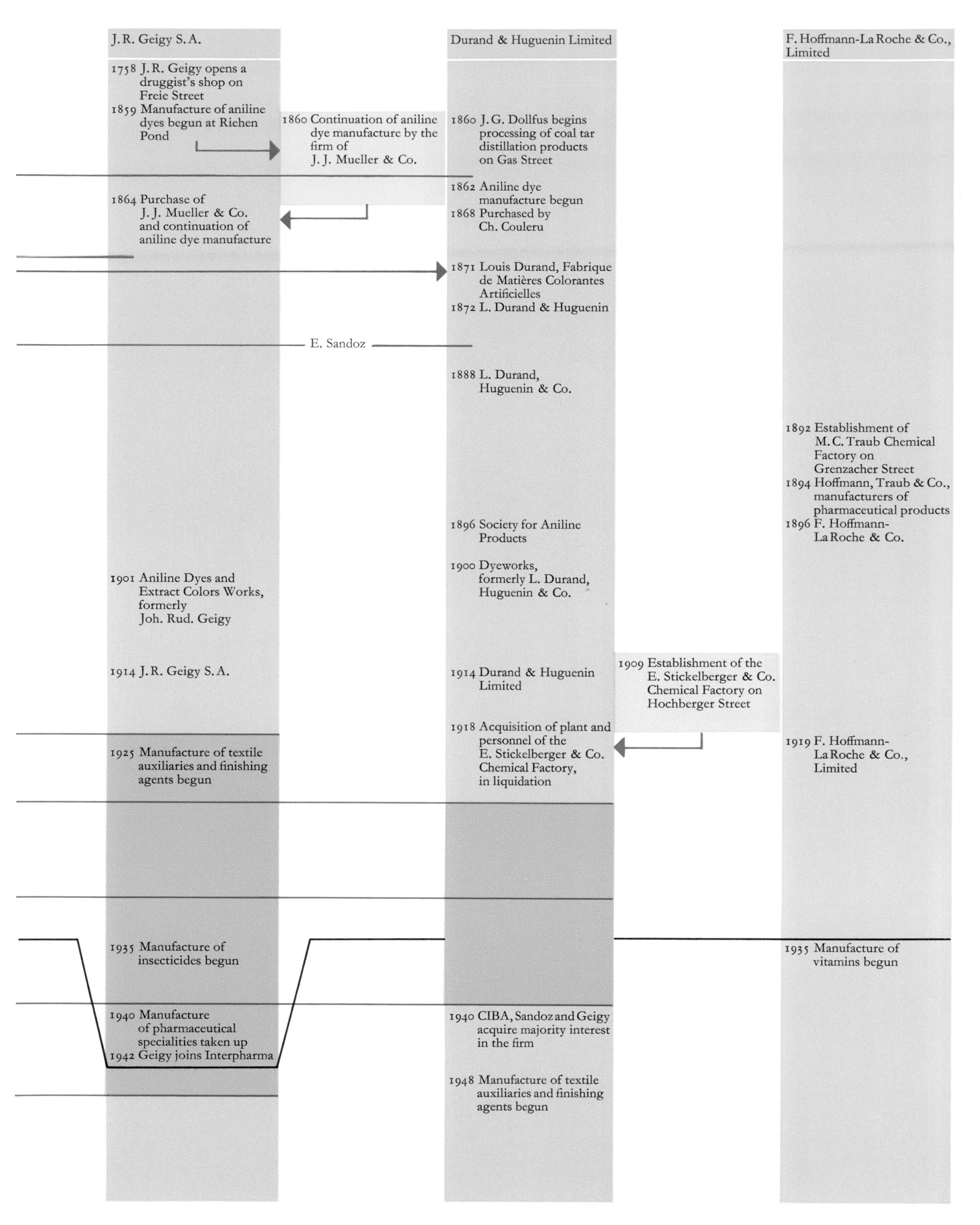

J. R. Geigy S. A.
Durand & Huguenin Limited
F. Hoffmann-La Roche & Co., Limited
1758 J. R. Geigy opens a druggist's shop on Freie Street
1859 Manufacture of aniline dyes begun at Riehen Pond
1860 Continuation of aniline dye manufacture by the firm of J. J. Mueller & Co.
1860 J. G. Dollfus begins processing of coal tar distillation products on Gas Street
1862 Aniline dye manufacture begun
1864 Purchase of J. J. Mueller & Co. and continuation of aniline dye manufacture
1868 Purchased by Ch. Couleru
1871 Louis Durand, Fabrique de Matières Colorantes Artificielles
1872 L. Durand & Huguenin
E. Sandoz
1888 L. Durand, Huguenin & Co.
1892 Establishment of M. C. Traub Chemical Factory on Grenzacher Street
1894 Hoffmann, Traub & Co., manufacturers of pharmaceutical products
1896 Society for Aniline Products
1896 F. Hoffmann-La Roche & Co.
1900 Dyeworks, formerly L. Durand, Huguenin & Co.
1901 Aniline Dyes and Extract Colors Works, formerly Joh. Rud. Geigy
1909 Establishment of the E. Stickelberger & Co. Chemical Factory on Hochberger Street
1914 J. R. Geigy S. A.
1914 Durand & Huguenin Limited
1918 Acquisition of plant and personnel of the E. Stickelberger & Co. Chemical Factory, in liquidation
1919 F. Hoffmann-La Roche & Co., Limited
1925 Manufacture of textile auxiliaries and finishing agents begun
1935 Manufacture of insecticides begun
1935 Manufacture of vitamins begun
1940 Manufacture of pharmaceutical specialities taken up
1942 Geigy joins Interpharma
1940 CIBA, Sandoz and Geigy acquire majority interest in the firm
1948 Manufacture of textile auxiliaries and finishing agents begun

How and Why Chemical Industry Grew in Basle

Traditional crafts were the buds from which the chemical industry sprouted. But in order for the crafts to grow into industries, they had to be planted in the fruitful soil of a viable economy. The entrepreneur needs raw materials, labor, and capital to set up manufacture, and a market ready and able to absorb the products he offers.

A "picture map" of Basle, done in 1847 by Friedrich Maehly. The old line of fortifications is clearly discernible, breached only by the Alsatian railway at right. Historical Museum, Basle.

How did it stand with these economic prerequisites in Basle around the middle of the last century, when the foundations of the local chemical industry were laid? The most important raw material for dyeworks was, as we have said, gas tar. In the beginnings of the chemical industry it was worked up in the dyes factories themselves to the starting products – benzene, toluene, aniline. The Basle gasworks was able to cover only a part of requirements; large amounts of gas tar, and later on of intermediates, had to be procured from England, France, and Germany. The short and convenient lanes of traffic leading to Basle may have been one of the reasons, though certainly not the decisive

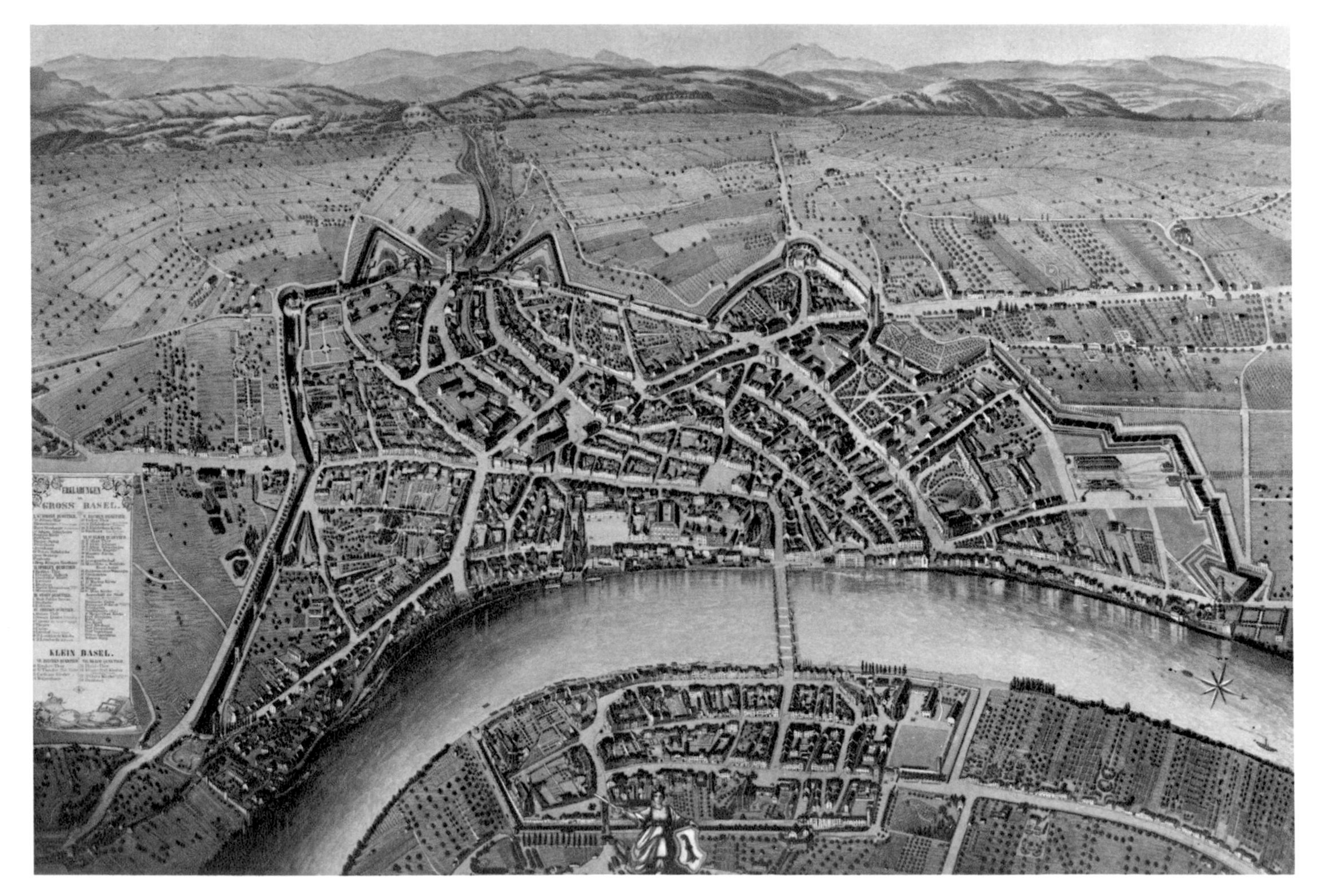

one, why the Swiss coal tar dyes industry developed mainly in this town.
The opportunity to dispose of waste via the Rhine was also of importance. In the early stages of fuchsine manufacture appreciable quantities of arsenic-containing water were given off which had to be got rid of conveniently.
Then too, of course, there was the rising demographic curve. From 1840 to 1860 the population of Basle

View of an old quarter near the Aeschen Gate c. 1876. The third building from the left housed the first office of the Swiss Bank Corporation. Watercolor by J. J. Schneider. Basle Public Records Office.

Right: The rise in the town's population paralleled industrialization. Graph based on figures in the Statistical Yearbook of Canton Basle Town.
Below: View from the market square up what is still the main shopping street of Basle, c. 1850. "Runners' carts" such as the one shown here were a familiar sight on the streets in those days. They transported goods from the silk ribbon manufacturers in town to weavers in the country and back again. Detail from a watercolor by J. J. Schneider. Basle Public Records Office.

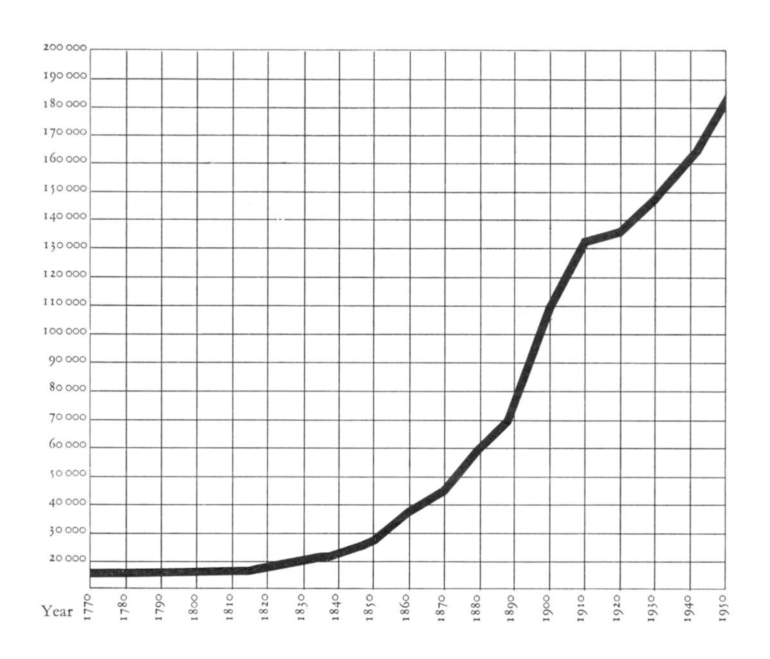

doubled, reaching about 40,000 in the latter year – sufficient to cover the labor requirement of the young chemical industry. The first dyes chemists came from France, whose schools of chemistry had already attained a specially high standard. In 1855 the Federal Polytechnic Institute was founded in Zurich; here the first Swiss technical cadres were trained.
The local banking system was well developed; in 1862 there were twenty private banks in Basle. The strong position of the town on the capital market was due to its lively business activity and industrious working population, as well as to the eminently thrifty habits of the Basle families, upheld down through the generations. The up-and-coming chemical industry was able to cover its needs from the supply of capital thus accumulated.
The sale of coal tar dyes offered no problem, thanks to a flourishing silk ribbon industry. In 1860 the town numbered twelve silk dyers with 337 hands. In spite of high prices and inferior fastness qualities, the first coal tar dyes were in great demand, for the finished dyeing was distinguished by pure shades which could not be obtained with natural coloring agents.

Culture and Chemistry in Basle in the late 19th Century

In 1859, the year when Basle began tearing down its town walls, Alexander Clavel commenced the manufacture of aniline dyes in his silk dye works. If the demolition of the walls marked the end of the old order dominated by the gilds and crafts, Clavel's undertaking heralded the florescence of the chemical industry in Basle.
The middle of the 19th century brought with it the upshot of the social unrest which had first broken out violently in the French Revolution of 1789. In 1847 and 1848 uprisings occurred in France, Austria, Germany, and Switzerland, directed at abolishing the ancient prerogatives of the nobility, the aristocracy, and privileged circles from the ranks of the burghers. The age of liberalism had truly begun.
In Switzerland, the economic barrier of cantonal boundaries was done away with, and the league of states became one federal state. Through the Federal Constitution of 1848 commercial and professional freedom and the freedom of settlement were, and still are, guaranteed by law. The monetary, customs, and postal systems were taken out of cantonal hands and unified on a federal basis.
Basle joined the railway networks then abuilding: the Alsatian in 1844, that of Baden in 1855, and in 1858, with the Hauenstein cut through, the Swiss Central Railway as well.
The progressive and liberal spirit which characterized the age was also reflected in the educational system. Natural sciences obtained a foothold in the teaching program. In 1852 subjects outside the classical curriculum were introduced in the secondary schools. In

The coming of the new age.
Above: Inauguration of the first railway station in Basle, December, 1845. The "French station" was the terminus of the Alsatian railway. From "Illustration" magazine.
Left: Demolition of the old town walls near the Steinen Gate in the summer of 1866. Photo by Hoeflinger, Basle.

1855 Karl Ludwig Ruetimeyer was called to the newly established chair of comparative anatomy and zoology at the university; even before Darwin, Ruetimeyer had made his name with studies on the origin of species. Some years later, in 1872, the physiological laboratory of the university was established and placed under the direction of Johann Friedrich Miescher, renowned for his research on the nucleus of the cell. The fame of Christian Friedrich Schoenbein, professor of chemistry from 1828 to 1868, extended far beyond the borders of Switzerland. With his "gun-cotton", nitrocellulose, he laid the foundation of modern explosives chemistry and plastics chemistry. Celluloid, we may recall, has nitrocellulose as one of its chief components.
Two institutions demonstrate the extent to which the way had been prepared for this new spirit of science and technology in Basle. In 1806 Christoph Bernoulli opened his "Philotechnical Institute", a private educational establishment dedicated, as its name indicates, to technical instruction. Bernoulli later became professor of applied arts at the University of Basle. In 1816/17 the Basle Society for Natural Research was formed, a group which was active in disseminating knowledge of natural science among the people and in university circles.
The attitude taken by the authorities was particularly important, since they could promote the development to industrialization by co-operating generously – or act as a drag on it with hamstringing regulations.
By an enactment of 1853 the manufacture of chemical products in Basle was made subject to the permission of the municipal Executive Council. Such a concession was granted only if no objections were forthcoming from the board of works and the public health committee after careful examination of the building project and the manufacturing program in question. Alexander Clavel was forbidden to continue manufacture on November 7th, 1863. For, according to the experts, a "full-fledged chemical factory" had sprung up, meaning an undertaking which needed a licence to operate. They pointed out further that the plant failed to meet both the official sanitary requirements and the fire-safety standards. This incident led Clavel to purchase a plot of land outside the town in 1864, located between Klybeck Street and the banks of the Rhine – the site of present-day CIBA. On June 8th, 1864 he obtained permission to build and operate an aniline dyes factory from the Council. With this licence there were enjoined upon him sanitary and building regulations intended to protect workers and neighboring residents against any effects detrimental to health and safety.

Opposite: St. Martin's church and the old university seen from the Lesser Basle bank of the Rhine, 1845. At that time the university housed upper high-school forms as well as its own faculties and institutes. Watercolor by Constantin Guise. Private collection, Riehen. Overleaf: Licence for operating an aniline dyes factory issued to Alexander Clavel in 1864. Basle Public Records Office.

Copie.

Concession

für die Anilinfabrik des Herrn Alexander Clavel.

Auf das Ansuchen des Herrn Alexander Clavel, Färbers, um Bewilligung zur Erstellung eines Laboratoriums für Fabrikation von Anilin- und andern Farben, nebst Dampfkessel und Herd, laut Plan auf seiner Liegenschaft Sect. A N° 777 zwischen der Klybeckstraße und dem untern Rheinweg, wird nach vorausgegangener Begutachtung löbl. Baukollegiums und löbl. Sanitätsausschusses:

wird dem Petenten die Concession für die Fabrikation von Anilin- und andern Farben unter folgenden Bedingungen hiemit (bewilligt) ertheilt.

1. daß bei der Bereitung von Farbstoffen solche technische Vorrichtungen getroffen werden, wodurch das Verflüchtigen der Stoffe und die in Folge davon entstehenden Dämpfe verhindert und die Umgebung vor schädlichen Einflüssen gesichert wird;

2. daß im Allgemeinen für Abwendung von Nachtheilen für die Gesundheit der Arbeiter Vorsorge getroffen werde, namentlich aber, daß entweder die Stoffe in feuchtem Zustande gemischt, oder die ganze Operation in geschlossenen Apparaten vorgenommen werde, verbunden mit einer schützenden Vorrichtung, welche verhindert, daß der Arbeiter nicht durch die beim Rühren sich entwickelnden Anilindämpfe unmittelbar belästigt werde;

3. daß die Vorräthe von Arsenik, Arseniksäure und sonstigen gefährlichen Stoffen in einem besondern Lokal und unter gehöriger Aufsicht aufbewahrt werden;

4. daß sämmtliche flüssigen Abgänge in das Tiefwasser des Rheins abgeleitet werden mit dem Beifügen, daß das Baukollegium im Hinblick auf den künftig zu erstellenden Rheinweg dem Petenten jetzt schon die für die Anlage seiner Leitung nöthigen Weisungen ertheilen wird.

Die festen Abgänge sind in den Rhein zu entleeren und dürfen unter keinen Umständen in der Nähe des Laboratoriums aufgehäuft oder auf dem dazugehörenden Areal vergraben werden;

5

5. daß Petent dafür sorge, daß das Laboratorium gehörig verlüftet werden könne und die nöthigen Kamine zur Ableitung der bei der Fabrikation sich entwickelnden Dämpfe errichten lasse;

6. daß das Laboratoriumsgebäude nach Plan in Stein und Eisen erstellt und diejenigen Räume, in welchen Flüssigkeiten aufbewahrt oder umgegossen werden, mit Plattenboden belegt oder wasserdicht cementiert werden;

7. daß Petent während des Betriebs seiner Fabrikation sich allen Weisungen der betreffenden Behörden, namentlich des Sanitätsausschusses und dessen Beamtungen zu unterziehen habe, selbst wenn hiedurch eine Beschränkung in dem Gewerbsbetrieb im Ganzen oder in einzelnen Zweigen desselben herbeigeführt werden sollte.

8. In Bezug auf den zu erstellenden Dampfkessel und die mit demselben verbundenen mechanischen und baulichen Einrichtungen hat Petent die in der hiefür besonders zu ertheilenden Bewilligung vom obrigkeitlichen Techniker vorzuschreibenden Bedingungen genau zu befolgen und endlich seine Gebäulichkeiten so zu stellen, wie ihm durch den Kantonsingenieur nach der vom E. E. Rath genehmigten Baulinie am untern Rheinweg die nähere Anweisung ertheilt werden wird.

Alles unter Vorbehalt nachbarlicher Rechte.

Obiger Concession wurde folgender Zusatz beigefügt:

Wird die Errichtung dieser Fabrik nach vorgeschlagener Concession bewilligt; den Bedingungen der letztern wird noch beigefügt, daß Petent gehalten sein soll, allfällige Theervorräthe nicht in Senkgruben, sondern in freistehenden eisernen Behältern zu verwahren. —

Von E. E. Rath genehmigt den 8ten Juni 1864

Disposition der Fabrikationsräume bei H. Oehler Sohn

Contor

Nord

offener Schopf

Hof

Eingang

Weg gegen die Elisabethenstrasse

Seife

Jodäthyl

Corallin

offene Seite

Bereitung von Fuchsin aus Anilin

Gewinnung des Anilins aus den Laugen

Darstellen der Eisenbeize

Grün

Weissgelb

Dampfkessel

Laboratorium

Blau & Violet

Anilinroth

Abdampfkessel für stark arsenhaltige Laugen

Hühnerhof

Rhein

Opposite: Ground plan of Clavel's aniline dyes factory. This sketch was prepared in 1864 to help document Clavel's application for an operating concession from the town. Organized along the same lines as traditional dyeworks, Clavel's establishment included a department for soap manufacture (left). The sheds and buildings for the various stages in aniline dye production have since been superseded mainly by pharmaceutical facilities, but a chicken coop still exists at lower right. Basle Public Records Office.

The early chemical plants were not greeted with unmixed pleasure by the populace. Complaints to the Executive Council about tainted air, damage to fields, and spoiled laundry were frequent. Agitation swept through the town when, in 1864, arsenic-containing refuse from fuchsine manufacture at the Mueller factory poisoned a well in Lesser Basle, resulting in serious illnesses and even fatalities.
In the face of these disagreeable consequences, the stand which the authorities took was extremely important. The simplest solution would have been either to forbid aniline manufacture or impose intolerable restrictions. But the official attitude proved more reasonable and farsighted. The government had recognized authorities come to Basle to give expert counsel: Prof. A. Escher von der Linth from Zurich, Prof. H. von Fehling from Stuttgart, and A. Scheurer-Kestner, a Mulhouse industrialist. They visited the dye manufacturing plants, and in their report submitted proposals for getting rid of the harm already done to the surface water, as well as advice on how to improve the factory installations in order to preclude such mishaps in future.
The "municipal chemists" and the town physician dealt with the rest of the citizenry's complaints by investigating each case conscientiously. In reporting their findings to the government they stated that the cause of the protests could be removed without having to throttle manufacturing with impossible demands. This sane policy is expressed in the official report dated August 1st, 1866 drawn up by factory inspectors Dr. Ch. Mueller, Dr. C. Bulacher, and Dr. F. Goppelsroeder: "... we may appropriately bring tolerance to bear upon this problem, particularly as concerns distinguishing between what is more or less unpleasant and what is actually harmful in its effects. This applies above all if, in the natural course of affairs, a branch of industry while following the path of progress changes shape as it goes along."
Another reason for the lively development of the early chemical industry in Basle is to be found in the lack of official protection for inventors.
The French patent law of 1844 was based on the principle of extending protection to substances, i.e. the inventor enjoyed protection of a final product, as well as of the process employed in its manufacture. When Verguin discovered fuchsine, the first synthetic dyestuff after mauveine, and an even more important one practically, the silk dyeworks Renard Frères et Franc in Lyons had it placed under patent protection. Verguin heated crude aniline in the presence of tin chloride. A half-year later Jean Gerber-Keller of Mulhouse, together with his son Armand, found that the tin chloride might be replaced with mercuric nitrate. Azaleine, as they called their dyestuff, colored purer than fuchsine. The inventors of this circumventive process had their dyestuff made in the Lyons dyeworks of Monet et Dury. In May 1860, however, they were fined for infringing the fuchsine patent, since the court found fuchsine and azaleine to be chemically identical. Father and son were therefore obliged to turn their discovery to use in a place where the French patent law did not apply. In 1864 Armand Gerber and Wilhelm Uhlmann, a tradesman, built an "établissement" for the manufacture of azaleine between Klybeck Street and the Rhine, next to the Clavel factory transferred to that site the same year. In 1898 this factory was united with the Society of Chemical Industry.

Scientific Knowledge and its Technical Utilization

At the time when the early chemical factories were being established, chemistry, the science of matter, had completed the most important phase in its development: it had become a rational discipline.
No matter how many substances there may be, they are all built up from a few basic ones. In his "Sceptical Chymist", published in 1661, Robert Boyle formulated the basic conception of the chemical element.
Elements combine in fixed quantitive relationships to form compounds. In 1781 Antoine-Laurent Lavoisier noted that "water is not a simple substance; it is, rather, composed weight for weight of inflammable air and of vital air". He had just discovered that 15 grains of the inflammable gas (hydrogen) and 85 grains of the vital air (oxygen) yield exactly 100 grains of water. Taking these quantitative studies as a basis, John Dalton worked out the concept of the atom in his "New System of Chemical Philosophy", the first part of which appeared in 1808. Atoms, the "ultimate particles" of the elements, unite to form molecules, the "ultimate particles" of compounds: one oxygen atom joins with two hydrogen atoms to make one molecule of water.
The work of rationalizing chemistry was completed by Friedrich Woehler. In 1824 he synthesized oxalic acid, a compound found in the leaves of the wood sorrel *(Oxalis acetosella* L.*)*. With this accomplishment the last remaining irrational idea of chemistry – the *vis vitalis* – collapsed. The structure of vegetable and animal, or "organic", substances was now seen not to depend on the vital processes of the organism. Such substances could also be formed in the test tube and retort.
The victory of rationalism was not limited to the theory of matter alone. Its premises were adopted by all of the natural sciences. Nor did its influence stop here: the rational-scientific method of pursuing knowledge became the salient characteristic of Occidental thought and achievement. Beyond this, it extended to

THE
SCEPTICAL CHYMIST:
OR
CHYMICO-PHYSICAL
Doubts & Paradoxes,
Touching the
SPAGYRIST'S PRINCIPLES
Commonly call'd
HYPOSTATICAL;
As they are wont to be Propos'd and
Defended by the Generality of
ALCHYMISTS.
Whereunto is præmis'd Part of another Difcourfe
relating to the fame Subject.

BY
The Honourable *ROBERT BOYLE*, Efq;

LONDON,
Printed by *J. Cadwell* for *J. Crooke*, and are to be
Sold at the *Ship* in St. *Paul's* Church-Yard.
MDCLXI.

Above: Title page of Robert Boyle's "The Sceptical Chymist"; London, 1661. In this celebrated work the "great Lover of Chymical Experiments" advanced the modern conception of the element as a substance which cannot be split up into simpler ones.

René Descartes' rules of investigation were: never to take anything as true which he "did not know evidently to be so"; to divide, examine, and resolve; to proceed in orderly fashion from the simple to the complex; and to strive for completeness.
Below: Descartes' "Principles of Philosophy" was published in Amsterdam in 1644.
Right: The mechanism of sight, with the soul in the pineal gland functioning as impulse transmitter. A woodcut from Descartes' "Treatise on Man"; Amsterdam, 1677.

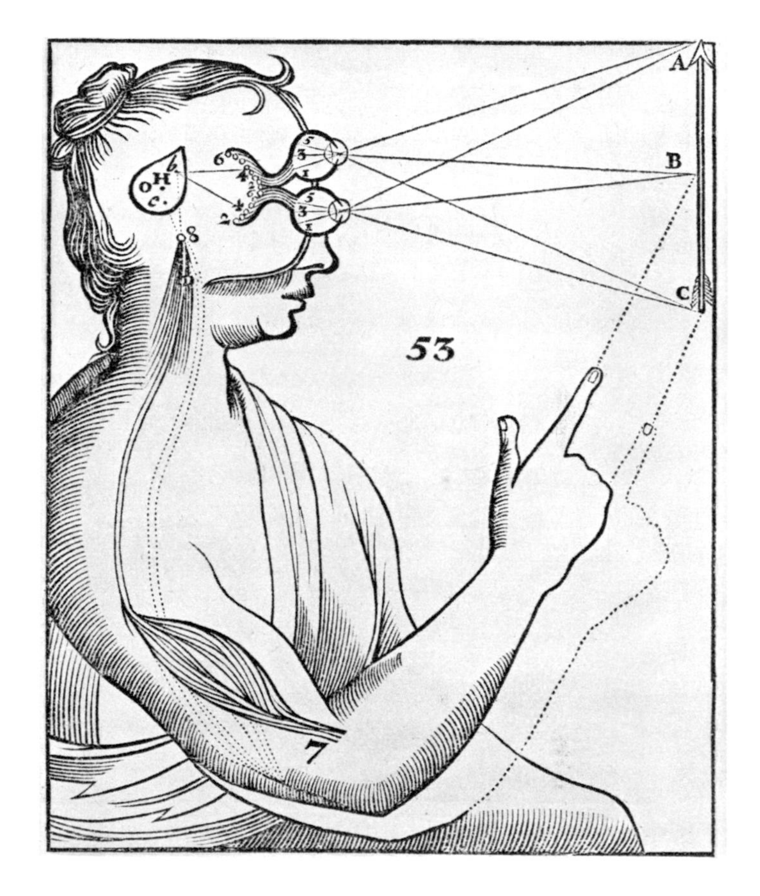

RENATI

DES-CARTES

PRINCIPIA

PHILOSOPHIÆ.

AMSTELODAMI,

APUD LUDOVICUM ELZEVIRIUM,

ANNO CIↃ IↃC XLIV.

Cum Privilegiis.

areas outside the West, "Europeanizing" other civilizations as it spread.
We have heard how the basic tenet of rationalism was formulated in 1644 by René Descartes in his "Principia Philosophiae", when he divided the universe into mind and matter (the realm of extended things). Nature detached from spirit can be correctly understood by means of mechanics. All "scientifically elucidated" phenomena are deducible from the concepts of extension and motion, which constitute a mechanical system. The astronomer observes the mechanics of the heavenly bodies; the chemist studies the mechanism of reaction; the physician practices his art on the mechanism of disease.
Rationalistic thought lives and moves in the sphere of matter *(res corporea)*, rather than in the realm of mind

(ego cogito). What distinguishes the evolution of natural science is the fact that spiritual phenomena are converted into material ones, that they may be made accessible to rational observation. Thus the "Creation of the World" became the "history of evolution", the "healing power of physick" became the "effective substance", the "blessed fruitfulness of the fields" became the "physico-chemical ecology of the soil". This process of materialization proved successful in an amazing number of fields – so many, in fact, that as recently as the beginning of our century exponents of the materialistic philosophy believed it possible to explain the workings of the whole universe in exclusively rational terms.

Reflecting the development of chemistry is the sign language employed by the chemist. Even back in the age of alchemy, substances and reactions were not described with words alone. The signs that alchemists used to annotate them were a kind of shorthand – and may also have served to conceal the adept's knowledge from non-initiates.
The signs used in earlier chemistry were symbols laden with many meanings. A triangle imposed on a cross – 🜍 – not only signified the substance sulfur but also the very essence of combustibility. A circle and arrow – ♂ – was the symbol for the metal iron, but at the same time it stood for the planet Mars and the male principle. These signs, plainly, were not rational.

Left: Old-fashioned chemical shorthand used on a bottle from a Swiss apothecary's shop. The label with its "chemical character" stands for Cremor tartari, or tartar, used as a cosmetic. Swiss Museum of Pharmaceutical History, Basle.
Opposite: Table of solubilities with the chemical signs and symbols current in mid-18th century. Solvents are given in horizontal row at top, while the substances to be dissolved are listed in vertical columns. From "Metallurgical Chemistry" by C. E. Gellert; Leipzig, 1750.

Tabelle von den Auflösungen verschiedener Körper

1.	2.	3.	4.	5.	6.	7.	8.	9.	10.	11.	12.	13.	14.
▽o	▽o	▽	▽	▽	⊖▽	⊖△	✠	⊖	⦶	⊕	℞	⦶.	△
C♁.	▽	▽	C♁	C♁	W. ⚯	☉	W.	⚯	♃ zum Theil	⚯	☉	W.	K.
C♄.	▽	▽	C♄	C♄	K.	☽.	♄	☿	⚯	♛♁	♛♁	K.	⚯
⏢	▽	C♁	⏢	⏢	♛♁	☿	♀	♛♁.	☽	W.	♄	♛♁	☿
⊖▽	C♁	C♄	⊖▽	⊖▽	♃	W.	♂.	W.	♛♁	☿	☿	♃	♛♁
⊖△	C♄	⏢	⊖△	⊖△	♄	♀	X.	♄	☿	♄ Nur zum Theil	W.	♄	W.
	⏢	⊖▽	✝ zum Theil	✠	♀	♂	△	♃	♄	♃	⚯	⚯	☽
	⊖▽	⊖△		⊖	♂	X.		♀	W.	☽	♃	♀	♄
	⊖△	⊕ zum Theil		⦶	X	✠		♂	♀	♀	♀	♂	♃
				⊕	✳	⊖		X	K	♂	K	X	♀
					⊖	⦶		△	♂	X	♂	△	♂
					⦶	⊕			X	△	X		
					⊕	△			△		△		
					△								

15.	16.	17.	18.	19.	20.	21.	22.	23.	24.	25.	26.	27.	28.
⊖△	K.	⚯	♛♁.	⟜♁	W.	X.	♄	♃	♂.	♀	☽.	☿	⟜o
K.	⚯ zum Theil	♛♁	☉	☽.	☉	♄ zum Theil	♀	☉	♀	☽.	☉	♛♁	C. ☿
X.	☽	☉	W.	♂	☽	♃	♃	☽.	☽	☉		♀	C.X.
W.	♄	☽	☽	♄	♄	☉	☉	♀	☉			♄	C.W.
♛♁	W.	♄	♄	♃	♃	☽	☽.	♂				♃	C.♂.
♃	♛♁	♃	♃	♀	♀	♂.						X	C.♀.
♄	X	♀	♀	X.	♂	♀						W.	C.☽.
♀	♃	♂	♂									☽.	C.☉.
♂	♂	X	X.									☉	C.♛♁.
☽	♀												C.K.
☉													C. ♄.

Körper so sich von denen in jeglichen Reihe zu oberst stehenden Körper nicht auflösen lassen

1.	2.	3.	4.	5.	6.	7.	8.	9.	10.	11.	12.	13.	14.
	▽o	▽o	▽o	▽o	☉		☉	☉	☉	☉	☽	☉	☉
			▽		☽.		☽	☽ Doch dieses zum Theil im trockenen Wege				☽.	X
							♃☿						

15.	16.	17.	18.	19.	20.	21.	22.	23.	24.	25.	26.	27.	28.
		W.		W.	X.		♂					♂.	
												K.	

110 **Art, durch Formeln die Zusammensetzung**

Ta	Tantal	Co	Kobalt
Ti	Titan	Ni	Nickel
Os	Osmium	Fe	Eisen
Au	Gold	Mn	Mangan
Ir	Iridium	Ce	Cerium
R	Rhodium	Al	Alùminium
Pt	Platin	Zr	Zirkonium
Pd	Palladium	Y	Yttrium
Hg	Quecksilber	Be	Beryllium
Ag	Silber	Mg	Magnesium
Cu	Kupfer	Ca	Calcium
U	Uran	Sr	Strontium
Bi	Wismuth	Ba	Baryum
Sn	Zinn	L	Lithium
Pb	Blei	Na	Natrium
Cd	Cadmium	K	Kalium.
Zn	Zink		

Diese Anfangsbuchstaben hat man gewählt aus der lateinischen Nomenclatur, weil sie den Naturforschern aller Länder angehört, von ihnen allen gebraucht werden kann, ohne daſs es nöthig ist, jene nach der jedesmaligen Sprache zu ändern. Daſs dieſs ein wesentlicher Vortheil ist, kann wohl nicht bestritten werden, auch haben die Meisten, die sich derselben bedient haben, dieſs eingesehen. Ein französischer Schriftsteller*) hat die National-Eitelkeit gehabt, sie mit den Anfangsbuchstaben in der französischen Sprache zu vertauschen. Wenn dieses von den englischen, deutschen, italienischen Schriftstellern nachgeahmt wird, so geht, ohne den geringsten Vortheil, viel von der Bestimmtheit und Faſslichkeit dieser Formeln verloren; man darf indeſs von den klaren Ansichten der Mehrzahl der wahren Naturforscher erwarten, daſs sie diesen Nutzen nicht einer so kindischen Eitelkeit aufopfern. „Die Wissenschaft," sagt Humphry Davy **) so vor-

*) *Beudant, Essai d'un cours élémentaire et général des sciences physiques. Minéralogie.*

**) In seiner Rede als Präsident der K. Gesellschaft zu London bei Ueberreichung der Copleyschen Medaille für Hrn. Arago, für die

J. J. Berzelius introduced the modern method of chemical annotation in 1814. This is a page from the German translation of his "Textbook of Chemistry", prepared by his pupil F. Woehler from the manuscript in Swedish (4th ed., Dresden and Leipzig, 1836).

Those employed by modern chemistry, on the other hand, are. They were introduced by the Swede Joens Jacob Berzelius in 1814, taking "the first letter in the Latin name of each basic substance". Today the chemical symbol expresses both the substance as such and its quantity: S signifies the substance sulfur in the amount of one atom. H_2O means that two atoms of hydrogen and one atom of oxygen are combined in one molecule of water. The irrational alchemical symbol, in short, was transformed into the rational chemical formula of today.

Chemical research gains scientific knowledge through experimentation in the laboratory. The classic abode of research is the university, but with the establishment of chemical factories industrial laboratories also came into being. In his memoirs, Carl Duisberg wrote of the beginnings of the Bayer works in Leverkusen: "Our wide experience with chemists and instructors working in technical capacities at universities has led us to the conclusion that nowadays, in order to produce fruitful and successful results for technology, the chemist must no longer work in the universities, but in technology itself." This means that fields of science ripe for practical development are cultivated primarily by industrial research.

Today the chemical industry in Basle works on five main groups of substances: dyestuffs, pharmaceuticals, plastics, and textile application products, as well as insecticides. The development of each group necessitates research efforts in two directions: synthesis and application.

Progress in any of these fields depends on the "law of the minimum". The pace is not set by the direction, whether synthesis or application, in which development has proceeded furthest. Rather, the tempo of development parallels progress in a line of effort which has yet to be extended. Thus the impulses that affected the furthering of dyes originated in synthetic-organic chemistry; a considerable body of knowledge concerning the application of dyestuffs to textile material had already accumulated during the times when natural coloring agents were used. Developments in the field of plastics are very closely related to the proliferation of knowledge concerning macromolecular chemistry. Conversely, pharmaceutical research was stimulated by medicine, and research in the field of textile application products by textile finishing, at a time when the art of organic synthesis was already quite far along.

Inside a modern laboratory of the chemical industry.

Dyestuffs

Natural coloring agents – substances and extracts – still used in huge quantities a hundred years ago, have disappeared from the market since that time. Synthetic dyestuffs have captured the position they once held.

The First Coal Tar Dyes: the Empirical Age of Dyestuff Chemistry. Two problems occupied chemical science around the middle of the last century: the study of products derived from coal tar and the investigation of natural substances. With their investigations Dumas and Liebig had developed the quantitative analysis of organic compounds. The products resulting from the combustion of an organic substance – nitrogen, carbon dioxide, water – are measured, and from the data obtained the summary formula is computed. Using this technique, in 1831 Justus von Liebig found the quinine molecule to be composed of 10 carbon atoms, 12 hydrogen atoms, and one oxygen and nitrogen atom each. The empirical formula is therefore $C_{10}H_{12}ON$. On the basis of this formula William Henry Perkin, a student at the Royal College of Chemistry in London, attempted to prepare quinine synthetically. He oxidized $C_{10}H_{13}N$, the allyl toluidine obtained from the distillation products of coal tar, with potassium dichromate and sulfuric acid. The resulting substance, instead of being the medicament he sought, was a dark mass from which a bluish-red dyestuff could be ex-

Opposite: Apparatus for performing elementary organic analysis according to the method developed by Dumas and Liebig. Copperplate from the atlas to Dumas' "Traité de chimie appliquée aux arts"; Paris, 1828/30.

Below: Around 1840 Liebig's laboratory was a Mecca for young chemists from many countries. This notice offers a laboratory course in analytical chemistry. Swiss Museum of Pharmaceutical History, Basle.

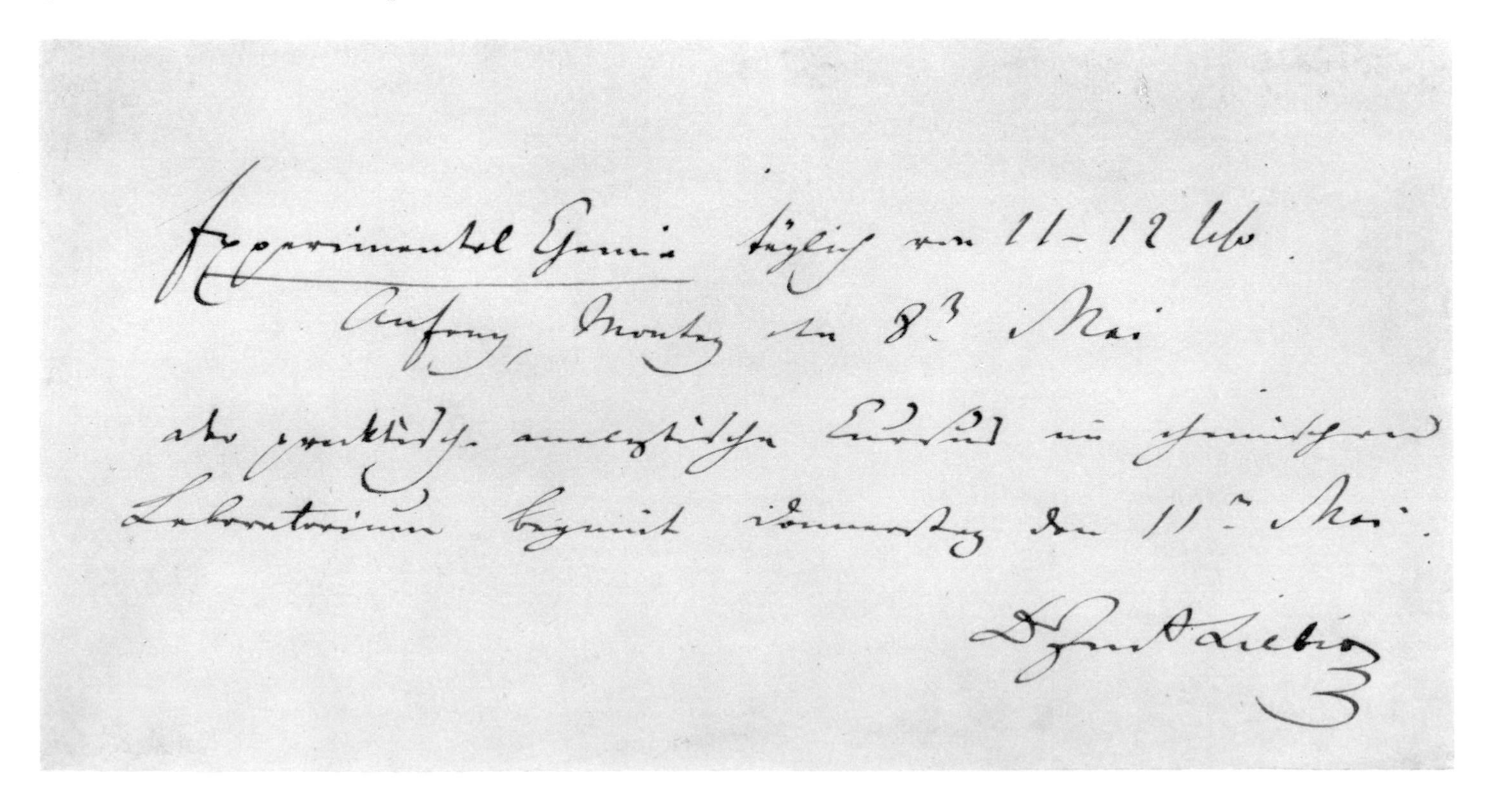

Experimental Chemie täglich von 11–12 Uhr.
Anfang Montag den 8ten Mai
der praktische analytische Cursus im chemischen
Laboratorium beginnt Donnerstag den 11ten Mai.

Dr Just Liebig

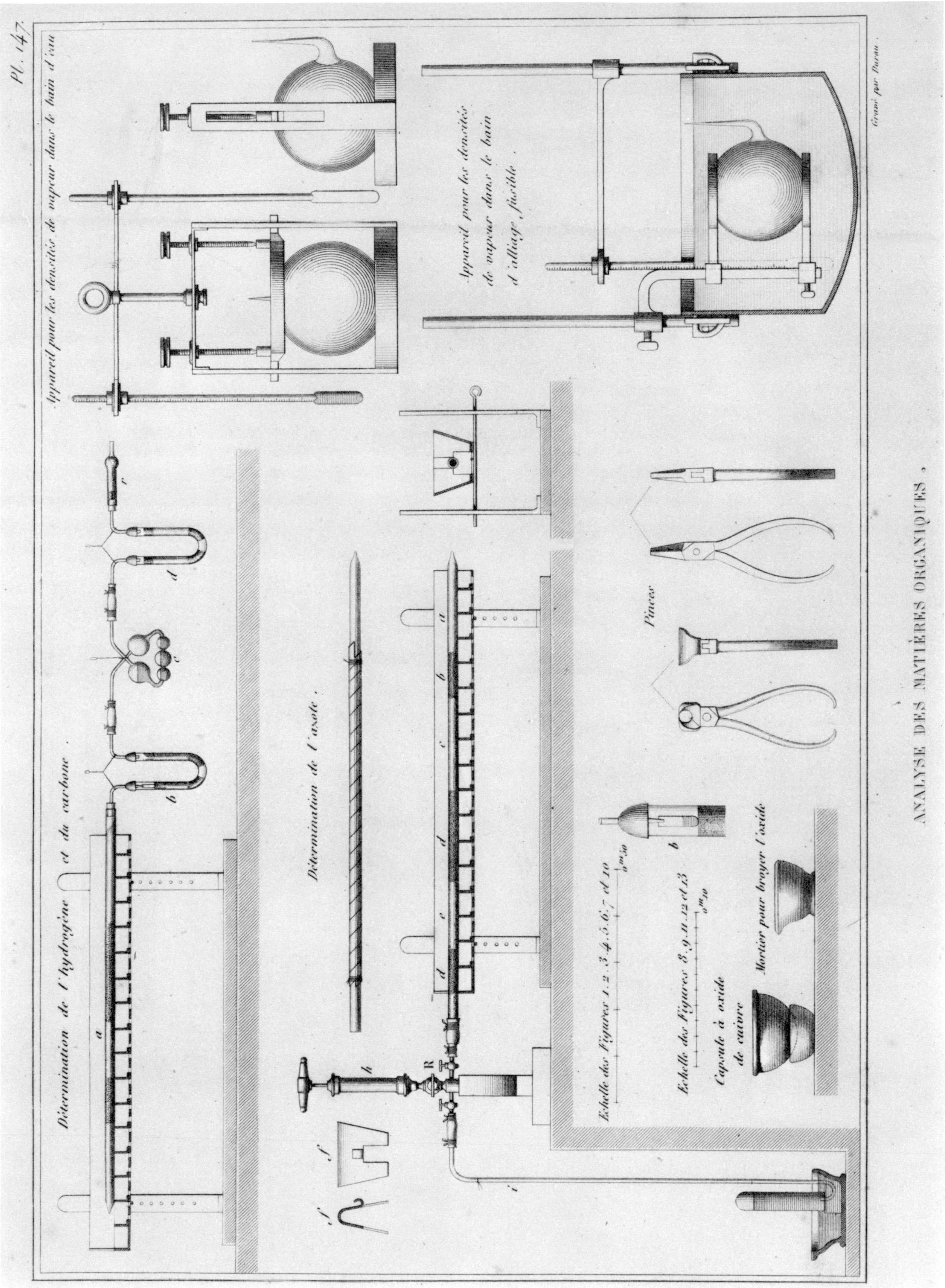

Pl. 147.

Détermination de l'hydrogène et du carbone.

a b c d r

Appareil pour les densités de vapeur dans le bain d'eau

Détermination de l'azote.

f f h R d e d c b a i

Appareil pour les densités de vapeur dans le bain d'alliage fusible.

Echelle des Figures 1. 2. 3. 4. 5. 6. 7 et 10

0m30

Echelle des Figures 8. 9. 11. 12 et 13

0m10

b

Capsule à oxide de cuivre

Mortier pour broyer l'oxide

Pinces

Gravé par Durau.

ANALYSE DES MATIÈRES ORGANIQUES.

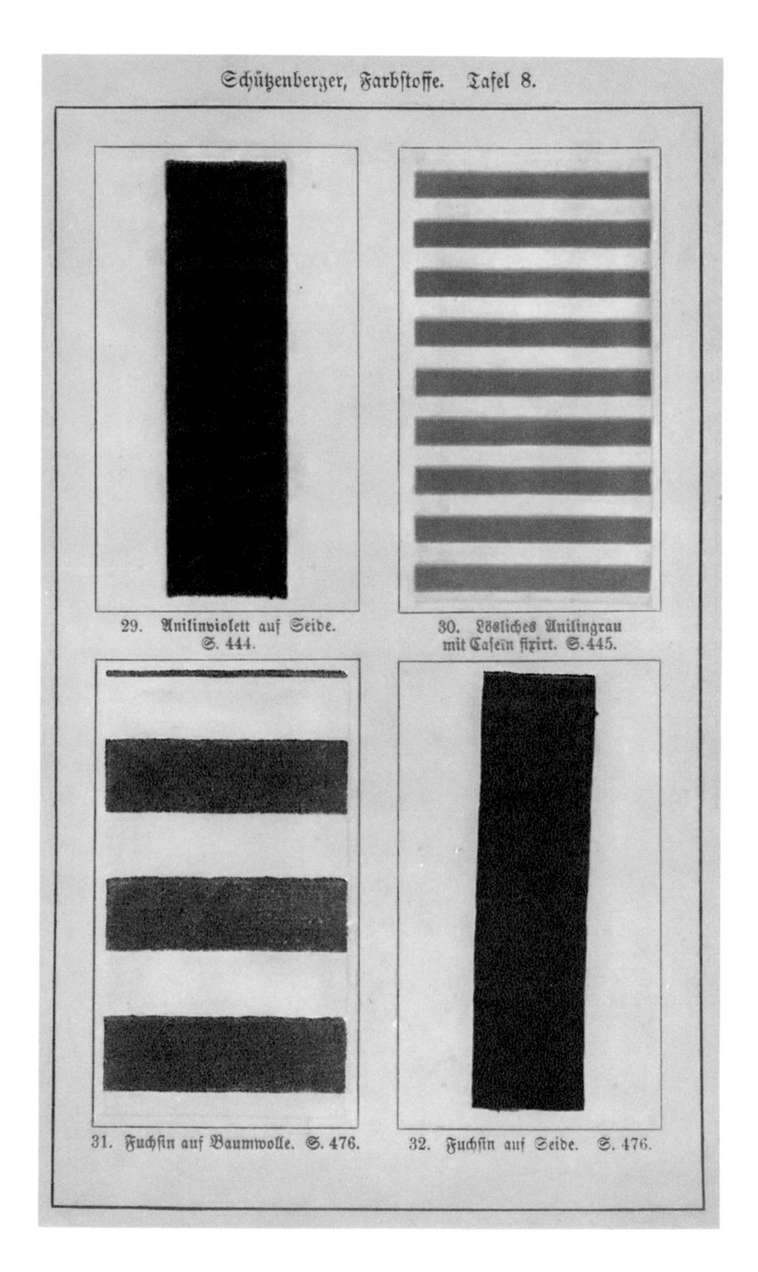

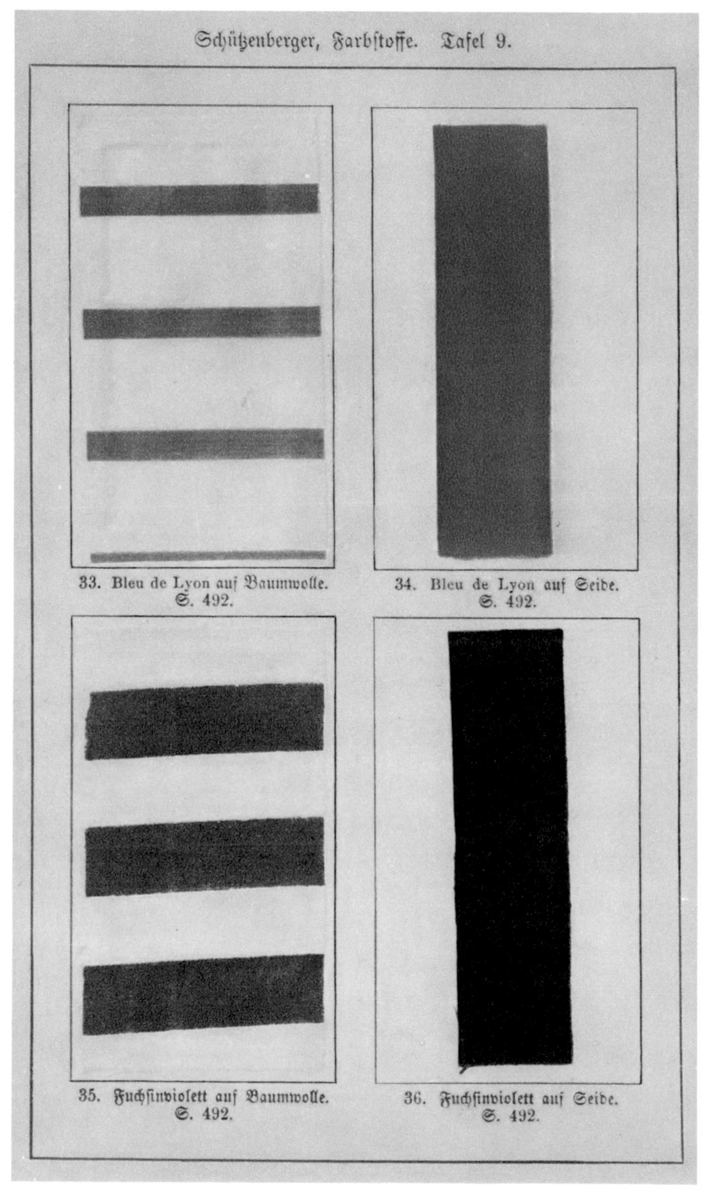

tracted with alcohol. Simple crude aniline used in the place of allyl toluidine resulted in a similar dyestuff, violet-colored mauveine. After having obtained patent protection for the manufacturing process in August 1856, Perkin began producing this dyestuff at Greenford Green near Harrow in 1857.

Because of its pure, pronouncedly blue-tinted red color, mauveine met with an enthusiastic reception among silk dyers. This particular shade could not be obtained with any of the natural coloring agents previously used. The simple dyeing process was also a point in its favor, only necessitating turning the material in a boiling dyebath for one hour.

Perkin's mauveine did not remain the only coal tar

Schützenberger, Farbstoffe. Tafel 10.

37. Hofmann's Violett auf Baumwolle. S. 497.

38. Hofmann's Violett auf Seide. S. 497.

39. Anilinbraun. S. 502.

40. Rosanilingrün. S. 503.

color for long. Analogous reactions of crude aniline with other oxidation and condensation agents made their bid too. Independently of one another, and almost simultaneously, A.W. von Hofmann, Perkin's teacher, and E. Verguin, in London and Lyons respectively, prepared aniline red in 1858/59. Aniline red, later called magenta or fuchsine, imparted lovely brilliant red shades to silk in the same simple way that mauveine colored purplish.

During the period from 1860 to 1862 Hofmann showed that by means of simple chemical operations (heating with aniline, ethyl iodide, methyl chloride), fuchsine can be converted into violet, blue and green derivatives.

Like mauveine, fuchsine and its derivatives belong to the class of basic dyes. Applied to animal textile fibres,

Opposite and above: Pattern cards showing material printed with the first synthetic dyestuffs. Perkin's mauveine is indicated as "aniline violet" (No. 29, top left). Tables from M. P. Schützenberger's work which originally appeared as "Traité des matières colorantes" in Paris, 1867. It was the first comprehensive work on synthetic colors. Right: Reaction vessel for fuchsine manufacture. Xylograph from Louis Figuier's "Marvels of Industry", published in the 1870s.

especially to silk, they do, it is true, give very pure shades. The fastness to light and washing of these dyes and their behavior in the wash, however, leave much to be desired.

In 1859 – the same year in which Verguin discovered fuchsine – Alexander Clavel, we may remember, commenced manufacture of this dyestuff in the laboratory of his Basle silk dyeworks. A short time later J. J. Mueller-Pack took up production of the same dye in the extraction factory of Geigy. These first manufacturers of aniline dyes in Basle were followed in 1862 by J.-G. Dollfus near the St. Johann Gate and in 1864 by A. Gerber with W. Uhlmann on Klybeck Street. To recapitulate local history, all of these works developed into large-scale chemical enterprises. Clavel's silk dyeworks was the nucleus of CIBA; the present-day J.R. Geigy S.A. grew from Mueller's extraction plant; Dollfus' coal tar dyes factory became Durand & Huguenin. In 1898 the Gerber-Uhlmann enterprise merged with what was then known as the "Society of Chemical Industry in Basle", the forerunner of our present-day CIBA.

Model of the benzene molecule. Note the formal resemblance to Ouroboros (page 50). Its ring structure was discovered by Kekulé when he was teaching at the University of Ghent in 1865.

At that time there were gaps in what was known about the reaction mechanisms of the first dyestuff syntheses. Chemists had as yet no clear picture of the structure of the molecules involved. Dyestuff chemistry was still a purely empirical field.

Architecture of the Molecule – Synthesis of Alizarin. The empirical formula provides information on the kind and number of atoms in a molecule, but about their arrangement it says nothing. A knowledge of the sorts and quantities of bricks used does not mean we know how the house built of them actually looks. Only a knowledge of the architecture, be the structure a house or a molecule, can give us a clear idea of the spatial disposition involved.

Towards the middle of the 19th century numerous chemists voiced their opinions concerning the architecture of the molecule. Here the observations of Friedrich August Kekulé von Stradonitz, a pupil of Liebig and professor of chemistry in Heidelberg, Ghent and Bonn, and of his less renowned contemporary, the Scotsman Archibald Couper, proved particularly fruitful. Kekulé recognized that carbon atoms could join to form chain-shaped and ring-shaped molecules. In 1865 he put forward his theory which held that a hexagonal ring structure may be assigned to benzene, and four years later he published the formulation still in use today. From the molecular formula C_6H_6 he derived the constitution of benzene; merely by using the data relating to material and amount, a differentiated geometric image was developed.

Kekulé's structure theory became foundation of benzene chemistry, and thus of dyestuff research. His formulae are abstractions, enabling us to perceive properties and reaction possibilities. In this way they furnish a basis for systematically undertaken chemical modifications.

Benzene

In the chemical laboratories of Switzerland and Germany the importance of Kekulé's structure theory was recognized at once; in England and France the tendency was to reject it. This may have been one reason why, during the second half of the century, the centre of gravity of the dyes industry shifted. The countries where it had originated, England (mauveine) and France (fuchsine), relinquished their leading position to Germany and Switzerland.

The consequences of the new structure theory soon became manifest. Working in Baeyer's laboratory at the Technical Academy in Berlin, Carl Graebe, later a professor in Geneva, and Carl Liebermann, afterwards a professor in Berlin, in 1868 clarified the structure of alizarin, a dioxyanthraquinone which is the red color principle of the madder root. They managed to synthesize this vegetable coloring matter the following year:

Alkali fusion

1,2-Dibromanthraquinone from coal tar anthracene

Alizarin 1,2-Dioxyanthraquinone

The light fastness properties of a fuchsine (top) and an alizarin dyeing on silk compared. A circular sample of each test run was exposed to sunlight for the same length of time. Whereas the alizarin dyeing (below) was not affected to any notable extent, the fuchsine was decomposed.

For the technological utilization of the alizarin synthesis Graebe and Liebermann joined forces with Heinrich Caro, a calico-printer turned chemist of BASF. In June 1869 an elegant and industrially feasible synthesis – the fusion of anthraquinone-2-sulfonic acid, using alkali – was submitted for patenting by these researchers from university and industry, only a day before Perkin filed a specification for essentially the same process.
The manufacture of synthetic alizarin from coal tar began. In 1869 the alizarin plant of BASF was opened in Ludwigshafen, the same year that Perkin inaugurated his in Greenford Green. The cultivation of madder lapsed into complete desuetude within a few years. A dyestuff that for thousands of years had only been obtainable from a plant was now being made in the chemical factory.
But it is not for this reason alone that alizarin occupies a prominent place in the history of coal tar dyes, for it was also the first synthetic dyestuff possessing satisfactory fastness to light and washing.

In Basle, too, alizarin was being manufactured. In 1873, as previously noted, Robert Bindschedler and Albert Busch-Steiner purchased Clavel's factory on Klybeck Street. From a description of the "manufacturing methods" dated 1874 we learn that of 85 workmen employed in the factory, 35 were in the alizarin plant. Towards the end of the 1880s, however, manufacture of this dyestuff had to be discontinued, since strong competition on the world market had brought a big reduction in price. In 1869, 20% alizarin paste was worth 34 Swiss francs per kilogram; a decade later this figure had sunk to 3 francs. Today alizarin has lost the predominance it once enjoyed. It has been succeeded by other dyestuff classes which are easier to handle and yield equally brilliant and fast shades.

Dyes research was not limited to the synthesis of this important natural red color. Within a short time other mordant dyestuffs were being synthesized on the basis of alizarin, differing in their shades from the natural prototype:

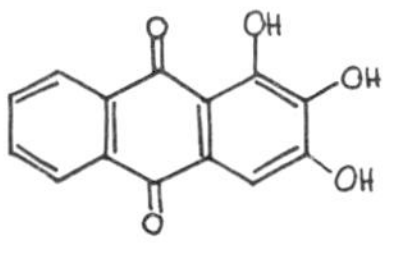

Alizarin Orange
1874

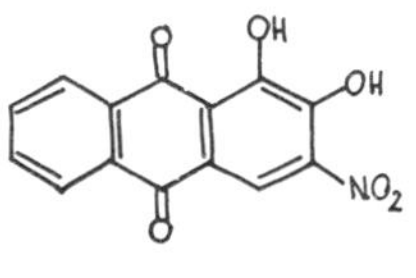

Alizarin Brown
1877

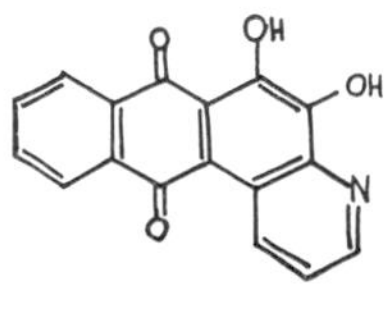

Alizarin Blue
1877

With the alizarin derivatives the three main emphases of industrial chemistry – and this included not only colors, but the later-flowering pharmaceutical chemistry as well – had been defined:
- Elucidation of natural substances and their synthesis (Example: alizarin)
- Chemical modifications of natural substances (Example: alizarin derivatives)
- Synthesis of substances with no prototype in nature (Example: mauveine, fuchsine, and derivatives)

Opposite and overleaf: A description of manufacturing methods employed in the Bindschedler & Busch coal tar dyes factory, relating to the production of alizarin. The first page concerns the working force; the following two give information on actual manufacturing procedures. Basle Public Records Office.

III h. No 3. Anilinfabrike Bindschedler & Busch 1874.
III 4

Beschreibung der Fabricationsmethoden der
chemischen Fabrike von
Bindschedler & Busch in Basel

Die Fabrike producirt
a. Anilinfarbstoffe
b. künstliche Alizarin.

Die Fabrication der Anilinfarbstoffe beschäftigt circa 50 Arbeiter, die des Alizarin circa 35 Arbeiter. Total der Arbeiter c. 85. – überwacht & geleitet in jedem einzelnen Fabricationszweige durch 3 Chemiker & c. 6 Contremaîtres.

Beim Eintritte in die Fabrike passirt jeder Arbeiter Visite des Fabrikarztes Herrn Dr. Lichtenhahn, werden nur von ihm gesund befundene Arbeiter angestellt. Einige Male per Jahr werden sämtliche Arbeiter nochmals ärztlich untersucht & namentlich die Arbeiter strenge angehalten, sich der grössten Reinlichkeit zu befleissen & ihnen zu diesem Behufe Seife & Badegelegenheit geboten.

Die technischen Einrichtungen für die verschied. Fabricationen sind derart, dass die Arbeiter nie durch schädliche Dämpfe & Dünste belästigt werden. Arsenik wird in der Fabrike gar nie angewandt.

Zur Alizarinfabrikation sind die Ateliers
No. 5. 7. 8. 10. 33. 34 & 36 benützt.
Der Fabrikationsgang ist folgender:
Das Rohprodukt, das Anthracen wird in
verschiedenem Grade der Reinheit, (30 à 70 %)
gekauft & in Atelier No 10 einer Reinigung
durch Waschen mit Alcool unterworfen.
Durch Oxydation mittelst Schwefelsäure &
doppeltchromsaurem Kali erhält man aus
dem gereinigten Anthracen das Anthrachinon,
welches mit Wasser ausgewaschen & in
No. 8 & 34 getrocknet wird. In No 36 wird
das trockene Chinon durch Erhitzen mit
Schwefelsäure & rauchender Schwefelsäure in
emaillirten Gefässen in Anthrachinonsulfo-
säure umgewandelt. Bei dieser Operation
entwickelt sich etwas gasförmige Schweflige
Säure gemengt mit Schwefelsäuredämpfen.
Um die Arbeiter völlig vor dem Einflusse
dieser Dämpfe zu schützen, sind die emaillirten
Kessel zugedeckt & werden die sich entwickelnden
Dämpfe in einem paraffinirten Holzkanal
in ein zum Theil mit Wasser gefülltes Fass
geleitet, in welchem sich die Dämpfe
condensiren. Der obere Theil des Fasses ist
wiederum durch einen Holzkanal mit

dem grossen Dampfkamin verbunden. Es
entsteht hiedurch eine sehr kräftige Aspiration,
welche die geringste Spur der Dämpfe aus den
emaillirten Kesseln durch die Rohre in das
Freie führt, & so diesen Fabrikationszweig für
die Arbeiter durchaus unschädlich macht.
Im Atelier No. 7 wird die Anthrachinonsulfo-
säure in das Kalk- & nachher in das Natron-
Salz verwandelt & das letztere fest zur
Trockne eingedampft. Indem man den
in No. 34 das Natronsalz durch Schmelzen mit
Natronhydrat hydroxylirt erhält man das
Alizarinnatron in fester Masse; diese wird
in No. 33 in kochendem Wasser gelöst & mit
Salzsäure das Alizarin ausgefällt, dieses
in Filterpressen filtrirt & gewaschen wird
in Form einer Pâte v. 10 à 20 %
Trockengehalt versandt.

Basel d. 30 April 1874

Bindschedler & Busch

Page from an old pattern card showing combination dyeings of the first azo colors on woollen felt (Orange II, Roccelline, Benzyl-violet).

The Flowering of Color Chemistry: Azo Dyes. The precipitate development of the azo dyes gave further testimony of how valuable Kekulé's structure theory was.

In 1877 Johann Peter Griess took out an English patent for the manufacture of a yellow azo dyestuff made from picramic acid and phenol (carbolic acid). Although this product failed to meet with any commercial success, dyes chemists were quick to grasp the great importance of the discovery. During the ensuing five years no fewer than 52 German patents in the azo field were granted to various applicants.

The first azo dye, though of no practical use, had made its appearance two decades earlier when, in 1856, Perkin caused potassium nitrite to act on hydrochloride of α-naphthylamine. Griess, an "original" who, like Perkin, worked for some years with A. W. von Hofmann in London and subsequently was affiliated with Allsopp & Sons, brewers of Burton-on-Trent, as a scientific consultant, made a thoroughgoing study of the diazo compounds. His first publication on the subject, a "preliminary notice", appeared in "Liebig's Annals of Chemistry" in 1858. The first technically important diazo dyestuff was discovered by a friend from Griess' student days, Carl Alexander von Martius. In 1862 von Martius, afterwards founder of Agfa in Berlin, obtained Bismarck Brown by causing nitrous acid to act on m-phenylene diamine (diazotization and self-coupling). The new color was placed on the market three years later by Roberts, Dale & Co., Manchester.

As an azo dye, Bismarck Brown remained in a class all by itself for many years. Only after its constitution and mechanism of formation had been explained on the basis of the new structure theory could the azo dyes field be systematically cultivated. Martius, Griess and Kekulé perceived the azo group to be the characteristic structural principle, consisting of two nitrogen atoms: $-N=N-$. The groupings of the other atoms in the dye molecule determine whether a compound belongs to the class of mordant, basic or acid dyestuffs.

Vorläufige Notiz über die Einwirkung von salpetriger Säure auf Amidinitro- und Aminitrophenylsäure;

von *Peter Griefs.*

Wird in eine alkoholische Lösung von Amidinitrophenylsäure ($C_{12}\left(\begin{array}{c}H_2\\2\ NO_4\\H_2N\end{array}\right)O, HO$) ein rascher Strom von salpetriger Säure geleitet, so fällt, nachdem die Einwirkung längere Zeit angedauert hat, ein Körper in messinggelben Schuppen nieder. Dieser läfst sich leicht durch Umkrystallisiren aus Alkohol reinigen. Die Mutterlange, aus welcher der Körper sich abschied, enthält Dinitrophenylsäure. Ich glaubte, der neue Körper würde seiner Bildungsweise gemäfs die Zusammensetzung $HO, C_{12}\left(\begin{array}{c}H_5\\2\ NO_4\end{array}\right)O_3$ haben; die Analyse belehrte mich jedoch, dafs sich seine Zusammensetzung durch die empirische Formel:

$$C_{12}H_2N_4O_{10}$$

ausdrücken läfst. Die Verbrennung des bei 100° getrockneten Körpers gab im Mittel:

C 34,2
H 1,1,

die obige Formel verlangt:

C 34,3
H 0,9 pC.

Die nach Bunsen's Methode ausgeführte Stickstoffbestimmung ergab das Verhältnifs des Stickstoffs zum Kohlenstoff = $\frac{1}{3}$. Diese neue Substanz hat durchaus nicht den Character einer Säure. Mit Alkalien zerfällt sie unter Gasentwickelung in Dinitrophenylsäure.

Die von Laurent und Gerhardt dargestellte Aminitrophenylsäure $HO, C_{12}\left(\begin{array}{c}H_3\\NO_4\\H_2N\end{array}\right)O$ erleidet durch salpetrige Säure eine ähnliche Zersetzung. Es bildet sich ein gelber krystallinischer Körper, dessen Zusammensetzung sich durch die Formel:

$$C_{12}H_3N_3O_6 + HO$$

ausdrücken läfst. Die Verbrennung des über SO_3 getrockneten Körpers ergab:

C 41,5
H 2,4.

Diese Zahlen entsprechen der angeführten Formel, welche verlangt:

C 41,4
H 2,3.

Das Verhältnifs des N zum C ergab sich = $\frac{1}{4}$

Dieser Körper erträgt nicht die Hitze des Wasserbades, sondern zersetzt sich durch dieselbe unter heftiger Explosion. Alkalien lösen ihn unter Gasentwickelung mit rother Farbe, wobei er möglicherweise in Nitrophenylsäure übergeführt wird.

Ich habe auch noch Brom und Untersalpetersäure und Chlor und Untersalpetersäure enthaltende Aminsäuren der Phenylsäure dargestellt und diese mit NO_3 behandelt. Diese geben, wie es scheint, ähnliche Zersetzungsproducte.

Die Bildungsweise, Eigenschaften und eigenthümliche Zusammensetzung dieser Körper verleihen, wie ich glaube, denselben einiges Interesse. Ich enthalte mich übrigens, ehe ich ihre Zersetzungsproducte genauer kenne, mit deren Studium ich schon seit längerer Zeit im Laboratorium des Hrn. Prof. Kolbe beschäftigt bin, jedes Urtheils über ihre rationelle Constitution, hoffe jedoch in kurzer Zeit Mittheilungen über dieselbe machen zu können.

The pioneer paper by Johann Peter Griess on the diazotizing reaction, of particular importance in color chemistry, appeared in the "Annals of Chemistry and Pharmacy" in 1858.

Thanks to their simple processing and the pure color tones they gave on wool and silk, the acid azo dyes caused a great stir among dyers. In but a short time they had ousted the yellow and red natural colors and their extracts completely.

The manufacture of azo dyes was soon taken up in Basle also. The firm of Bindschedler & Busch, for example, produced many acid azo dyes, some of which are still in use today.

Acid Azo Dyes	Discoverer	Made by Bindschedler & Busch in 1883 as:
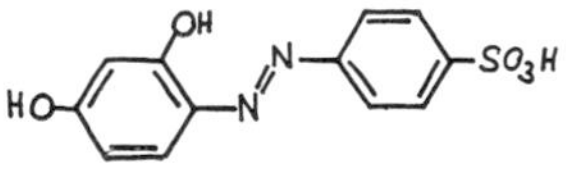	Griess 1875	Yellow T
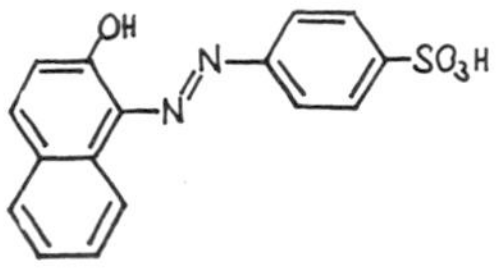	Roussin 1876	Orange II
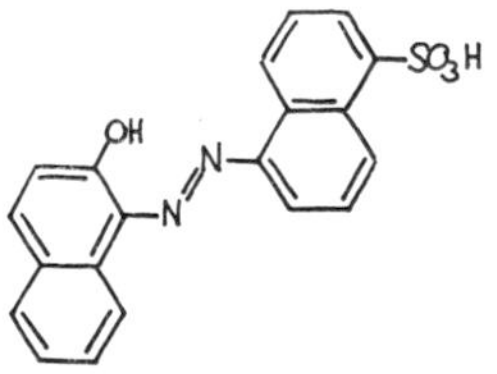	Caro Roussin 1877	Roccelline

To Rudolf Nietzki, professor of organic chemistry at the University of Basle from 1884 to 1911, azoic color chemistry owed many a forceful impulse. Even before his Basle period he constructed the first acid dyestuff with two azo groups, Biebrich Scarlet.

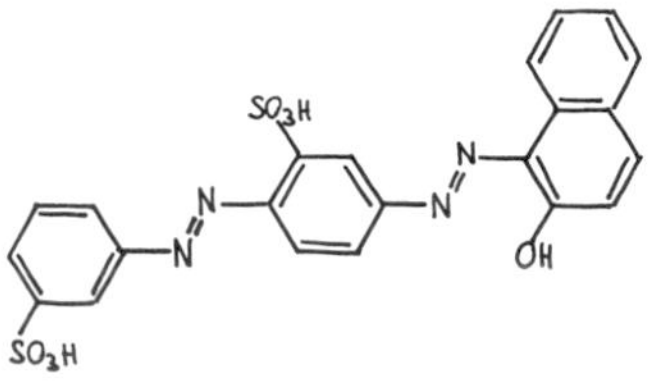

Biebrich Scarlet

This color, because of its pure red shade, was the most successful competitor of genuine scarlet, the dyeing from cochineal insects on tin-mordanted wool and silk.
In 1887 the first mordant azo dye was discovered by Nietzki in Basle. This was Alizarin Yellow GG.

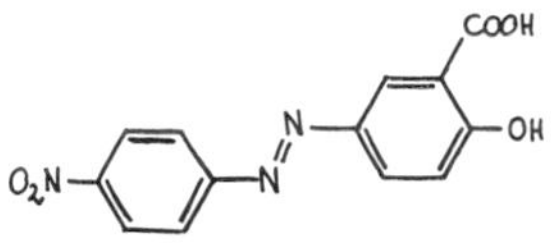

Alizarin Yellow GG

Alizarin Yellow in combination with chromium and iron mordants superseded the natural colors fustic and Persian (or buckthorn) berries.
Nietzki was quite as important for his teaching activities as for his research work in the field of colors. His textbook on the "Chemistry of the Organic Dyestuffs" was the classical compendium of its day, going through five editions from 1889 to 1906.

Opposite: First page of a petition from Prof. Rudolf Nietzki to the Basle Departement of Education in which he requests financial support for the teaching laboratory which he had been maintaining out of his own pocket. The Basle chemical firms backed this project, and thus induced the authorities promised to cover the operating expenses of the laboratory. Basle Public Records Office.

Basel 18 Febr. 1896

An

den Vorsteher des Erziehungsdepartements

Basel

Seit Beginn des Wintersemesters ist mein neues Laboratorium im Betrieb und es sind in demselben gegenwärtig 18 Praktikanten in ganz derselben Weise, wie früher im Bernoullianum mit wissenschaftlichen Arbeiten beschäftigt.

Obwohl durch diesen Erfolg meine Erwartungen erheblich übertroffen wurden, hat sich das Unternehmen in finanzieller Hinsicht als so wenig lebensfähig erwiesen, dass ich mich genöthigt sehe, für die weitere Fortführung desselben die Hilfe der hohen Regierung in Anspruch zu nehmen.

Ein im vorigen Jahre von mir an die hohe Behörde gestelltes Gesuch um eine Beihilfe von Fr. 5000 zur Einrichtung des Laboratoriums wurde mir abgeschlagen. Andererseits stellte mir die h. Curatel in der letzten Sitzung die Bedingung, dass ich dieselbe Höhe der Praktikantenkurse einhalten wolle,

The coal tar dyes on the market up to the 1880s simplified dyeing processes for the dyer, particularly with wool and silk. The basic dyes (the fuchsine group, for example) and the acid azo dyes can be applied to these materials without pre-mordanting.
Acid dyestuffs have practically no affinity for cotton, and the basic colors entail mordanting treatment of the fibres with tannin and tartar emetic. There existed only three natural direct coloring agents for cotton: for red, safflower, the blossom of *Carthamus tinctorius* L.; for orange, annatto, a waxlike pulp around the seeds of *Bixa orellana* L.; and for yellow, the Chinese turmeric. This was why the discovery of the first coal tar dyes for coloring cotton directly caused a sensation. In 1883 J. Walter of the Geigy firm discovered Sun Yellow by boiling p-nitrotoluene sulfonic acid with soda lye. Of even greater importance was the preparation a year later of Congo Red by the German chemist W. Boettiger.

Congo Red

With this coloring principle the way was opened to the development of a new dye class, one which today comprises hundreds of specimens of the substantive, or direct, cotton dyes.

Direct dyeing of cellulose fibres in 40-fold magnification. Direct dyestuffs have a pronounced affinity for cellulosic fibre. Top to bottom: beginning, middle, and end of the coloring process, with cotton red 10 B dyed onto viscose rayon.

Production of vegetable indigo. Branches of the plant are fermented in water in vat B. The workers on either side of vat C are adding oxygen to the aqueous extract by beating it, in order to precipitate out solid indigo. The sediment is then drawn off through tube E into canvas filtres G, drained, and dried. Copperplate from the Encyclopedia of Diderot and d'Alembert; volume dated 1762.

The Triumph of Color Chemistry: Synthesis of Indigo and Indigoid Vat Dyes. Dyes chemistry celebrated its greatest triumph with the synthesis of indigo, the most widely used natural coloring agent.

Many plants supply indigo, for example the indigo bush *(Indigofera anil* L.*)*, a native of East India, or dyer's woad *(Isatis tinctoria* L.*)*, indigenous to Europe. The dyestuff is not, to be sure, ready to hand in the plants but is formed in the course of a working-up process. The stalks and leaves of the indigo plant were subjected, right after harvesting, to fermentation lasting from a week to a fortnight in steeping tanks, during which time the colorless indican contained in the plant split up into indoxyl and glucose. The aqueous yellowish indoxyl solution was then decanted from the fermentation vat into a heating vat, where it was exposed to atmospheric oxygen by being beaten with sticks. This caused the indoxyl to be oxidized into water-insoluble indigo, which settled in grain or flake form to the bottom of the vat. After being pressed into cube-shaped pieces, the dried sediment found its way onto the market.

Adolf von Baeyer, a professor in Berlin who subsequently became Liebig's successor in Munich, dedicated a large part of his research work to the vegetable dyestuff indigo. In 1868 he published the first formula which, although not complete, pointed the way to synthesis. Twelve years later Baeyer succeeded in synthesizing indigotin via o-nitrocinnamic acid. Three years after this he was able to write that "the location of every atom in the molecule of this dyestuff has now been experimentally ascertained". Thus fifteen years of work culminated in the elucidation of the structure of indigo by analysis and synthesis.

Indigo

addirt sich nur ein Wasserstoffatom zu $C_8 H_5 N O$; es muß daher die Formel des Blau verdoppelt werden, wofür auch die amorphe Beschaffenheit desselben spricht. Die Formel für das Indigblau wird also folgende:

$$\left.\begin{matrix} C_6 H_4 C_2 H N \\ C_6 H_4 C_2 H N \end{matrix}\right\} O O$$

Bei der Reduktion zu Indigweiß wird ein Sauerstoffatom ausgelöst und die Substanz

$$\left.\begin{matrix} C_6 H_4 C_2 H N O H \\ C_6 H_4 C_2 H N H \end{matrix}\right\} O$$

gebildet, aus welcher bei fernerer Reduktion durch Verlust des zweiten Atoms Sauerstoff zwei Moleküle der Verbindung $C_6 H_4 (C_2 N H_2, OH)$ entstehen.

München den 3ten Sept. 83.

Lieber Herr Doctor

Left: Baeyer's indigo formula which he published in 1868, although not correct in every part, made possible the synthesis of this dyestuff. From Vol. 2 of the aforementioned work (page 121) by Schützenberger on "Dyestuffs"; Berlin edition, 1870.

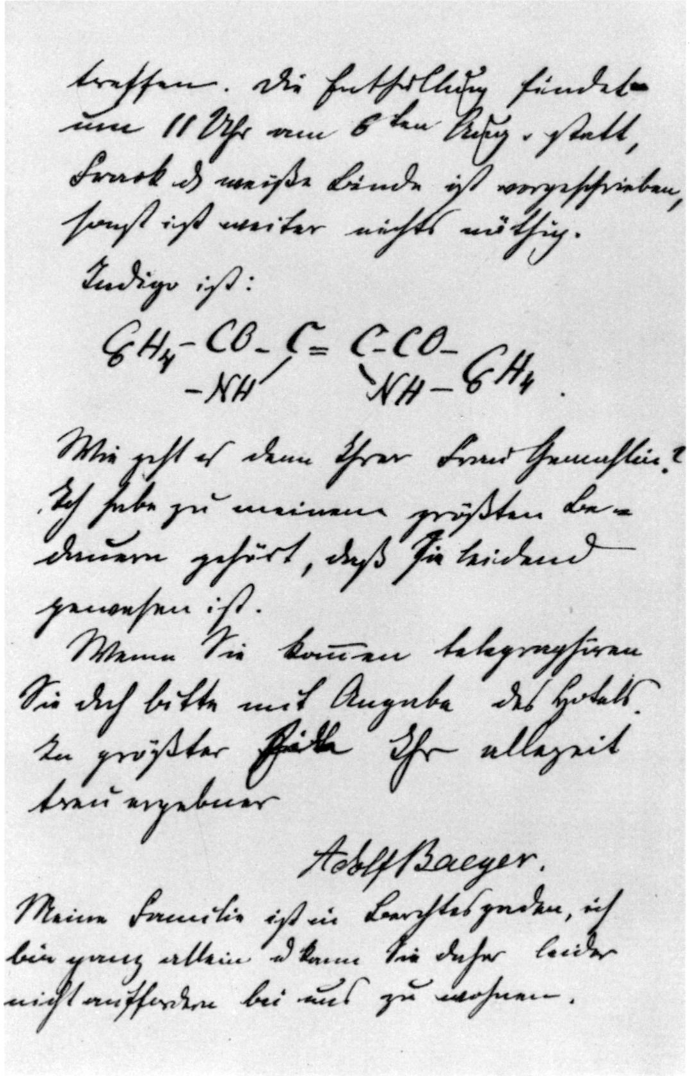

Baeyer's synthesis was, for practical purposes, prohibitively expensive. Both in Germany and in Switzerland chemists energetically sought a more economical means of preparing the color. In 1890 Karl Heumann, a professor at the Zurich Polytechnic, found two possibilities that finally led to this goal.

Synthesis "Heumann I":

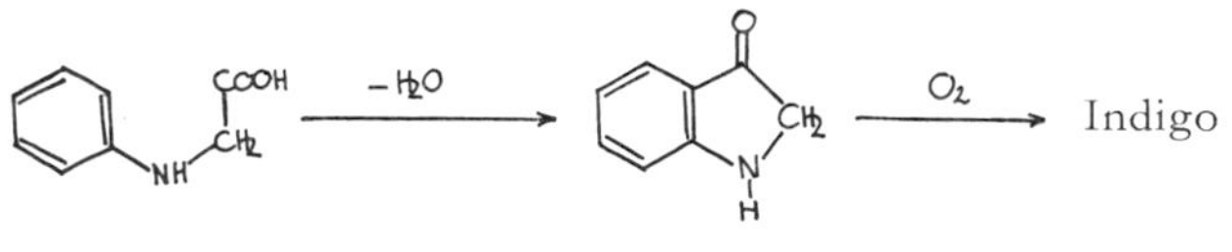

$-H_2O$; O_2 → Indigo

Phenyl-glycine — Indoxyl

Synthesis "Heumann II":

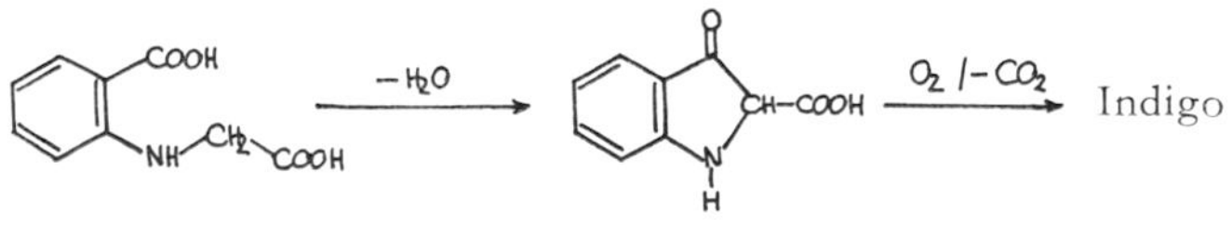

$-H_2O$; O_2 / $-CO_2$ → Indigo

Phenyl-glycine-o-carboxylic acid — Indoxyl-carboxylic acid

Above: The first recording of the correct formula for indigo, from a letter of Baeyer to Heinrich Caro. German Museum, Munich.

The "Heumann II" synthesis was turned to industrial use at BASF in Ludwigshafen; in 1897 the first synthetic indigo appeared on the market. The Dyeworks, formerly Meister Lucius & Bruening in Hoechst, worked on the basis of the "Heumann I" method, modified by the Frankfurt chemist Johann Pfleger who, among others, proposed fusing with sodamide in place of alkali amide. The firm of Hoechst placed their indigo on the market in 1902.

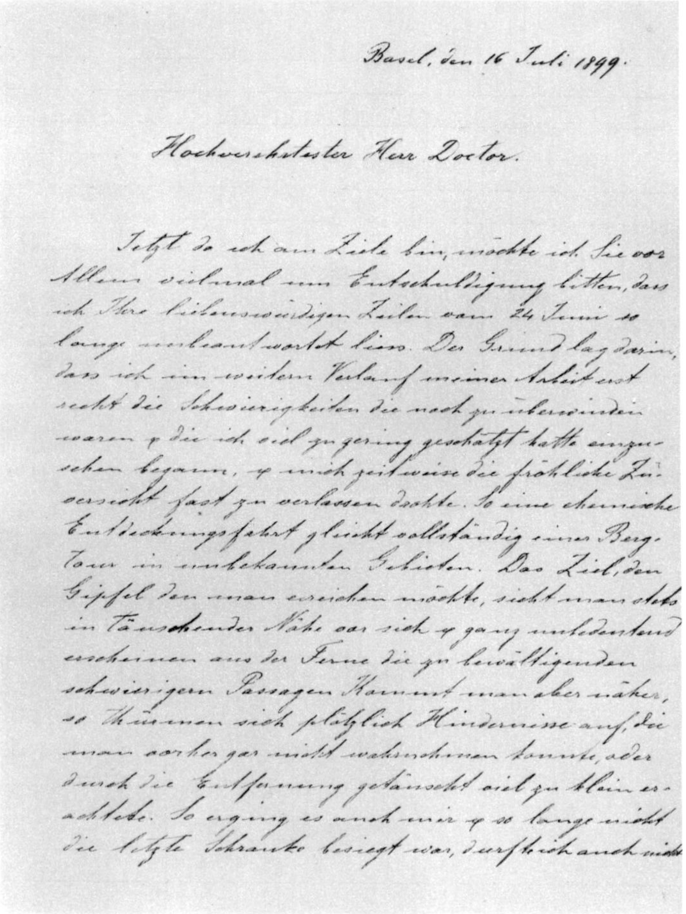

Basel, den 16 Juli 1899.

Hochverehrtester Herr Doctor.

Jetzt da ich am Ziele bin, möchte ich Sie vor Allem vielmal um Entschuldigung bitten, dass ich Ihre liebenswürdigen Zeilen vom 24 Juni so lange unbeantwortet liess. Der Grund lag darin, dass ich im weitern Verlauf meiner Arbeit erst recht die Schwierigkeiten die noch zu überwinden waren & die ich viel zu gering geschätzt hatte einzusehen begann, & mich zeitweise die fröhliche Zuversicht fast zu verlassen drohte. So eine chemische Entdeckungsfahrt gleicht vollständig einer Bergtour in unbekannten Gebieten. Das Ziel, den Gipfel den man erreichen möchte, sieht man stets in täuschender Nähe vor sich & ganz unbedeutend erscheinen aus der Ferne die zu bewältigenden schwierigern Passagen. Kommt man aber näher, so thürmen sich plötzlich Hindernisse auf, die man vorher gar nicht wahrnehmen konnte, oder durch die Entfernung getäuscht viel zu klein erachtete. So erging es auch mir & so lange nicht die letzte Schranke besiegt war, durfte ich auch nicht

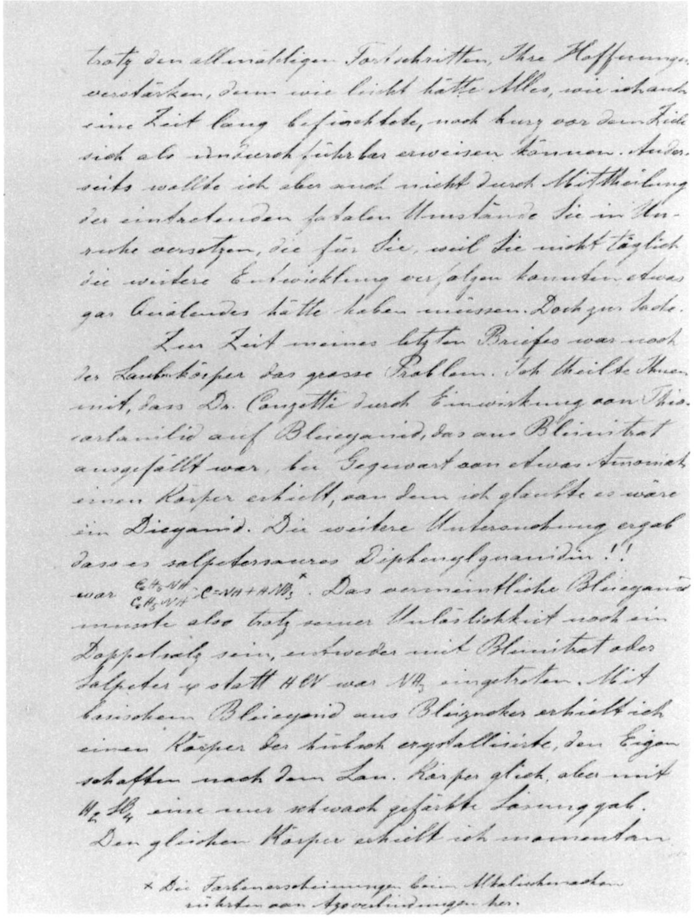

trotz den allmähligen Fortschritten, Ihre Hoffnungen verstärken, denn wie leicht hätte Alles, wie ich auch eine Zeit lang befürchtete, noch kurz vor dem Ziele sich als undurchführbar erweisen können. Anderseits wollte ich aber auch nicht durch Mittheilung der eintretenden fatalen Umstände Sie in Unruhe versetzen, die für Sie, weil Sie nicht täglich die weitere Entwicklung verfolgen konnten, etwas gar Quälendes hätte haben müssen. Doch zur Sache.

Zur Zeit meines letzten Briefes war noch der Zwischenkörper das grosse Problem. Ich theilte Ihnen mit, dass Dr. Conzetti durch Einwirkung von Thiocarbanilid auf Bleicyanid, das aus Bleinitrat ausgefällt war, bei Gegenwart von etwas Ammoniak einen Körper erhielt, von dem ich glaubte es wäre ein Dicyanid. Die weitere Untersuchung ergab dass es salpetersaures Diphenylguanidin!! war $\begin{matrix}C_6H_5NH\\C_6H_5NH\end{matrix}C{=}NH+HNO_3$ ×. Das vermeintliche Bleicyanid musste also trotz seiner Unlöslichkeit noch ein Doppelsalz sein, entweder mit Bleinitrat oder Salpeter & statt HCN war NH_3 eingetreten. Mit basischem Bleicyanid aus Bleizucker erhielt ich einen Körper der hübsch crystallisirte, den Eigenschaften nach dem Zw. Körper glich, aber mit H_2SO_4 eine nur schwach gefärbte Lösung gab. Den gleichen Körper erhielt ich momentan

× Die Farbenerscheinungen beim Alkalischmachen rühren von Azoverbindungen her.

In this letter dated July, 1899, Traugott Sandmeyer communicated the process he had worked out for indigo manufacture to Rudolf Geigy-Schlumberger. He aptly compares the labors of a chemist to a mountain hike over unfamiliar terrain. Works Archive of J. R. Geigy S.A., Basle.

In Basle, indigo was made on an industrial scale for the first time in 1899. Traugott Sandmeyer, a successful and pertinacious experimenter connected with the Geigy firm, discovered an indigo synthesis via diphenyl thiourea which was industrially feasible. But Geigy indigo had a short-lived commercial career, for Sandmeyer's method, as fine as it was, could not hold its own against the cheaper Heumann process.

The Heumann-Pfleger method of synthesizing indigo was taken over in modified form by the "Bindschedler Chemical Factory, Basle", established at Kleinhueningen in 1893. We have heard how this undertaking, as a manufacturer of indigo, purchased the electrochemical works at Monthey in 1904. A long series of technical difficulties that had to be overcome exhausted the resources of the Basle factory. Two years after its union with the Society of Chemical Industry in Basle was consummated in 1908, regular indigo output was begun at Monthey.
In a matter of fifteen years synthetic indigo pushed the natural product off the scene. Whereas in 1897 the British West Indies exported 19 million pounds of the

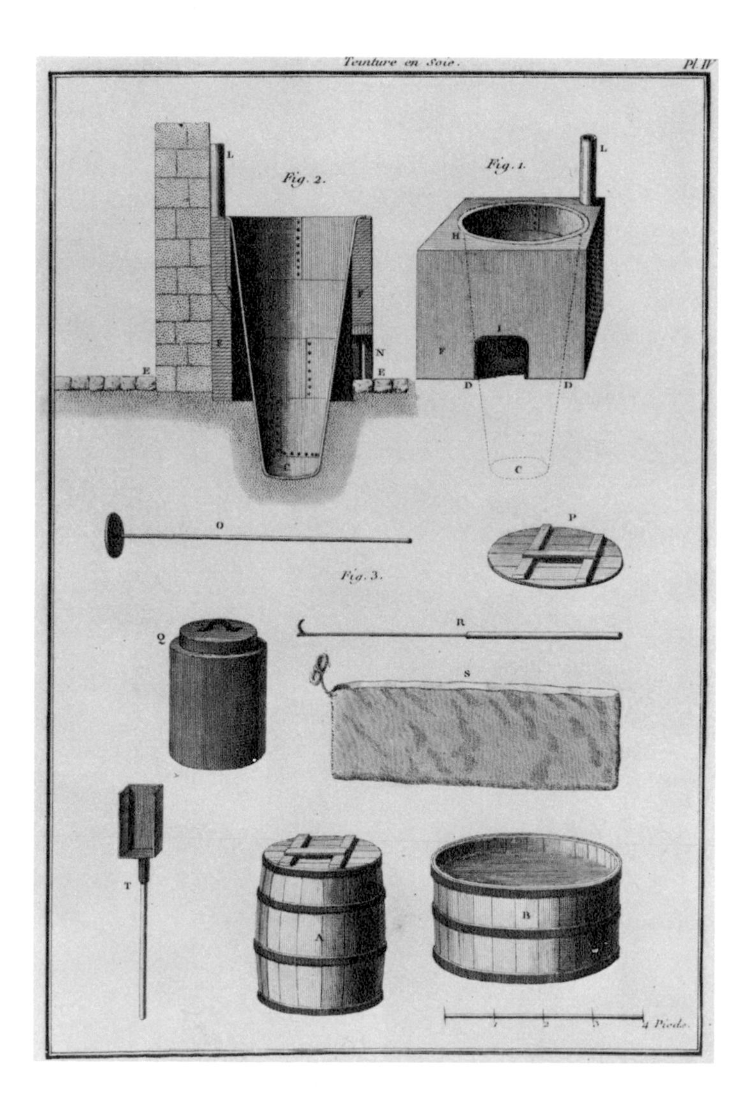

Right: A typical indigo article done in "blue printing". Known generically as the resist or reserve style, which dates back to ancient India, this technique gets its effects by masking the ornamental pattern with chemical substances before dyeing. The reserve paste prevents penetration of the coloring matter and is washed out after dyeing. The specimen shown is a blue printing on linen done a hundred years ago in the Tessin. Swiss Museum for European Ethnology, Basle.
Below: Indigo vat let into the ground, a common design in the 18th and 19th centuries. Lower part of drawing: gear, storage cask, and alum tub. Copperplate from *The Art of Silk Dyeing* by Pierre-Joseph Macquer in "Descriptions of the Arts and Trades"; Paris, 1763.

vegetable dyestuff, by 1913 this figure had sunk to slightly over a million. Since that time, natural indigo has been relegated to the museum.

Indigo is an exemplar of the vat dyes. The insoluble product has to be reduced by the dyer to the soluble "leuco" (= white) form. During the dyeing process this reduced form of the dye is taken up by the textile material; then, when the material is exposed to air, the insoluble product is re-formed by oxidation and fixed to the fibre so firmly as to be fast to washing. The reduction of the dyestuff, or vatting, was formerly carried out by fermentation. The dyer fermented the indigo together with sugar-containing fruit, bran, or bread in the dyebath, an operation that lasted for days or even weeks. Another old method is the Indian "orpiment vat", in which arsenic sulfide acted as the reducing agent. At the end of the 18th century the ferrous sulfate (or copperas) and lime vat, and in 1845 the zinc-lime vat, came into use.

All these ways of vatting disappeared. Hydrosulfite ($Na_2S_2O_4$) is a reducing agent, proposed as far back as 1869, which is amazingly simple and rapid in action, and as soon as its large-scale industrial preparation became possible at the beginning of this century it was used in dyehouses everywhere. Through the introduction of hydrosulfite, vat dyeing became a reliable,

331

1) 0,5 g p-Dichlorindigo (von Dr. Kraft dargestellt aus [illegible] → [illegible] → Dichlorindigo), 6 g Nitrobenzol, 0,5 g Brom werden im Laufe von ca. 3/4 Std. im Ölbad am Rückfl. auf ca. 221° erhitzt u. dann, und während ca. 1 Std. auf 226–228° gehalten, nach welcher Zeit die HBr-Entwickelung fast völlig aufgehört hat u. alles Brom verschwunden ist; nach 12 stünd. Erkalten filtriert, mit Alkohol gewaschen u. getrocknet: 0,42 g blauvioletter Krystallpulver, in conc. Schwefelsäure mit rotbrauner Farbe, aber bedeutend blaustichiger löslich als das Ausgangsmaterial, auf Zusatz von Wasser Niederschlag blauvioletter Flocken. [illegible]

	4 Br	8 Br
331 ——	320	640
0,5 ——	0,5	1 g

2) 0,5 g p-Dichlorindigo, 6 g Nitrobenzol, 1,2 g Brom werden wie 1) behandelt, nach der angegebenen Zeit scheint alles Brom verbraucht zu sein: 0,63 g blauschwarzes Krystallpulver, in conc. H_2SO_4 mit gelbbrauner Farbe löslich, mit Wasser erfolgt Ausscheidung reinblauer Flocken. [illegible]

Ausgangs-p-Dichlorindigo zum Vergleich: violettbraunes Krystallpulver, in conc. Schwefelsäure mit rotbrauner Farbe löslich; auf Zusatz von Wasser erfolgt Ausscheidung rotvioletter Flocken; in rauchender Schwefelsäure mit blauvioletter Farbe löslich, die sich beim Erwärmen kaum verändert; beim Ausgiessen in Wasser Bildung einer stahlblauen Lösung, aus welcher Watte in reinblauen Nuancen angefärbt wird; in Nitrobenzol in der Hitze mit violettroter Farbe & nur sehr schwer löslich [illegible]

speedy, and cheap process. And this breakthrough stimulated the development of further vat dyestuffs. A development which had already been perceptible in the case of alizarin and was later to occupy an important place in pharmaceutical chemistry now set in with indigo too. After the synthesis of the natural substance there began a period of chemical modifications. What these indigoid variations aimed at were dyes with other shades and improved fastness properties, yet applied in the same way.
The first step towards this goal was taken by Paul Friedlaender, a professor at the Technical Crafts Museum in Vienna. In a synthesis analogous to "Heumann II", he replaced the imino group with sulfur in 1905, obtaining the first red vat dye, thioindigo.

Thioindigo

Research was then taken up in Basle. Gadient Engi, a CIBA chemist guided by a sound instinct for real technological possibilities, worked on the chemistry of the indigoid vat dyes. Within a few years he systematically built up a vat dye series ranging from yellow to black. To mention but a few of his successfully concluded investigations: In 1907, by halogenating the indigo molecule, he scored a major success with *Ciba Blue 2 B* (5,5',7,7'-tetrabromindigo) which, in its affinity and in its fastness to washing, chlorine and light, surpasses indigo. Similarly, from thioindigo he obtained *Ciba Bordeaux B* (5,5'-dibromthio-indigo), which is bright and fast to washing.

Ciba Blue 2B

Ciba Bordeaux B

Opposite: Gadient Engi's laboratory notes on the halogenation of indigo. Engi found that halogen atoms caused alterations in shade and, in many cases, also influenced affinity and fastness properties for the better.
Below: Dyeings of tetrabromindigo *(Ciba Blue 2 B)*, constructed by Engi, on cotton yarn. An early pattern card.

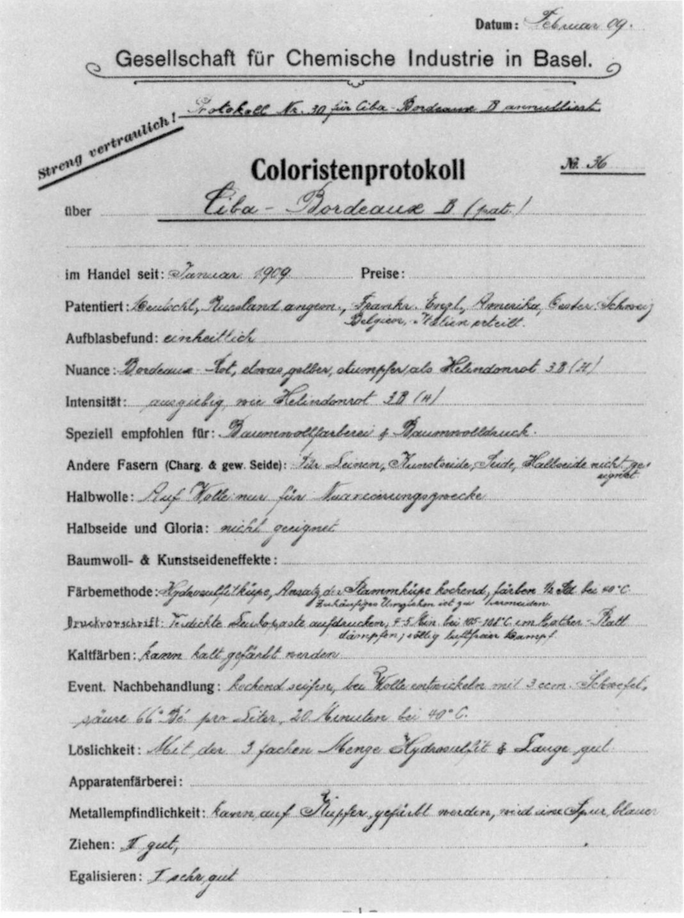

Datum: Februar 09.

Gesellschaft für Chemische Industrie in Basel.

Streng vertraulich! Protokoll Nr. 30 für Ciba-Bordeaux B annulliert.

Coloristenprotokoll Nr. 36

über Ciba-Bordeaux B (pat.)

im Handel seit: Januar 1909 Preise:

Patentiert: Deutschl., Russland angem., Frankr. Engl., Amerika, Oester. Schweiz, Belgien, Italien erteilt.

Aufblasbefund: einheitlich

Nuance: Bordeaux-Rot, etwas gelber, stumpfer als Helindonrot 3B (H)

Intensität: ausgiebig wie Helindonrot 3B (H)

Speziell empfohlen für: Baumwollfärberei & Baumwolldruck

Andere Fasern (Charg. & gew. Seide): Für Leinen, Kunstseide, Seide, Halbseide nicht geeignet

Halbwolle: Auf Wolle nur für Nuancierungszwecke

Halbseide und Gloria: nicht geeignet

Baumwoll- & Kunstseideneffekte:

Färbemethode: Hydrosulfitküpe, Ansatz der Stammküpe kochend, färben ½ Std. bei 40°C. Zu häufiges Umziehen ist zu vermeiden.

Druckvorschrift: Verdickte Teigpaste aufdrucken, 4-5 Min. bei 105-108°C im Mather-Platt dämpfen; völlig luftfreier Dampf.

Kaltfärben: kann kalt gefärbt werden

Event. Nachbehandlung: kochend seifen, bei Wolle entwickeln mit 3 ccm Schwefelsäure 66° Bé per Liter, 20 Minuten bei 40°C.

Löslichkeit: Mit der 3 fachen Menge Hydrosulfit & Lauge gut

Apparatenfärberei:

Metallempfindlichkeit: kann auf Kupfer gefärbt werden, wird eine Spur blauer

Ziehen: I gut,

Egalisieren: I sehr gut

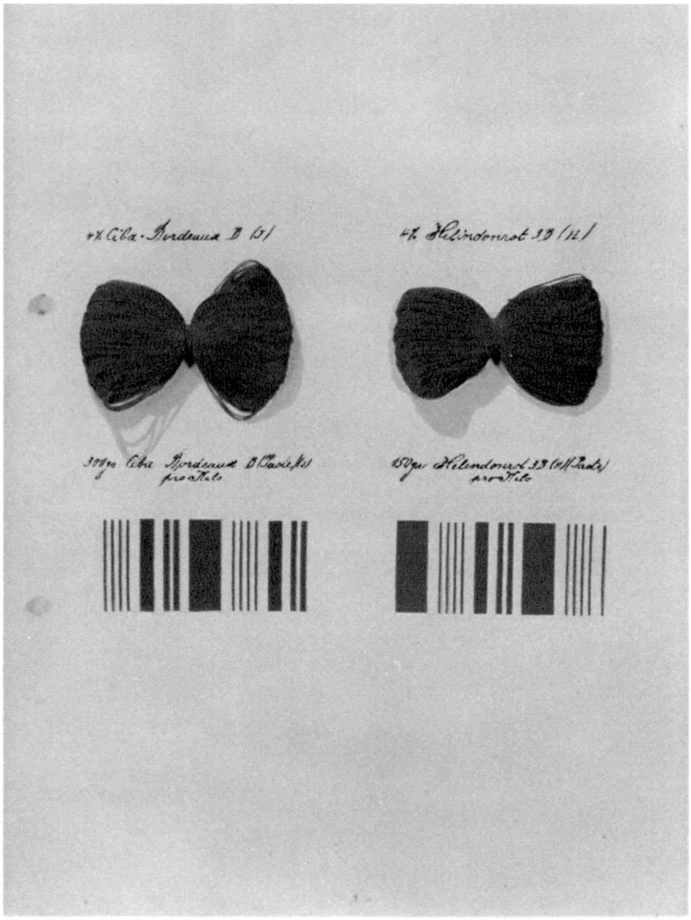

The synthesis of asymmetrical indigoid molecules was of great theoretical and practical interest. When this came about, the way was open to the manufacture of grey and violet vat dyes such as *Ciba Violet 3B*.

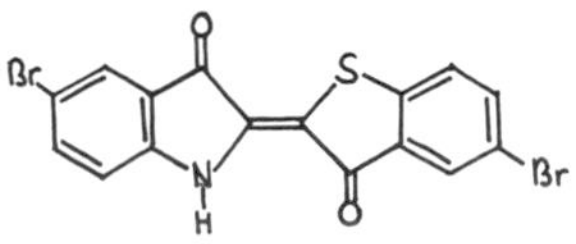

Ciba Violet 3B

Extract from the confidential "colorist's protocol" containing technical information concerning tests of the properties of Dibromthioindigo *(Ciba Bordeaux B)*, which Engi developed for dyeing and textile printing.

Stringent Fastness Requirements: Anthraquinone Vat Dyes. Anthraquinone is the basic substance of alizarin. The logic of matters suggested taking this base for vat dyes too. René Bohn, an Alsatian chemist with BASF, hit on the idea of preparing anthraquinone indigo by alkali fusion of β-amino anthraquinone. And he did in fact obtain a blue-coloring vat dye, though this was not, in its chemical structure, the indigo derivative sought, but rather a new dyestuff principle, *Indanthrene Blue RS*. In 1901 this vat dye made its appearance on the market.

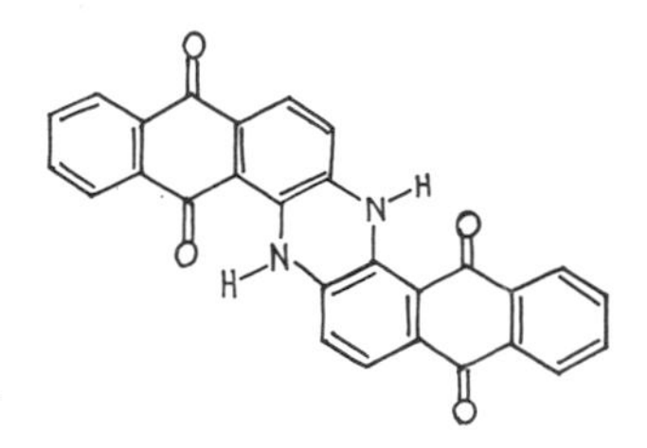

Indanthrene Blue RS

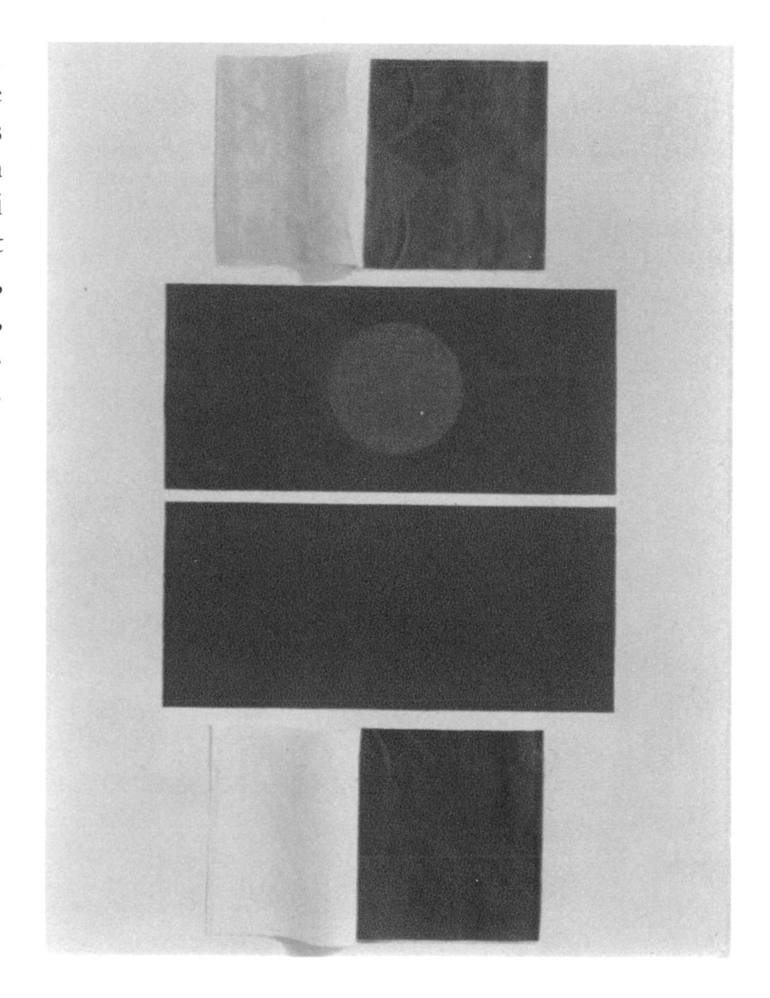
The fastness properties of indigo (upper half) and *Indanthrene Blue RS* (lower half) on cotton fabric compared. For the light test, a circular area of each dyeing has been exposed to sun rays for the same length of time. For the washing test, pieces of dyed fabric together with undyed cotton have been treated for half an hour under identical conditions in a solution containing 10% soda at the boil.

The discovery of indanthrene blue touched off a spate of research activity, and the class of anthraquinonoid vat dyes was built up.
These dyes can be applied like the indigoids. The dyeings, however, possess greater stability in use. Anthraquinonoid vat dyes constitute the fastest dyestuff series known.

The story of how anthraquinonoid vat dyes were developed also provides an interesting illustration of the liaison between the school of technology and industry. Besides carrying on research, the centre of higher learning trains scientists for key positions in industry. The initial development phases of the anthraquinonoid vat dyes, industrially so important, lay almost exclusively in the hands of graduates of the Swiss Federal Institute of Technology in Zurich. René Bohn and many of his co-workers contributed greatly to the repute of this school.

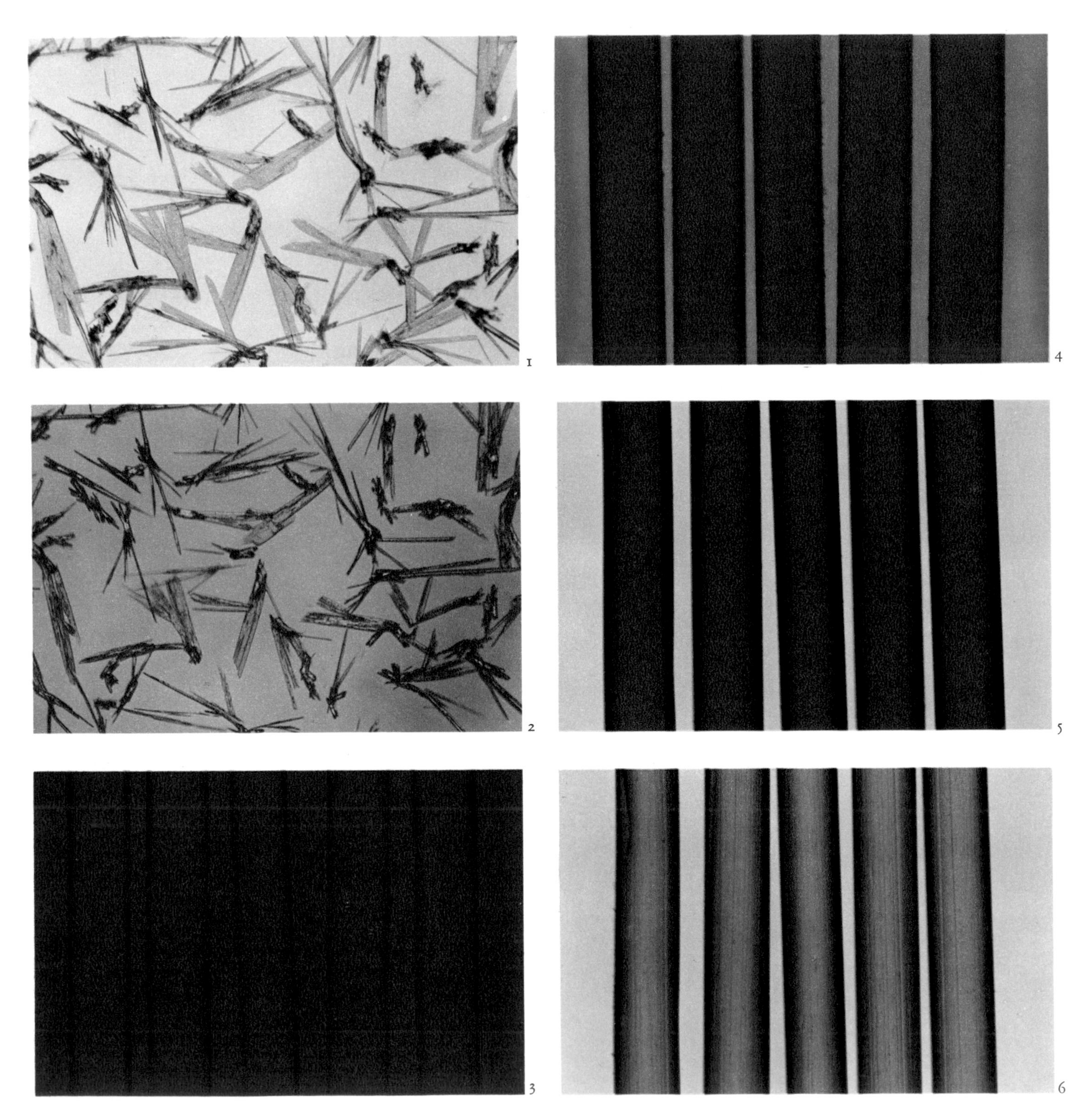
1
2
3
4
5
6

In Basle, CIBA chemists were not long in recognizing the possibilities inherent in the field of anthraquinonoid vat dyes. Through the sulfur fusion of methyl anthraquinone and methyl benzanthrone, Bertram Mayer created yellow, orange, blue and black specimens of this class, a series from which there emerged, in 1911, *Cibanone Blue F3G* – still an important product for textile printing.

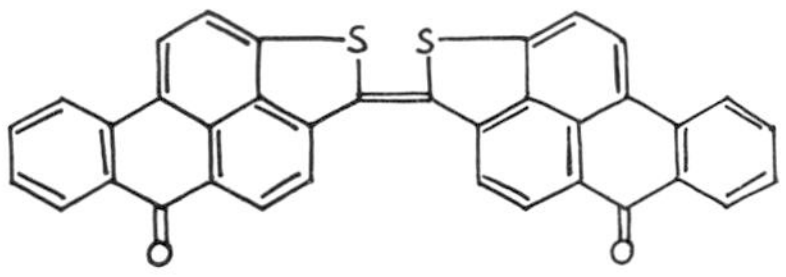

Cibanone Blue F3G*
* "F" = FELISOL Fastness Label, used in Europe.

The idea of introducing cyanuric chloride as a link in the structure of acylaminoanthraquinones proved a fruitful one. An example of this group is *Cibanone Red F4B,* patented in 1922.

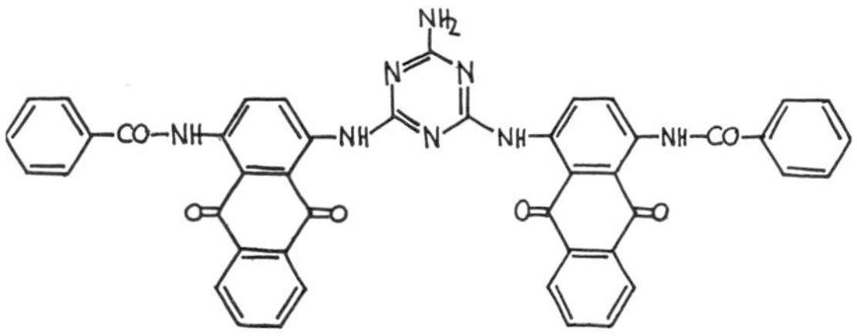

Cibanone Red F4B

Opposite: Coloring with vat dyes as seen under the microscope. Magnifications: Illus. 1 & 2, x 100; Illus. 3–6, x 40. *Cibanone Gold Orange 2 GT* (1) is covered with a solution of hydrosulfite and soda lye (2) for vatting. This reduces the dye to the leuco form; it dissolves, changing its color. Viscose rayon (3) is introduced into this "vat", and the leuco dye goes on to the textile material (4). After rinsing (5) the dyeing is oxidized in air, and the dyestuff in the fibre is changed back to its chemical starting form (6).

In Basle there were produced in 1940 for the first time anthraquinonoid vat colors with polycyclic aromatic hydrocarbons built into their molecules: *Cibanone Yellow Brown FG* contains chrysene.

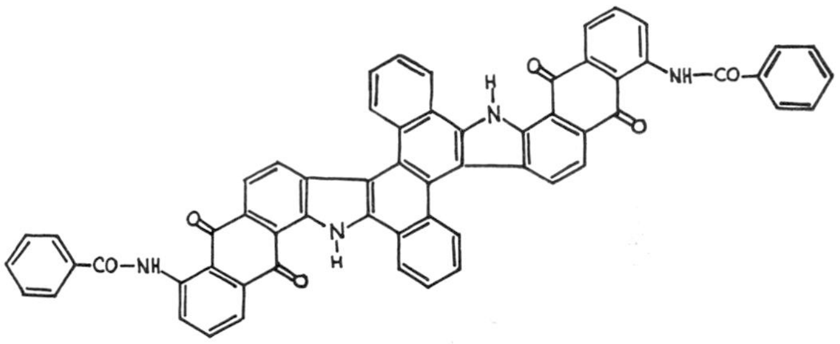

Cibanone Yellow Brown FG

Overleaf: Stages in the synthesis of *Cibanone Red G,* an anthraquinonoid vat dye. Shown next to the microphoto of the substance in polarized light (magnification x 100) are the model and the formula of the constituent substance.

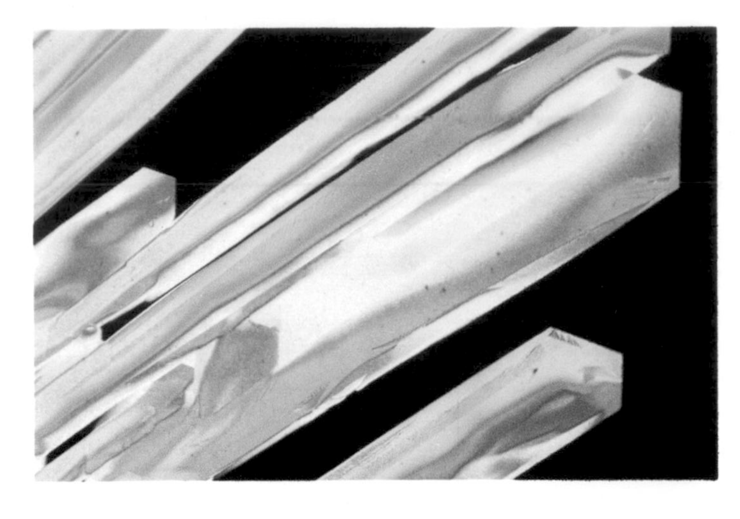

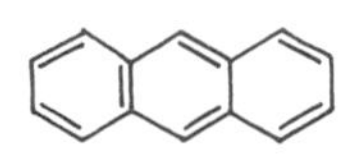

Anthracene

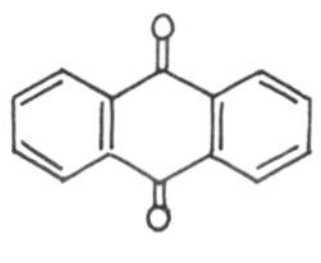

Anthraquinone

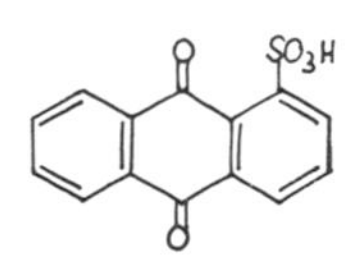

Anthraquinone-1-sulfonic acid

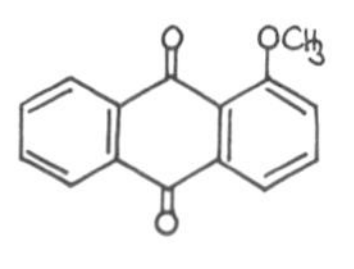

1-Methoxyanthraquinone

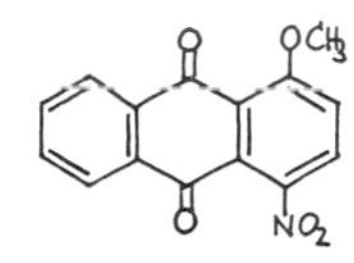

4-Nitro-1-methoxyanthraquinone

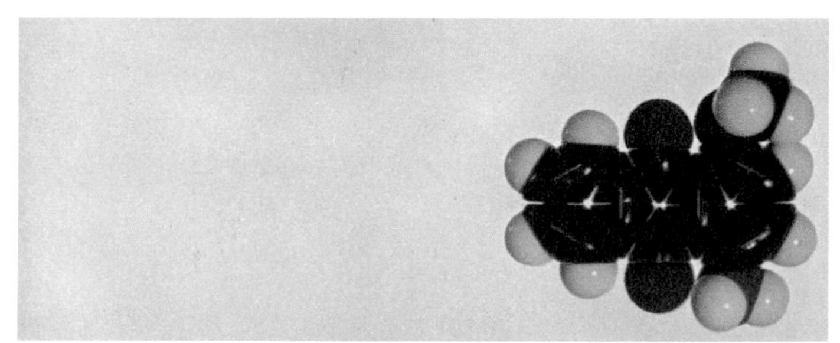

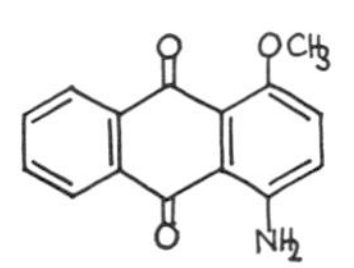

4-Amino-1-methoxyanthraquinone

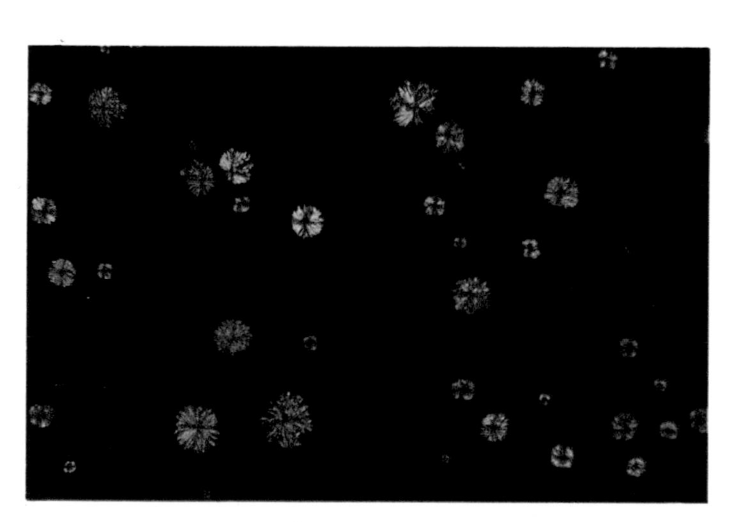

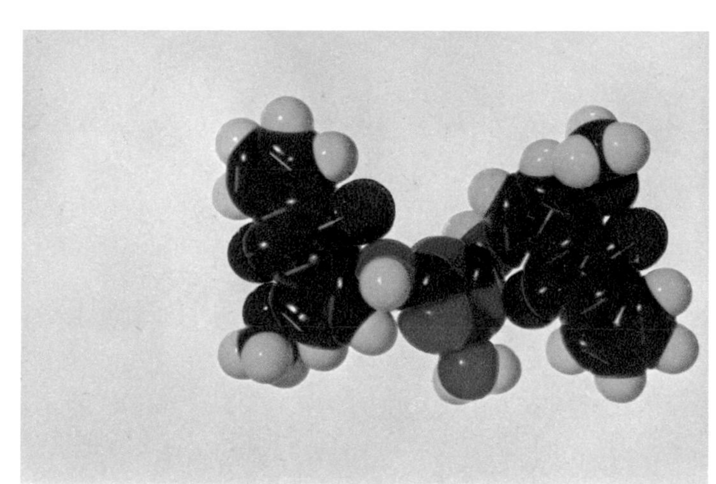

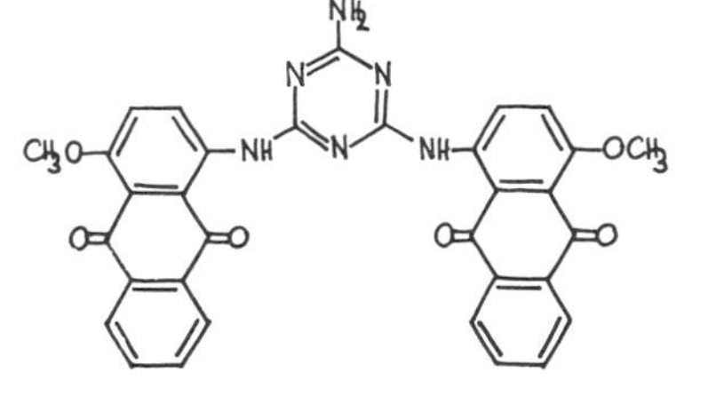

Cibanone Red G

Left: Cibanone Red G dyed onto cotton fabric.

The extension of existing ranges was not the only object of vigorous research activity; this was also applied to the improvement and simplification of dyeing methods and processes. After the introduction of hydrosulfite, the application of vat dyes was distinguished in the main by two milestones of progress: chemically, by the creation of the soluble vat dye leucoesters, and physically, by the development of finely divided trade products. Both improvements are closely connected with Basle.

Vat dye leucoesters are reduced vat dyes stabilized by esterification in this soluble form. The principle they exemplify was worked out by Marcel Bader, professor at the Ecole supérieure de Chimie in Mulhouse, and his co-worker Charles Sunder. Further development and the conversion to practical use as *Indigosol* brands were taken on by the Basle firm of Durand & Huguenin Limited.

Indigosol O

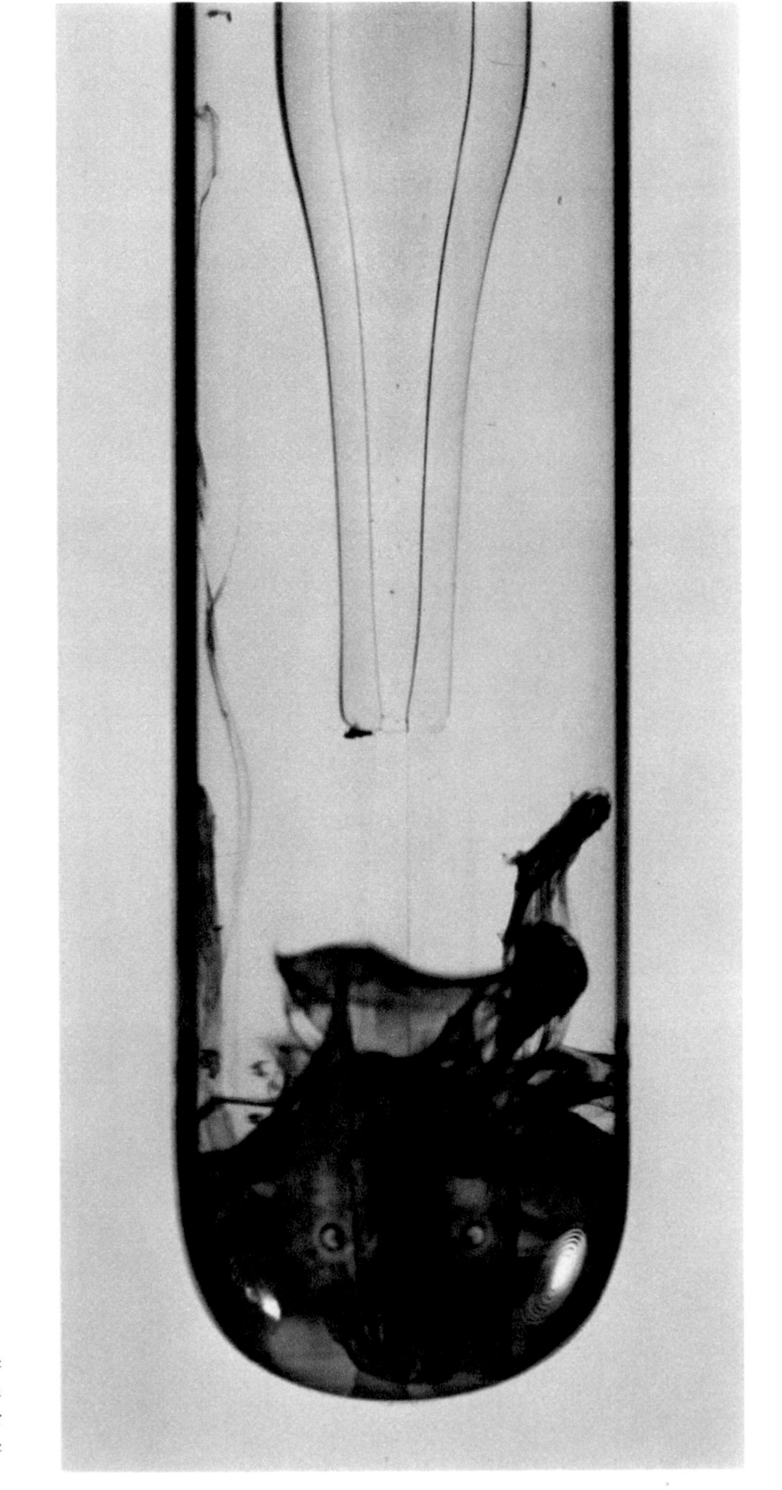

On textile fibre as in the test tube, soluble vat dye leucoesters can be reduced by use of acid and oxidizing agents to insoluble vat dyes. In the experiment pictured here, the solution of vat dye leucoester *(Cibantine Blue 2 B)* and sodium nitrite is flowing from the pipette into diluted acid. The dyestuff is precipitated out insoluble.

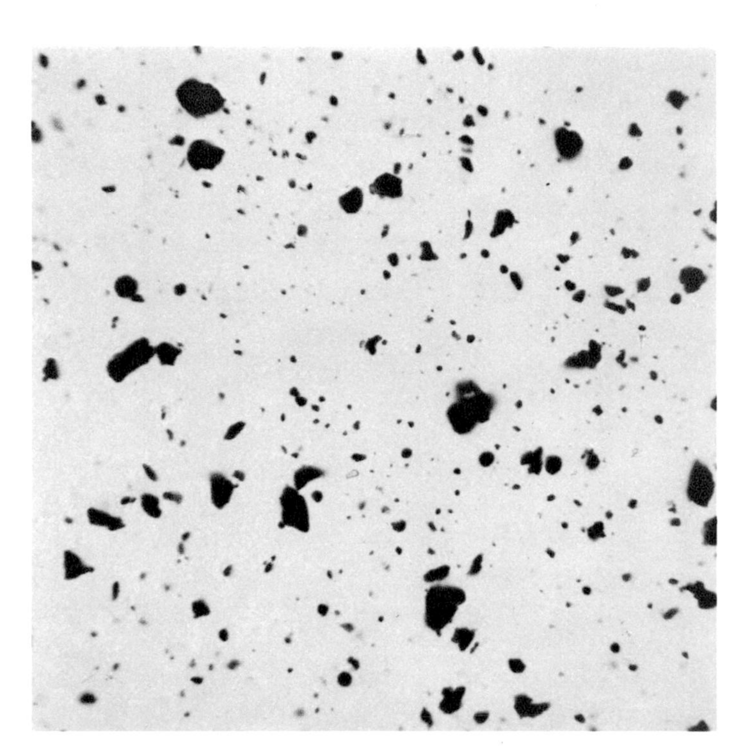

In 1931 CIBA manufactured the first Micro Powders and Micro Pastes from vat dyes according to a process patented by the company. In 1954 it marketed Micro Disperse powders and pastes. These extremely finely divided dyestuffs have made possible the economical application of vat pigments, which can also be used in continuous dyeing. The dye is applied unvatted, i.e. as a water-insoluble pigment, to the textile material and reduced to the dyeing leuco form only when on the fibre.

Microphotos of two market forms of the vat dye *Cibanone Brown FBR*, magnified x 750. Left: *Powder;* right: *Micro Disperse Powder,* particularly suitable for continuous dyeing.

Below: Continuous dyeing of cotton fabric with vat dyes using the "Pad-Steam" process developed by Du Pont de Nemours. Goods pass through the machine at a rate of up to 100 metres per minute. The fabric is impregnated with a suspension of the insoluble vat dye (1), then dried (2). Impregnation with hydrosulfite solution follows (3). Next, the vatted dye is vatted to the fixable leuco form in the steam chamber (4). After oxidation and de-soaping of the dyeing (5), the dyed length of fabric is deposited (6).

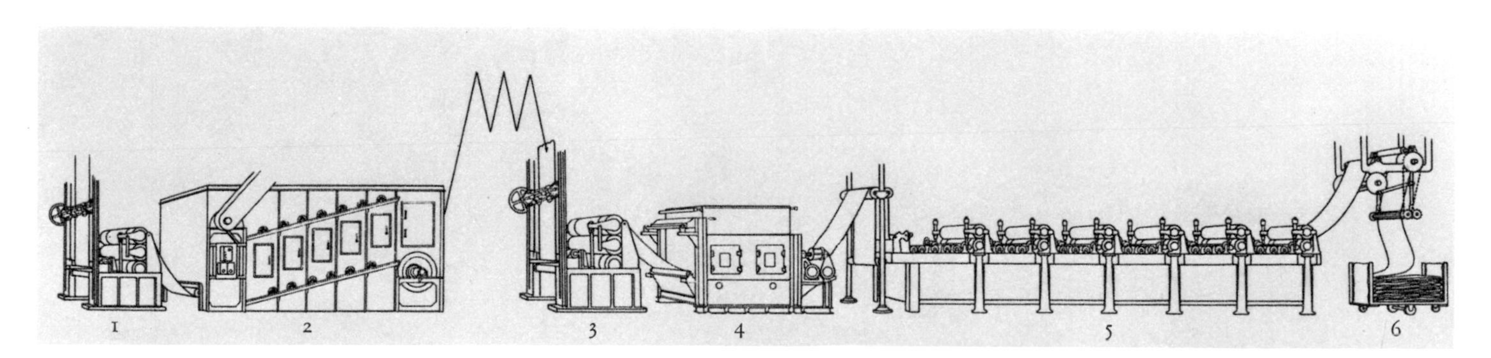

Co-ordination Theory: Metal-Containing Dyestuffs. Kekulé's structural theory provided the geometrical likeness of organic molecules, making them accessible to the chemist's imagination and thus enabling him to explore them systematically. In inorganic chemistry, this method of geometrical depiction was introduced half a century later. With the co-ordination theory presented in his book "New Views in the Field of Inorganic Chemistry", dated 1905, Alfred Werner, professor of chemistry at the University of Zurich, laid the foundation for the chemistry of complexes.

Around a metal atom – designated the central atom by Werner – atoms or groups are located in a spherical arrangement to form a complex. The number of positions around the central atom, termed the co-ordination number, is characteristic for a given metal: 6 for chromium, cobalt, iron, and aluminium, for instance, or 4 for copper and nickel. The groups co-ordinated about the metal atom can also belong to organic molecules, such as those of dyestuffs.

Immediately the co-ordination theory afforded an insight into the mechanism of mordant dyeing. In the course of the dyeing process the natural and synthetic mordant colors join with the metal of the mordant, which is the central atom, to form complexes in the textile fibre. "By means of appropriate experiments", wrote Werner in 1908, "I have shown that the compounds capable of forming complex salts internally also possess the property of coloring mordanted materials". With this demonstration, the field of dyestuff metal complexes had been drawn into the range of the chemist's vision.

At this stage the idea naturally suggested itself of building the metals into the mordant colors even before dyeing, in order to shorten and simplify the dyeing process. BASF took out a patent on the production of chromium complexes of sulfo acids analogous to alizarin which could be used in the dyes industry as intermediate products or as inks.

A decisive step along the way to turning chromium complex dyestuffs to industrial use was the patent application submitted by CIBA in 1915 for the chroming of azo compounds and a simple method for applying them to animal fibres. On the basis of this research, the class of 1:1-chromium complex dyestuffs (one chromium atom per azo group) was created. These comprised the *Neolan* dyes of CIBA and, somewhat later, the *Palatine Fast* dyes of BASF.

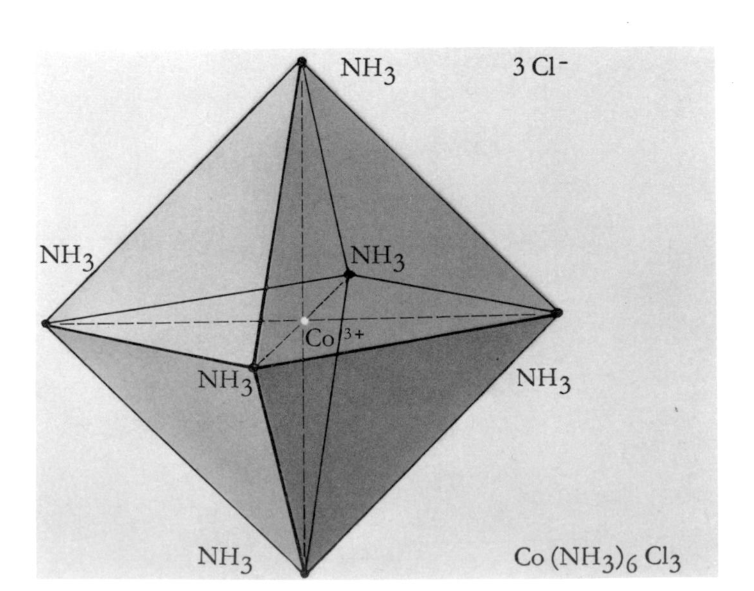

Neolan Green B

Model of a complex compound after Werner. In hexammine cobalt (3) chloride, $[Co(NH_3)_6]\ Cl_3$, six ammonia molecules are grouped around the central atom of cobalt in octahedral arrangement.

Basle became a centre of industrial research on metal complex dyes. In 1933, with its cobalt-containing Red 2B for nitro lacquer, now designated *Orasol Red 2B,* CIBA placed the first metal complex free of sulfo groups on the market, a complex containing two azo groups for each metal atom. BASF colorists showed that, by employing a special process, such "1:2 complexes" can also be applied onto wool. The appearance of Geigy's *Polar Grey BL* in 1949 marked the introduction of their dyestuff class into wool dyeing. In 1951 and 1952 a new range of 1:2 chromium and cobalt complexes free of sulfo groups was marketed under the trade names of *Irgalan* (Geigy) and *Cibalan* (CIBA).

Orasol Red 2B

In addition to the chromium and cobalt complexes, the copper complexes of azo dyes also became the subject of concentrated attention in Basle. In 1915, CIBA chemists synthesized copper compounds of substantive cotton dyes, recognizing at once their great practical importance: the dyeings of these copper complexes possess outstanding fastness to light. The *Chlorantine Fast* dyes range is the fruit of the research devoted to them.

Chlorantine Fast Violet 5BLL

Dyeings on cotton with the same color: left, in copper – free form; right: as a copper complex *(Chlorantine Fast Violet 5BLL)*. A circular area of each dyeing has been exposed to sunlight for the same length of time. On top left margin, washing tests performed in soap solution for one-half hour at 40°C. Building copper into the dye molecule helps above all to improve fastness to light.

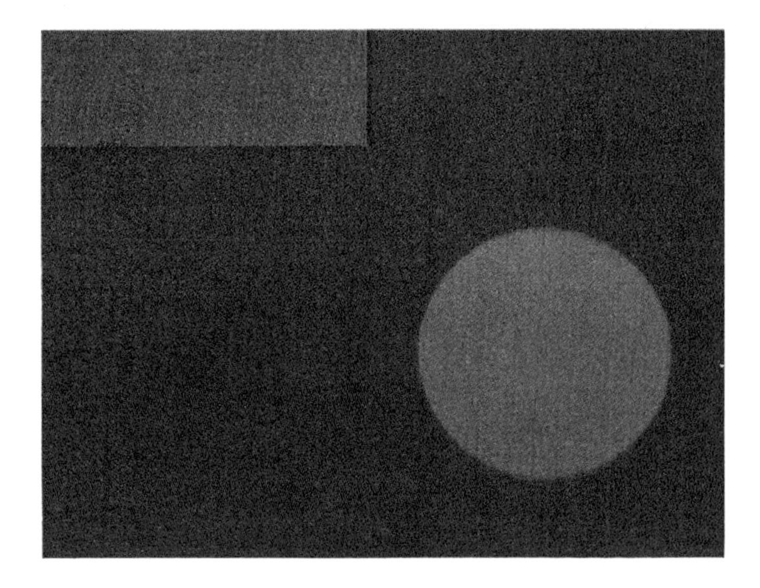

The Term Dyes Enlarged to Include Organic Pigments. In 1927 Henri de Diesbach, a professor at Fribourg, described the preparation of an organic compound containing copper which has two striking qualities: it is of an intense blue color and is very resistant to chemical reagents. Six years later the Imperial College of Science and Technology in London succeeded in elucidating the structure of the blue chromophore. Reginald P. Linstead noted the similarity of copper phthalocyanine, as he called the compound, to the pigments of the blood and of green leaves.

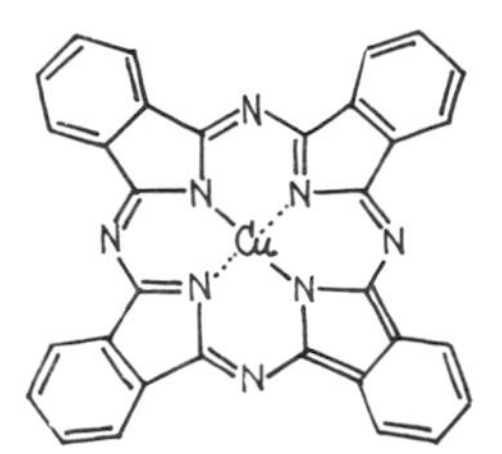

Copper phthalocyanine

This compound, brought out as *Monastral Blue B* by I.C.I. and *Heliogen Blue B* by I.G. Farben in 1934, is a pigment, i.e. completely insoluble in water. Thus it could not be applied to textile fibres by the usual techniques. But added to a spinning solution, for example, in very finely dispersed form, it imparted to man-made fibres a blue dyeing of extraordinary stability. With thermosetting synthetic resins as binders it can be fixed wash-fast onto textile material. Copper phthalocyanine is also used as a colorant in plastics, lacquers, and paints, just like long-familiar mineral pigments such as ochre, chrome yellow, or ultramarine blue.
The discovery of copper phthalocyanine and of the uses to which it could be put served greatly to extend the notion of what constitutes organic coloring materials. No longer restricted to soluble compounds for dyeing textiles, this idea now comprises insoluble (and thus, in principle, all) highly colored compounds as well.
With research aims thus clearly outlined, the task was to build up ranges of pigments distinguished, like copper phthalocyanine, by very good fastness properties. The basic blue colorant was soon joined by green phthalocyanine derivatives and selected vat pigments. CIBA chemists were at the forefront of this development in Basle. With their azo compounds marketed as *Cromophtal* colors in the 1950s, they have been following up new lines of approach.

Since pigments in solid form are incorporated into the substrate to be colored, their physical properties such as particle size and crystal form are of decisive importance for both the strength and purity of the shade. This is the reason why the chemist is no longer alone responsible for color research. Nowadays he works together with the physicist, who has tools such as the spectrograph, X-rays, and the electron microscope at his disposal for purposes of investigation.

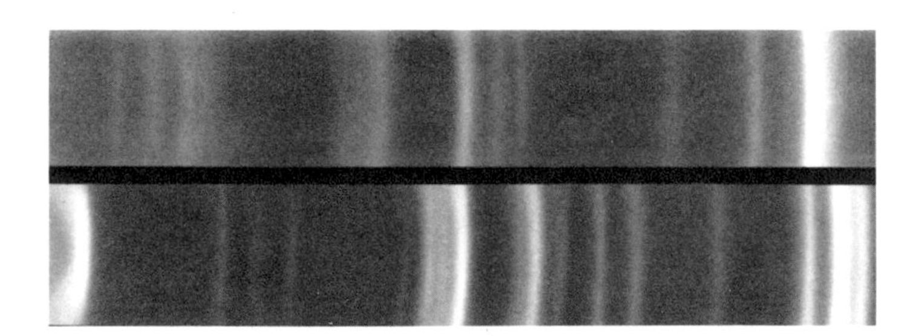

Polymorphism of an anthraquinone dye. One and the same dyestuff can be obtained in various crystal forms, differing from each other in their physical properties. X-ray diagrams illuminate the crystal structure: above, α-modification, melting point 298–299 °C; below, β-modification of *Cibanone Brilliant Rose F2R,* M.P. 312–313 °C.

Polymorphism of Cibanone Brilliant Rose F2R. Spectrophotometric absorption in the visible light range.

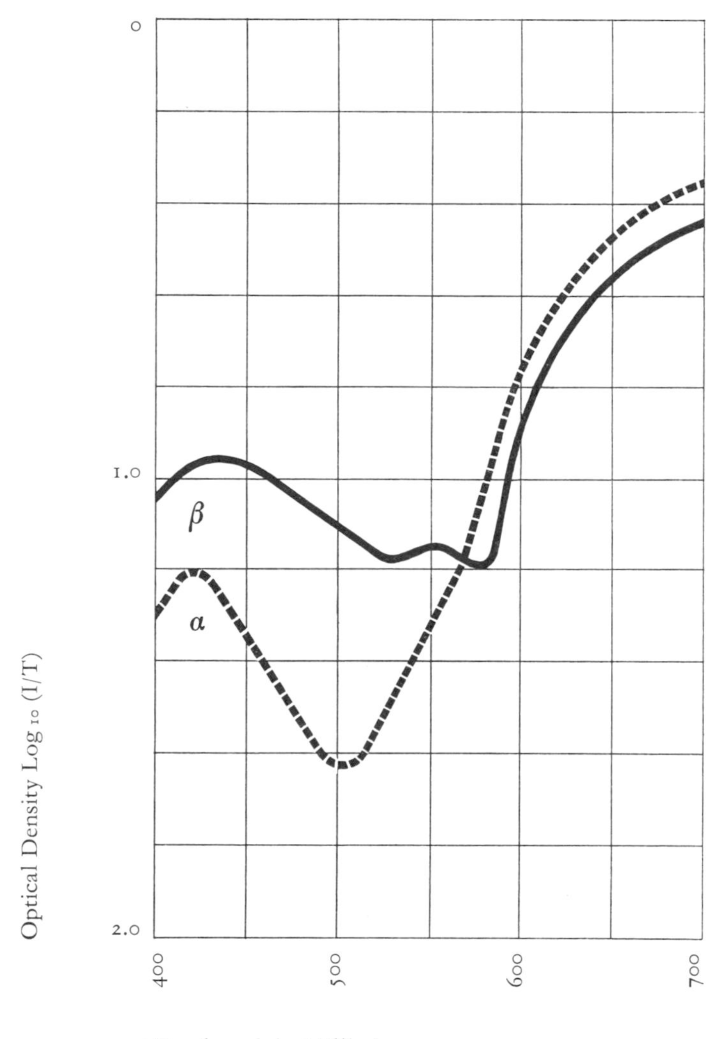

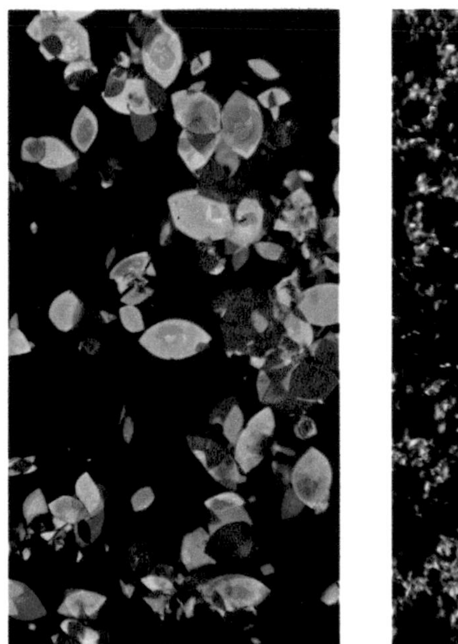

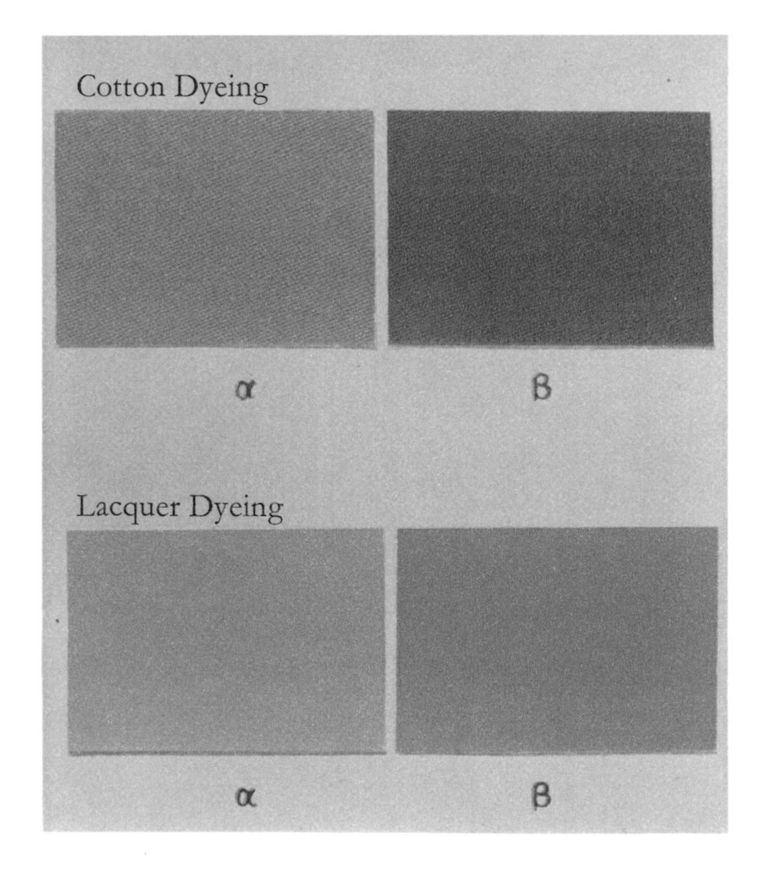

The α and β modifications of *Cibanone Brilliant Rose F2R* differ markedly from one another in color.
Above: Absorption curves.
Right: Microphotos of crystals of the α and β modifications (magnification x 300). In vat dyeings on cotton (top), the α modification is transformed into the β when soaping takes place. In the lacquer dyeing, the pigments of the two modifications show a pronounced difference in shade.

Reactive Dyestuffs: The Textile Fibre Drawn into the Dyeing Process. For a hundred years color chemistry took its key impulses from basic research pertaining to organic synthesis. The color chemist applied the knowledge disclosed by fundamental organic chemistry to his starting materials, easily available and therefore cheap heavy chemicals derived from coal tar and petroleum, and from these he built ever more complicated dyestuff molecules.

Measured by the plenitude of what was known concerning color synthesis, knowledge of the chemistry of dyestuff application was scanty up to the first half of the present century. It was known that most wool dyes were fixed on the fibre by a loose and easily decomposable salt bridge between the acid groups of the dye and the basic groups of the wool keratin (a protein). It was known, further, that the reduced, and thus soluble, vat dyes are deposited in the course of coloring as insoluble pigments in the fibre and that, by dint of secondary valences, the direct dyes are fixed to the cellulose chains of cotton. Finally, dyestuffs for acetate rayon constitute solid solutions with the substrate. There is one characteristic common to all these phenomena: the textile fibre, rather than participating in the chemical reaction, is and remains a substrate in the dyeing process.

So much being given, what was more logical than to try linking the dyes with the fibre by means of a firm chemical bond, rather than the less compact kinds of linkage just alluded to, and in this way arrive at maximum fastness to washing? Once the thought was followed up, color chemistry found an important new field to research. Textile fibres themselves were now drawn into investigations, as reaction partners in dyeing, and application research took on enhanced significance.

Opposite: Dyeing with *Cibacron Scarlet 2 G* on wool, with the textile auxiliary *Neovadin AN* added. Microphotos of the fibre in cross-section, magnification x 500.

1. 10 minutes after dyeing has begun, 17% of the dye has gone on to the fibre.
2. 20 minutes later, 93% of the dye together with the auxiliary has been deposited on the surface of the fibre.
3. In the next 60 minutes, the dye goes into the fibre.

An hour and a half after the beginning of the process, all of the dye has been absorbed by the textile material, which is now penetrated.

Below: Viscose rayon fabric colored with the reactive dye *Cibacron Brilliant Red B,* shown in cross-section. Magnification x 250.

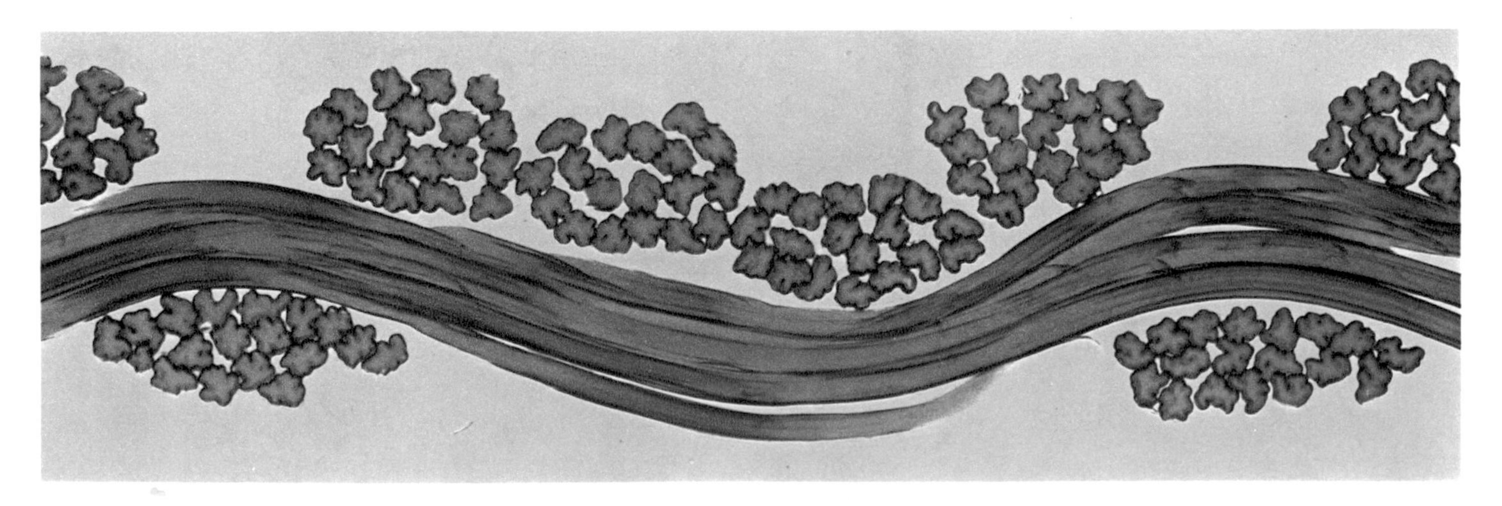

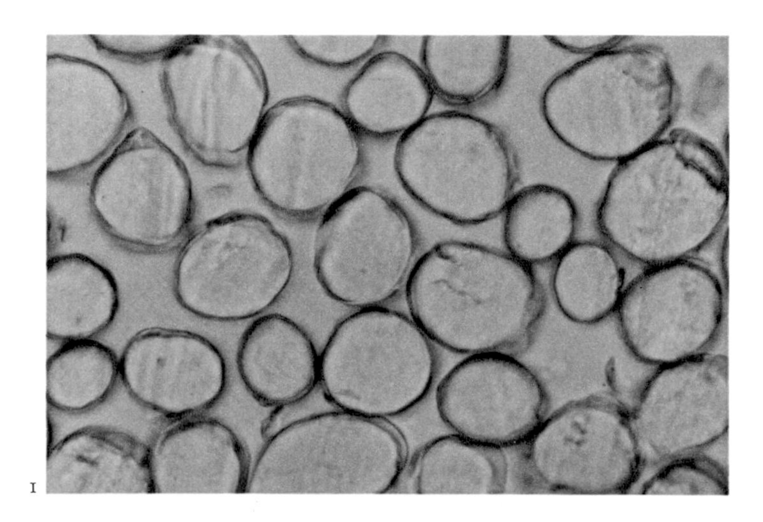

1

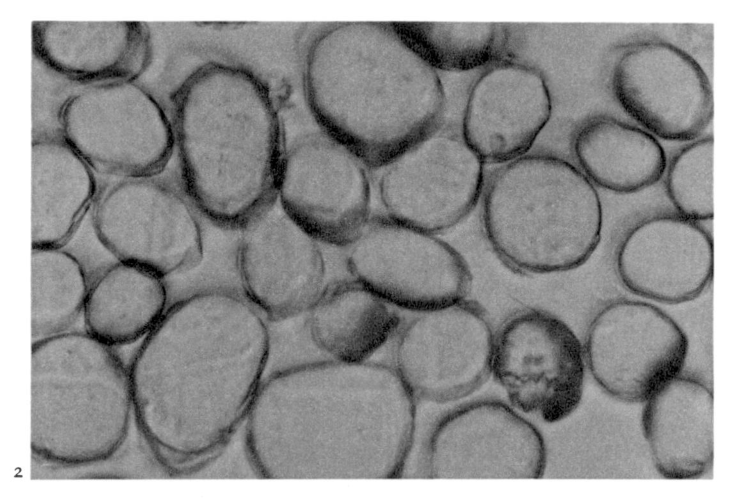

2

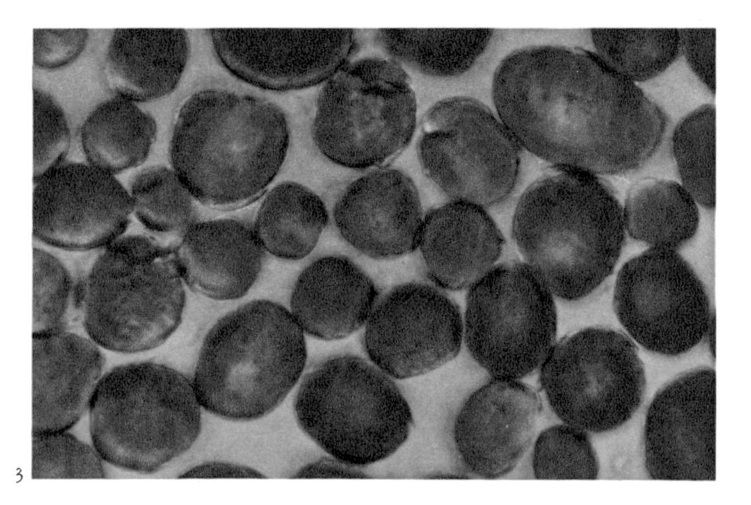

3

In 1953, while attempting to synthesize fast wool dyes, CIBA chemists chose trichlorotriazine as an intermediate.

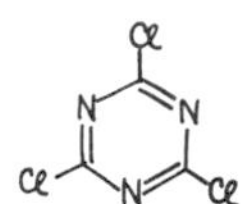

Trichlorotriazine

In the synthesis of these dyes two chlorine atoms were used to build up the dye molecule, while the third remained reactive. During the coloring process these dyes were affixed extremely wash-fast to the wool, the third chlorine atom reacting with the wool keratin to produce a firm chemical bond. The first reactive dyestuff of this type was marketed in 1954 under the trade name *Cibalan Brilliant Yellow 3GL*.
The reactive dye principle based on chlorotriazine could be applied to cotton dyeing too. I.C.I. chemists found that dyestuffs which contain two active chlorine atoms on the triazine ring enter into chemical combination with cellulose under carefully arranged dyeing conditions. Shortly thereafter it was discovered in the CIBA laboratories that, in principle, one active chlorine atom suffices to react with cotton to produce a compound which is highly stable, even to repeated and vigorous washing.
In 1956 I.C.I. brought out its reactive dyes for cellulosic fibres, designating them *Procion* colors. About a year later the *Cibacron* colors of CIBA appeared on the market.

The massive development which dyes chemistry has gone through is visibly reflected in the large number of dyestuff ranges and individual colors. New types of fibres require new types of dyes. Keen competition between the makers of dyes, bringing with it ever-increasing demands from consumers with regard to fastness properties, shades, methods of application, and prices, keeps the color chemist constantly on his toes.

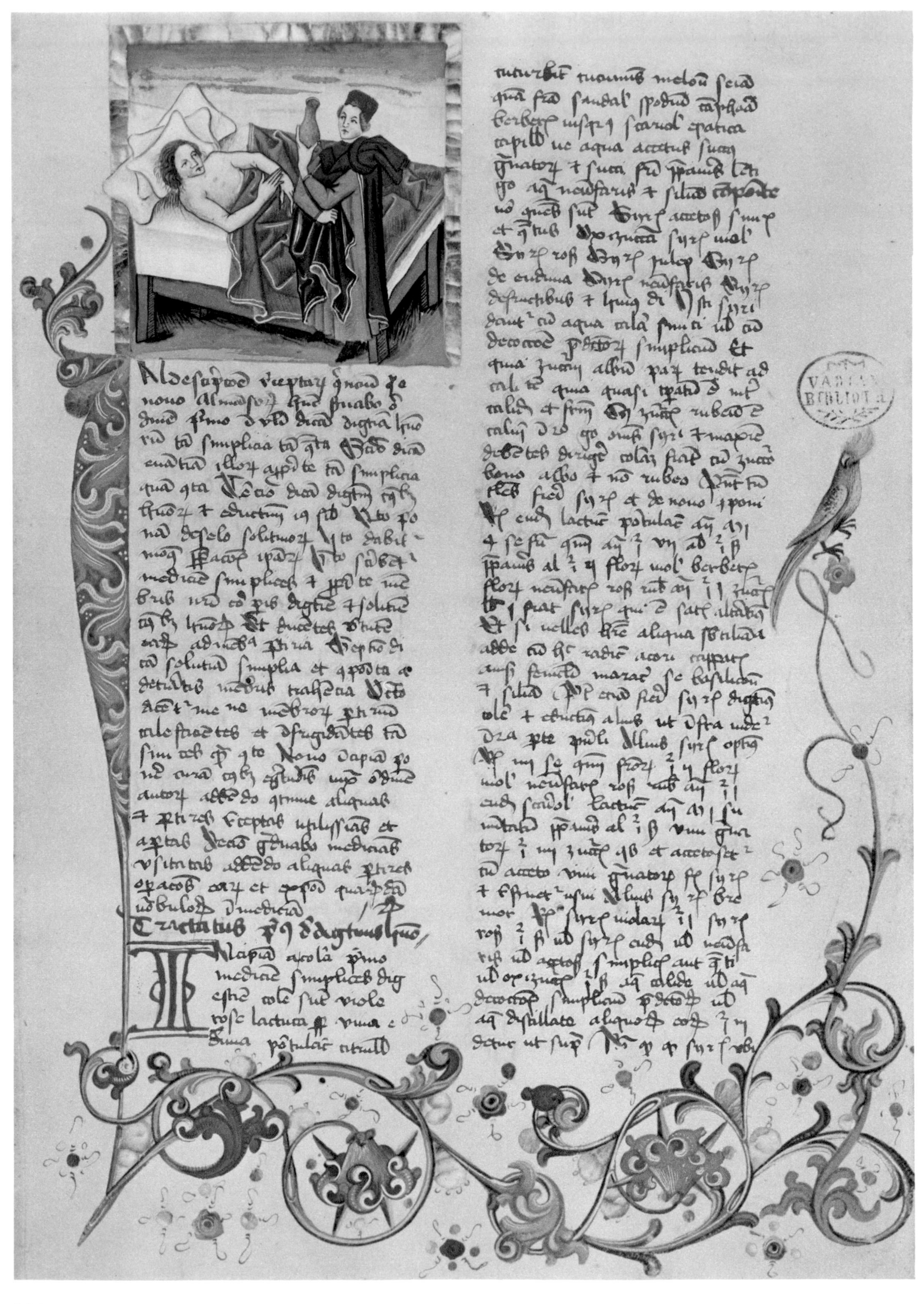

Pharmaceuticals

The rational era in medicine began around the middle of the 19th century. In 1838 the botanist and physician Matthias Jakob Schleiden perceived that plant tissue is cellular in structure. A year later the anatomist Theodor Schwann found the cell to be the structural element of animal tissue as well. In 1842 Justus von Liebig's work "Organic Chemistry in its Application to Physiology and Pathology", appeared. Life processes were shown to be chemical changes and exchanges occurring within a cellular framework.
In 1849, Rudolf Buchheim opened the first special institute for experimental pharmacology at Dorpat (Estonia). This establishment practiced the rational approach to disease, which views illness as a disruption of normal chemical processes in the body, to be regularized by the introduction of the active substances contained in medicaments.

Micro-organisms Disclosed as Pathogens: Antisepsis and Chemotherapy. In 1841 the French physician Joseph-François Malgaigne published the first statistics on mortality resulting from surgical operations. He found that in amputations an average of 60% of the patients died of the sequelae, generally because of wound fever. Mortality during birth was also high; in 1846 more than 10% of women in childbed at the obstetrical clinic in Vienna succumbed to puerperal fever. Similar conditions obtained in the clinics of other cities. This grave situation in the hospital treatment of wounds, however, shortly took a definite turn for the better. In 1847, Ignaz Philipp Semmelweis, an assistant at the aforementioned Viennese clinic, found that puerperal fever was infectious and imposed the strict regulation that all who examined or treated patients should wash their hands with chloride of lime solution.

The work of the chemist Louis Pasteur proved decisive for the successful treatment of wounds. Through his investigations of silkworm epidemics in the 1860s he found that contagious diseases, fermentation, and putrefaction are all due to the same cause, namely to the activity of micro-organisms.
These discoveries opened the way to applying the principles of asepsis and antisepsis, i.e. of sterile and germicidal treatment. Quite independent of one another, but both proceeding on the basis of Pasteur's

Opposite: A physician at the patient's bedside. Miniature from the first page of Pietro da Tossignano's "Recepta", 1465. MS. 433, Vadiana Library, St. Gallen.
Right: Ward in a 17th century French hospital. Ignorance of how infections developed from wounds was responsible for the high mortality rate in the hospitals of that time. Contemporary copper engraving.

work, the French chemist François-Jules Lemaire and the English surgeon Joseph Lister utilized phenol (called carbolic acid at the time), derived from coal tar, for treating wounds. This use of germicidal phenol for surgical purposes was described by Lister in his publication "On a New Method of Treating Compound Fracture, Abscess, etc., with Observations on the Conditions of Suppuration", which appeared in 1867. He later improved on the spraying technique, sometimes irritating, by developing sterilization of the surgeon's hands, the instruments, and dressings.

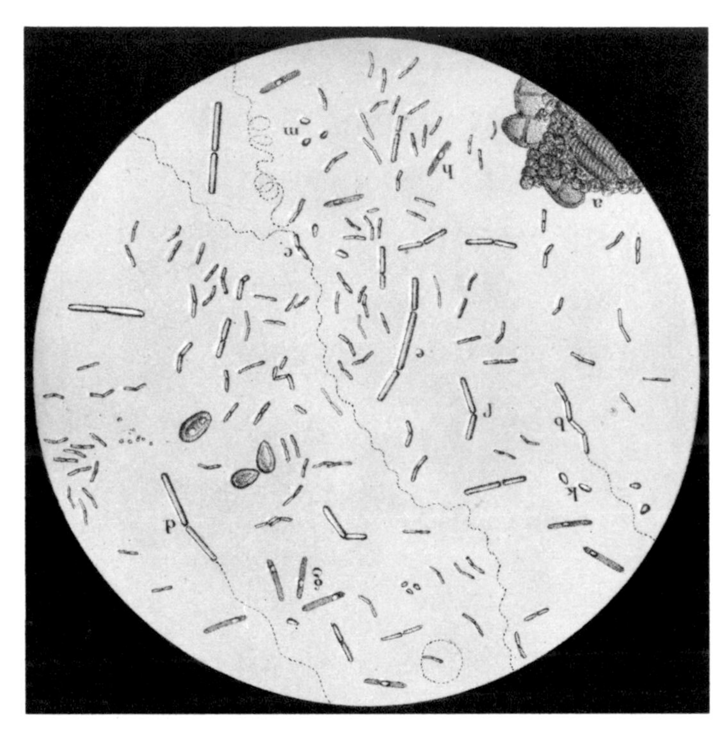

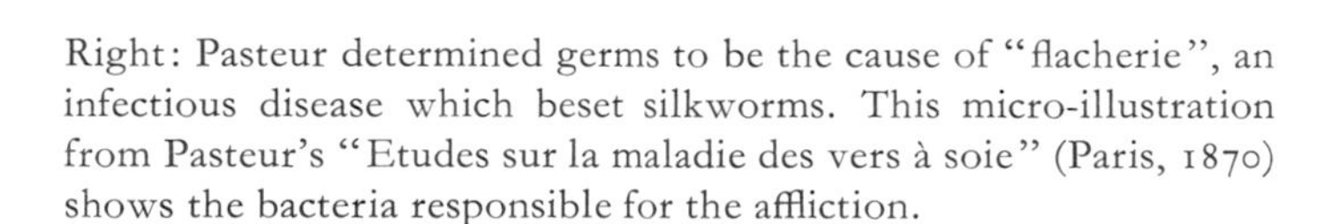
Right: Pasteur determined germs to be the cause of "flacherie", an infectious disease which beset silkworms. This micro-illustration from Pasteur's "Etudes sur la maladie des vers à soie" (Paris, 1870) shows the bacteria responsible for the affliction.

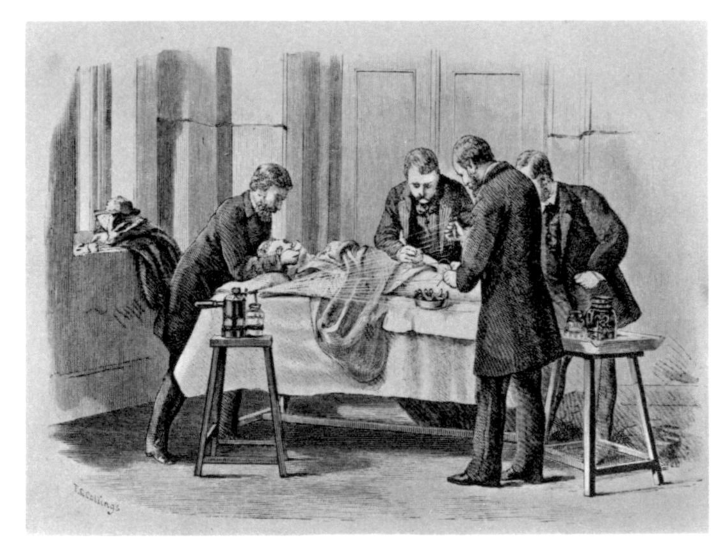

In 1865 Lister introduced the antiseptic treatment of surgical wounds.
Left: The carbolic acid spray used by Lister. In the collection of the Wellcome Historical Medical Museum, London.
Above: Actual spraying of the field of operation. Xylograph from "Antiseptic Surgery" by William Watson Cheyne; London, 1882.

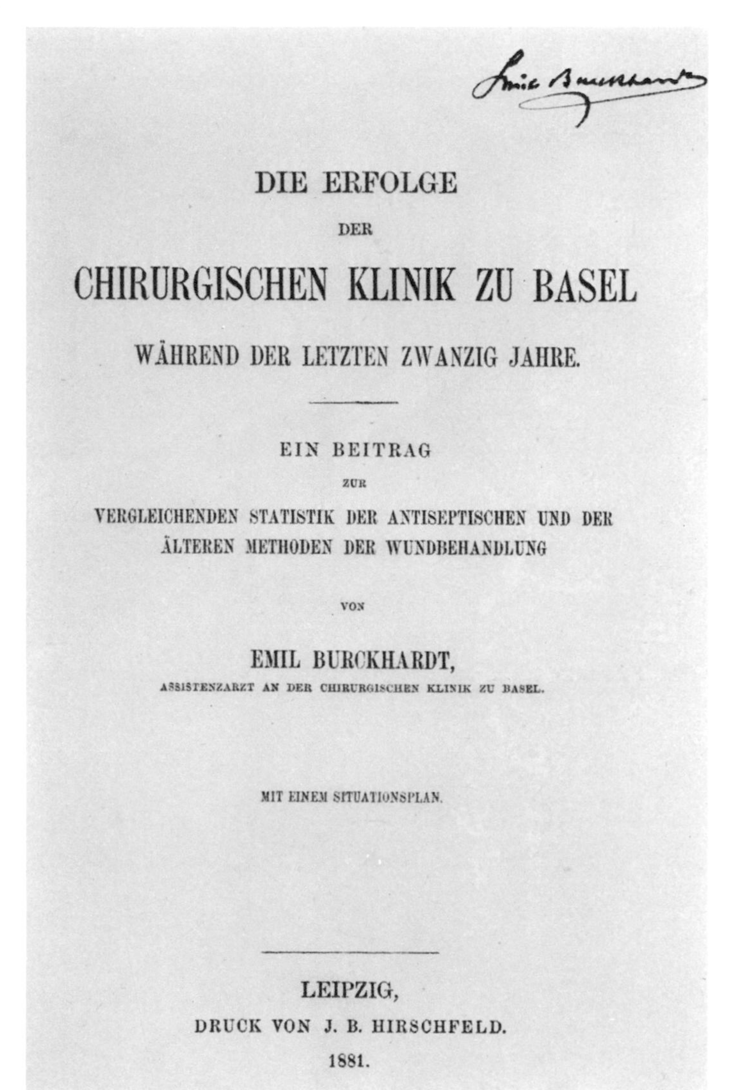

DIE ERFOLGE

DER

CHIRURGISCHEN KLINIK ZU BASEL

WÄHREND DER LETZTEN ZWANZIG JAHRE.

EIN BEITRAG

ZUR

VERGLEICHENDEN STATISTIK DER ANTISEPTISCHEN UND DER ÄLTEREN METHODEN DER WUNDBEHANDLUNG

VON

EMIL BURCKHARDT,

ASSISTENZARZT AN DER CHIRURGISCHEN KLINIK ZU BASEL.

MIT EINEM SITUATIONSPLAN.

LEIPZIG,

DRUCK VON J. B. HIRSCHFELD.

1881.

In Basle, August Socin, professor of surgery at the university, introduced antiseptic wound treatment with phenol in 1871. Ten years later his assistant Emil Burckhardt was able to report that the mortality rate following amputations had decreased from 43.7% to the low figure of 11.5%.

The insight into the bacterial origin of wound fever and puerperal fever gave rise to a new branch of natural science: bacteriology. In 1875 Carl Weigert, pathologist at the University of Frankfurt on Main, succeeded in making cocci in the tissue accessible to microscopic observation by staining them with methyl violet. This method of staining micro-organisms – not only with methyl violet, but also with other products of the young coal tar dyes industry – became one of the most important detection techniques in bacteriology.

Left: Lister's antiseptic method was adopted at an early date in Basle by Socin. This publication by the surgeon Emil Burckhardt described the successes attained with the method at the Surgical Clinic. Leipzig, 1881.
Below: Microorganisms in cultures outside of living tissue. From left to right: Sarcinia, Serratia marcescens, paratubercular bacillus, Chromobacterium "violaceum", Pseudomonas aeruginosa.

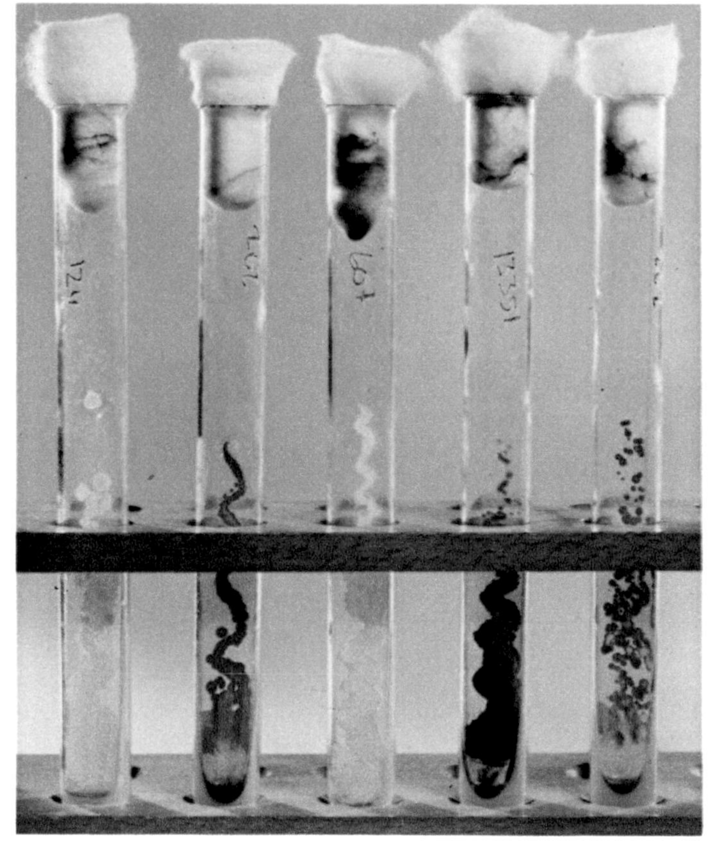

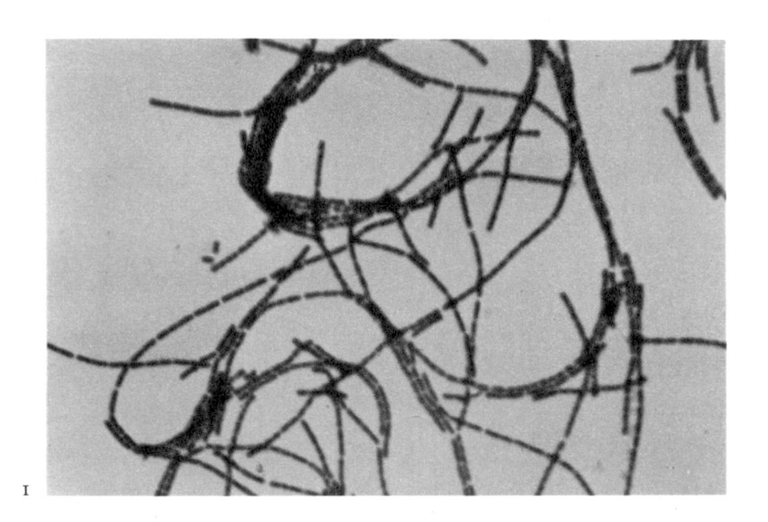

1

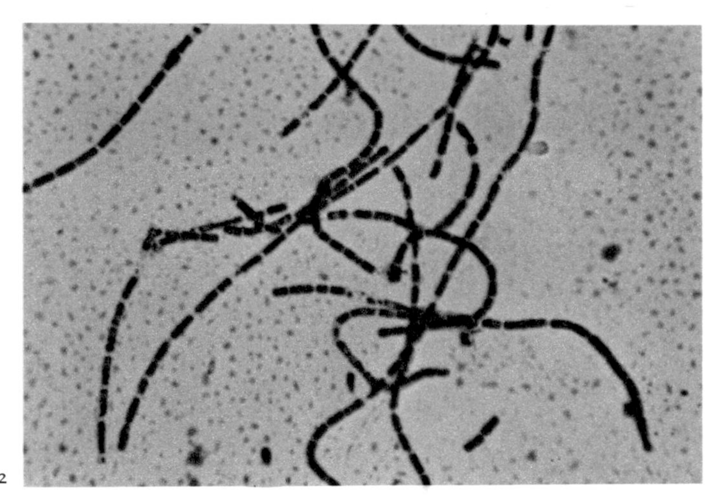

2

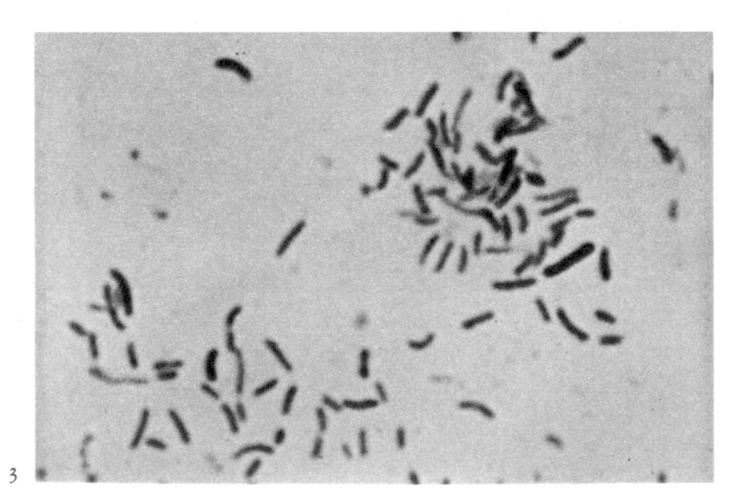

3

Robert Koch helped to extend bacteriological working techniques. Around 1880 he began cultivating bacteria *in vitro* at the Office of Health in Berlin, i. e. growing them in cultures outside of living tissue. The great number of bacilli which he and his school identified during the twenty years following spoke for the success of Koch's method.
The knowledge that micro-organisms cause infectious diseases also pointed the way to undertaking measures to forestall contagion. Pathogenic micro-organisms had to be prevented from entering the tissue. Antiseptic treatment destroys the micro-organisms in the tissue, while in aseptic treatment the material which comes into contact with a wound has been sterilized. Bacteriological technique, which uses cultures of pathogens and microscopy, makes it possible to test chemical agents for their effectiveness as antiseptics. The fight against infectious diseases was thus placed on a systematic and enlightened basis, and at this point industrial research could begin.

The aim of industrial research was the discovery and perfection of antiseptics more effective and less injurious to tissue than the products previously used – chloride of lime, iodine, phenol, formaldehyde, and iodoform.

Stained smears of pure cultures: anthrax and tubercle bacilli, discovered by Koch. Magnification x 1000.
1. Anthrax bacilli.
2. The more resistant spores.
3. Tubercle bacilli.
Preparations from the Institute of Hygienics, University of Basle.

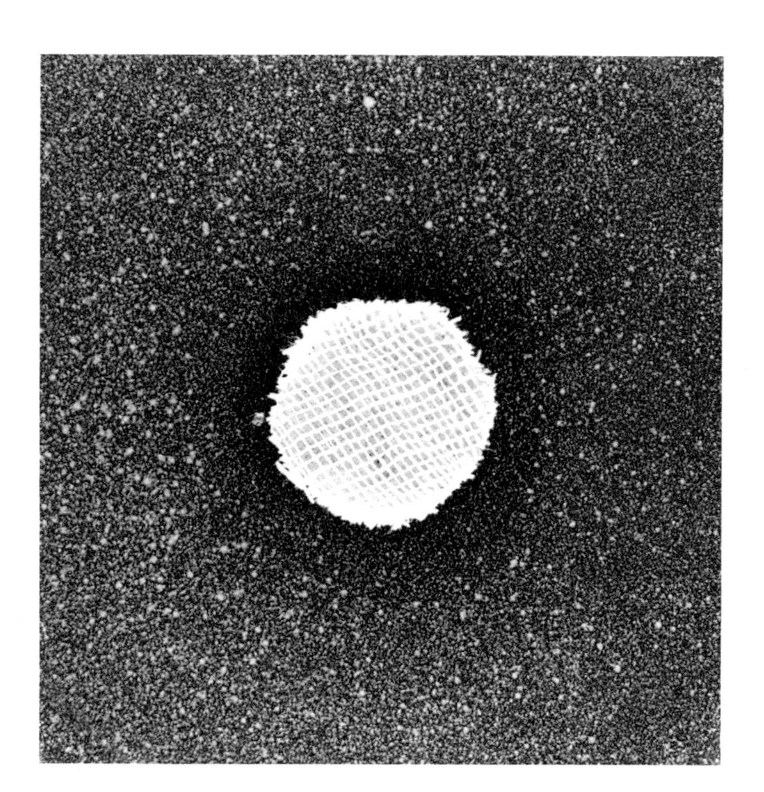

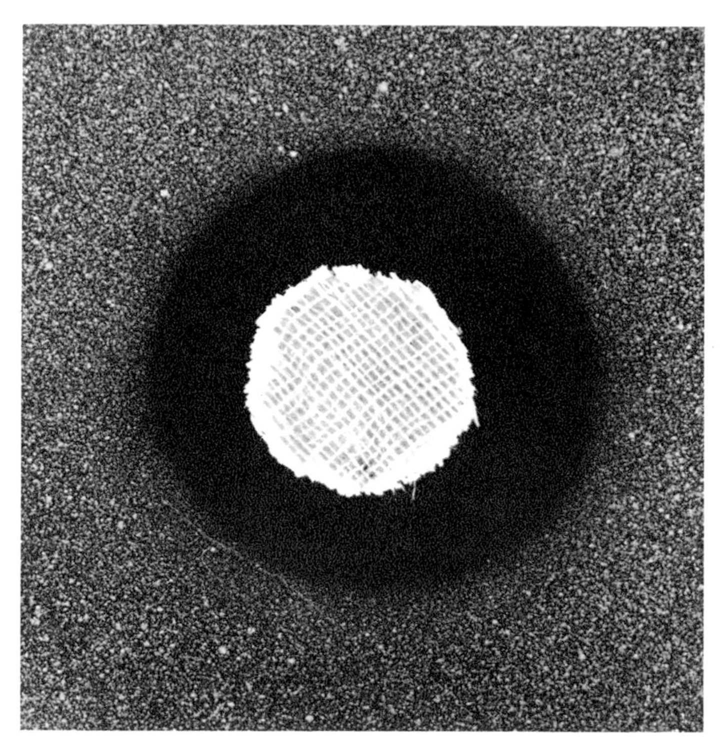

Thus it was found that certain phenol derivatives are more favorable in their effect than phenol itself; chlorophenol is more strongly antiseptic; and phenol esterified with salicylic acid (salol) damages tissue less – so little, indeed, that it can be taken by mouth as an intestinal antiseptic.
These preparations, however, were surpassed by derivatives of quinoline which, besides the phenolic principle, also contain iodine in their molecule: *Loretin* (Hoechst) and *Vioform* (Bindschedler Chemical Factory, Basle).

SO_3H, J, OH, N

Loretin
1893

Cl, J, OH, N

Vioform
1899

The introduction of the cationic detergents provides ample proof of the special care devoted to research concerning antiseptics in Basle. Substances of this sort have a wetting effect similar to that of soap but, in contrast to soap, the effect is exerted in an acid medium too. In order to make the antiseptic action of Vioform of use in the intestinal tract, CIBA combined it in 1934 with the cationic detergent *Sapamine* to produce the antiseptic *Entero-Vioform.*

$CH_3-(CH_2)_{16}-CO-NH-C_6H_4-N^{\oplus}(CH_3)_3 \quad CH_3OSO_3^{\ominus}$

Sapamine

The bacteriological test makes it possible to examine compounds for their efficacy as antiseptics. This is a culture of Aspergillus niger, a fungus causing infection of the outer ear.
Top: A control test.
Bottom: Zone of inhibited growth around gauze steeped in *Vioform.*

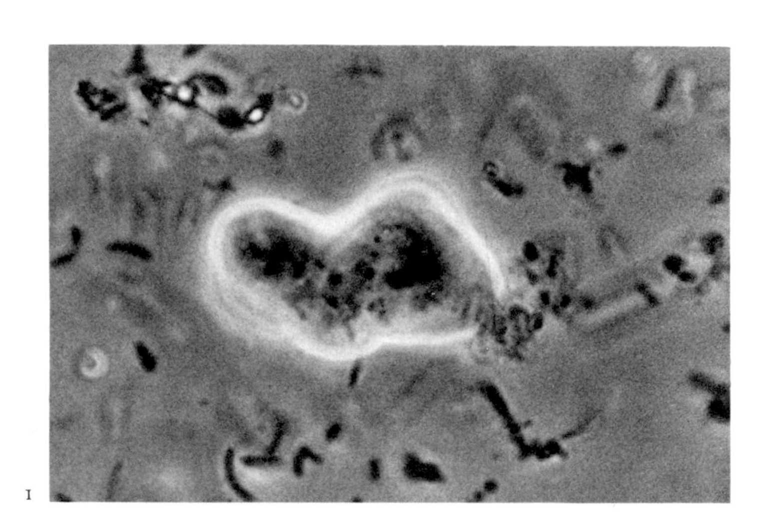

1

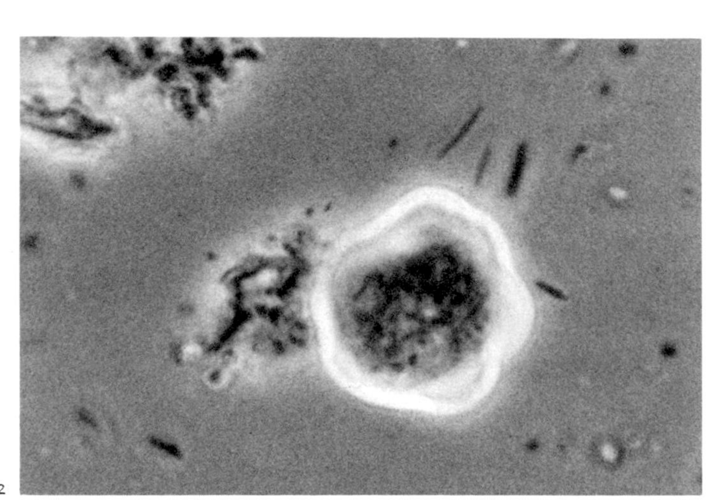

2

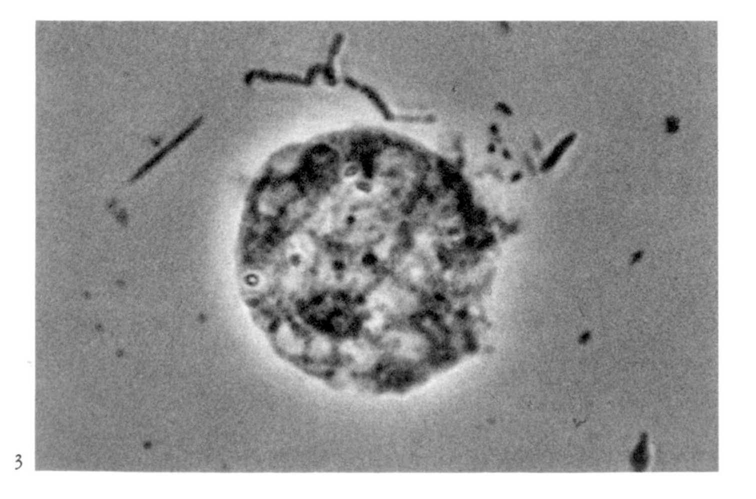

3

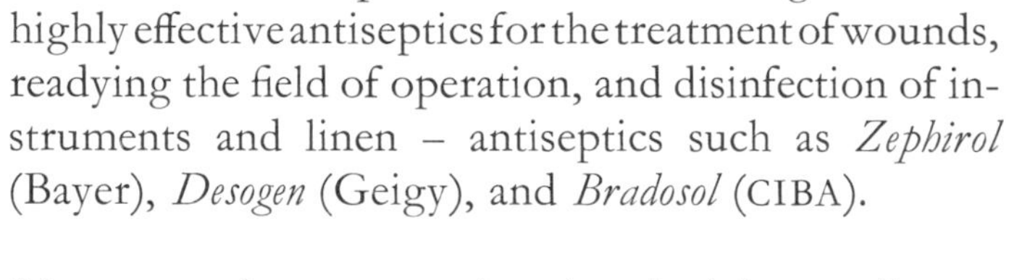

The further development of cationic detergents led to highly effective antiseptics for the treatment of wounds, readying the field of operation, and disinfection of instruments and linen – antiseptics such as *Zephirol* (Bayer), *Desogen* (Geigy), and *Bradosol* (CIBA).

More recently, a new antiseptic principle was discovered in phenanthrolinquinone. With *Entobex,* CIBA launched a preparation in 1957 which, thanks to its antiseptic action in the intestinal tract, effectively combats amoebic dysentery, a dreaded affliction in the tropics.

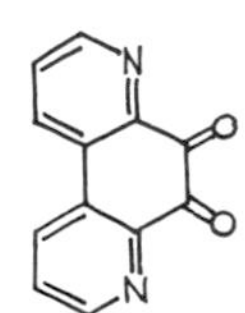

Entobex

Certain dyestuffs stain disease-causing micro-organisms, but not the tissue. This finding of Carl Weigert's was not responsible for the fruition of bacteriological technique alone, since it also paved the way for chemotherapy. Paul Ehrlich applied the principle of selective staining to living organisms. He was convinced that it should be possible to find agents which, if admitted to the bloodstream, would join only with pathogenic bacteria and would kill them, without harm to the diseased body. This, the antisepsis of the circulatory system, is the fundamental idea of chemotherapy.
In 1885 Ehrlich began testing dyestuffs for their pharmacological efficacy. Six years later he found methylene blue, or methylthionine chloride, to be effective against malaria.

Microphotos of an amoebicide in action. A fully mobile amoeba (1), when acted on by *Entobex,* loses its mobility, takes on a globular shape (2); and dies (3). Magnification x 1000.

Salvarsan, an organic arsenical compound, heralded chemotherapy. It is used in the treatment of diseases such as African sleeping sickness and syphilis caused by trypanosomes and spirochetes.
Top: Stained smear of blood with Trypanosoma equiperdum, which afflicts horses and asses. Magnification x 1000.
Centre: Stained smear of blood with corkscrew-shaped spirochetes of the Borrelia genus. Magnification x 1000.

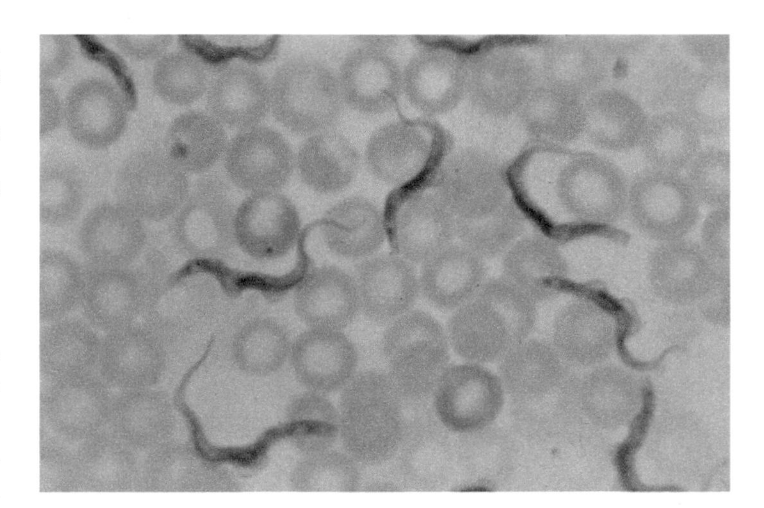

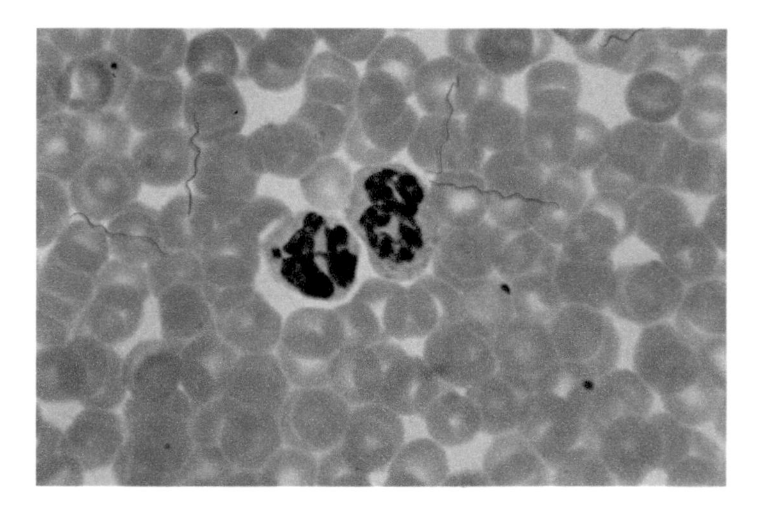

In the first years of this century Ehrlich, who had meanwhile become director of the Institute for Experimental Therapy in Frankfurt on Main, turned his attention to organic compounds of arsenic. He elucidated the chemical structure of Atoxyl (sodium arsanilate), which had shown promising success in the treatment of sleeping sickness and syphilis, though not without dangerous side effects. This substance he modified systematically. "My therapeutical program", wrote Ehrlich, "consists in preparing homologues and derivatives of all kinds and varieties from substances having a certain effectiveness, to investigate the action of each and, building on the results thus obtained, to arrive at ever-better therapeutic agents. This means learning to aim, and doing so by means of chemical variation."
The chemical variation of Atoxyl led him, working together with the Japanese physician Sahachiro Hata, in 1909 to *Salvarsan,* hydrochloric 3,3'-diamino-4,4'-dihydroxyarsenobenzene.

$2HCl/2H_2O$

Salvarsan

Salvarsan was the first sure remedy against syphilis and against other infectious diseases caused by spirochetes as well as by trypanosomes (protozoa). And as such Salvarsan represented the first triumph of chemotherapy.

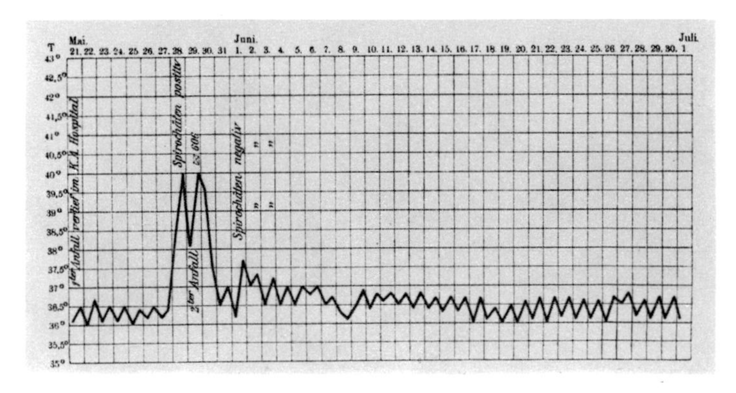

Fever chart of a syphilitic patient treated with Salvarsan (606). From "Experimental Chemotherapy of Spirillosis" by Ehrlich and Hata.

Dyestuffs were the point of departure in Ehrlich's investigations, and dyestuffs were to introduce a new phase of chemotherapy a half century later: the combating of infections due to spherical bacteria classified as cocci. In 1935 Gerhard Domagk, director of experimental pathology and bacteriology at I.G. Farben, reported the chemotherapeutic successes he had attained with the reddish-brown azo dye *Prontosil*.

Prontosil

Prontosil is an efficacious medicament against coccal infections such as pneumonia, meningitis, or tonsillitis.

Prontosil, the first sulfonamide to be used for medical purposes, is a dyestuff. These are dyeings of Prontosil on silk.

That the effect attained in these cases is not limited to the colorific nature of the substances concerned was shown by the work carried out in 1935/36 by a group of researchers in the Pasteur Institute. Fourneau, Tréfouël, Mme. Tréfouël, Nitti and Bovet found that Prontosil is broken down in the body by reduction to the simpler substance sulfanilamide. Responsible for the chemotherapeutic effect is a cleavage product, p-amino-benzene-sulfonamide.

p-Amino-benzene-sulfonamide

A rational explanation of the mechanism of action of p-amino-benzene-sulfonamide, and with it of sulfonamides in general, was found in 1940. Woods and Fildes saw that this substance intervenes in the metabolic chemistry of bacteria, interposing itself in place of endogenous p-amino-benzoic acid in bacterial metabolism, thus inhibiting the latter. Sulfonamides act as antimetabolites of p-amino-benzoic acid, essential to bacterial growth.

p-Amino-benzoic acid

Although the chemotherapeutic action of p-amino-benzene-sulfonamide was not yet entirely satisfactory, still the direction that industrial development would take was clearly marked out. Sulfonamides would have to be built up in such a way as to combine a maximum of chemotherapeutic activity with a minimum of unpleasant side effects. Hundreds of sulfonamides were synthesized, the most effective of them being sulfapyridine, or *Dagenan,* prepared in 1937 by the British firm of May & Baker.

The first preparation combining both properties desired – a high degree of efficacy and good tolerance – was made in Basle. Max Hartmann and his co-workers had synthesized many compounds. In 1938 they discovered 2-sulfanilamidothiazole which, after careful clinical trials, was made available to the medical profession under the name of *Cibazol.*

Cibazol

The field of sulfonamides proved capable of considerable development. In the last twenty years new chemotherapeutic agents have been prepared all over the world on this basis.

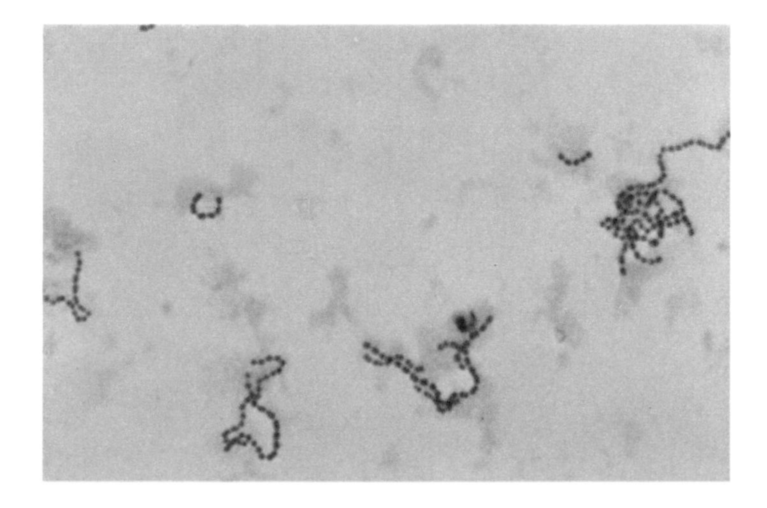

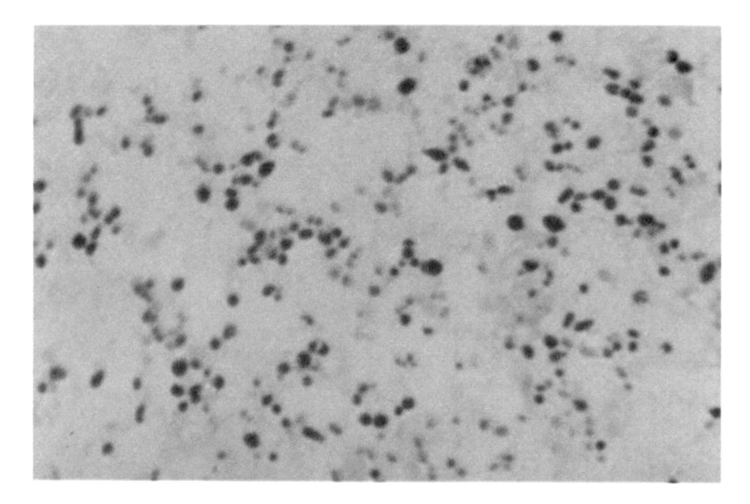

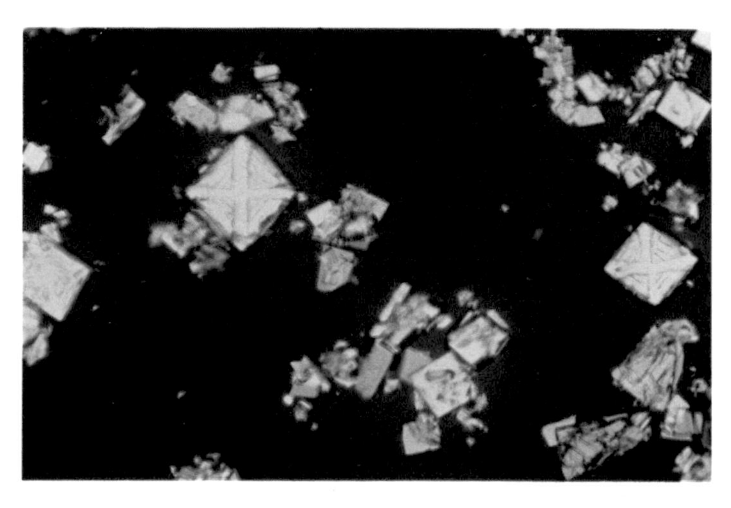

The sulfonamide drugs extended the range of therapeutic possibilities in a number of infectious diseases.
Top: Stained smear preparation of Streptococcus haemolyticus, or pus-producing cocci.
Centre: *Orisul,* a CIBA sulfonamide, inhibits the formation of streptococcal chains. Magnification x 1000.
Bottom: Orisul crystals in polarized light, magnification x 20.

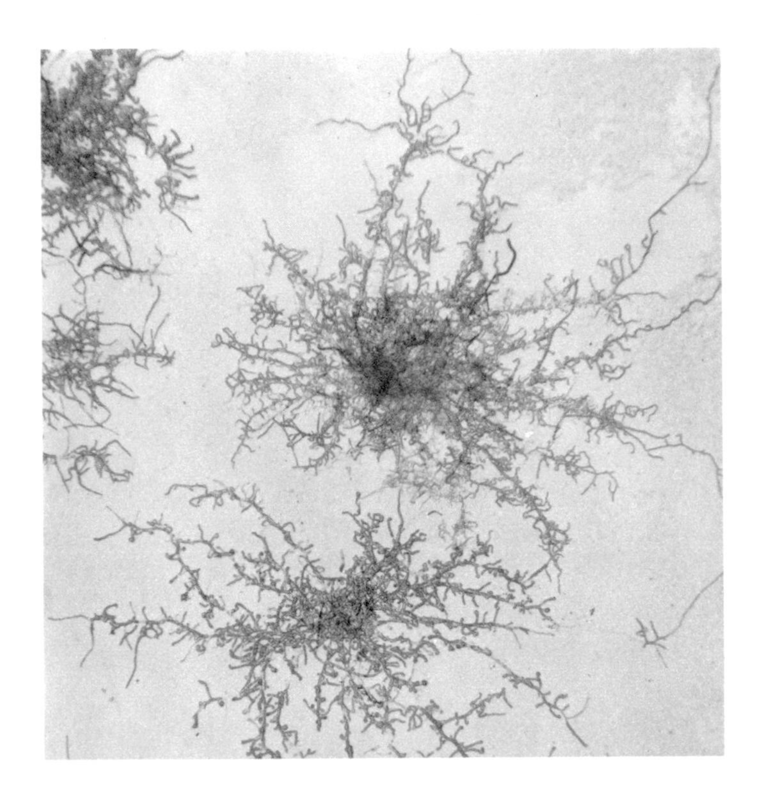

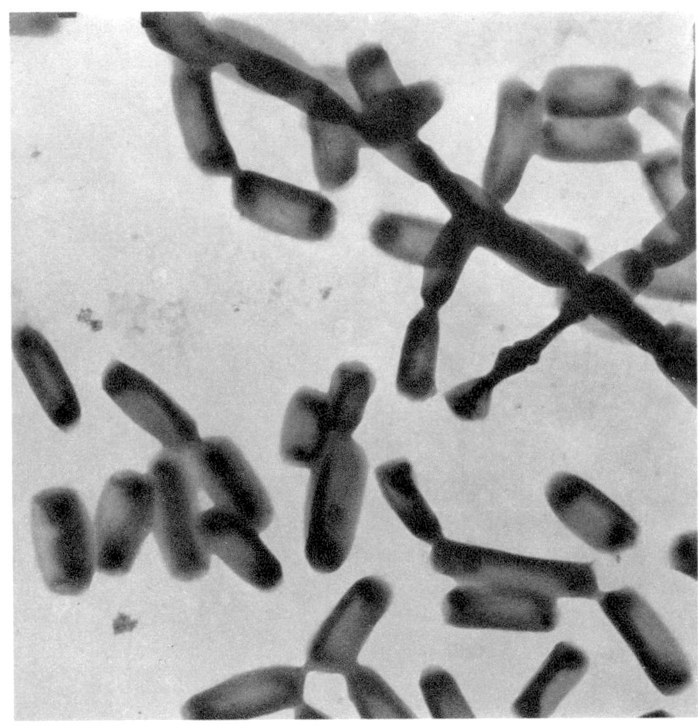

Antibiotics are chemotherapeutic substances derived from mould cultures.
Above left: Fresh preparation of Streptomyces griseus with ramified fungus filaments, magnification x 300.
Above right: Spores of Streptomyces griseus under the electron microscope, magnification x 15 000. Photo from the Institute for Special Botany, Swiss Federal Institute of Technology.
Left: Slightly magnified crystals of *Vionactane,* a CIBA antibiotic which acts against tuberculosis.

Throughout four decades chemotherapy was dominated by synthetic drugs. In 1938 Howard W. Florey, building on observations made by Fleming, began a systematic back-to-nature search at Oxford for chemotherapeutic substances in the products released by moulds. That these organisms have a certain anti-bacterial activity was a fact which had already been known for some time. Florey's work resulted in the isolation of penicillin from the fungus penicillium. This was the overture to the development of the antibiotics, a field in which American research teams now hold the lead.

Basle also deserves credit for the effectual treatment of a special form of bacterial infection: tuberculosis. In the 1950s a research group at Hoffmann-La Roche discovered, almost at the same time as Domagk of Bayer, the tuberculostatic action of isonicotinic acid hydrazide. Their discovery provided the physician with a highly potent weapon against this insidious disease.

Isonicotinic acid hydrazide

Another antimycobacterial preparation was developed at CIBA Summit in collaboration with the Basle parent house. 1958 saw the introduction of *Ciba-1906,* a diphenyl thiourea compound earmarked for use against leprosy, one of mankind's most ancient scourges.

Ciba-1906

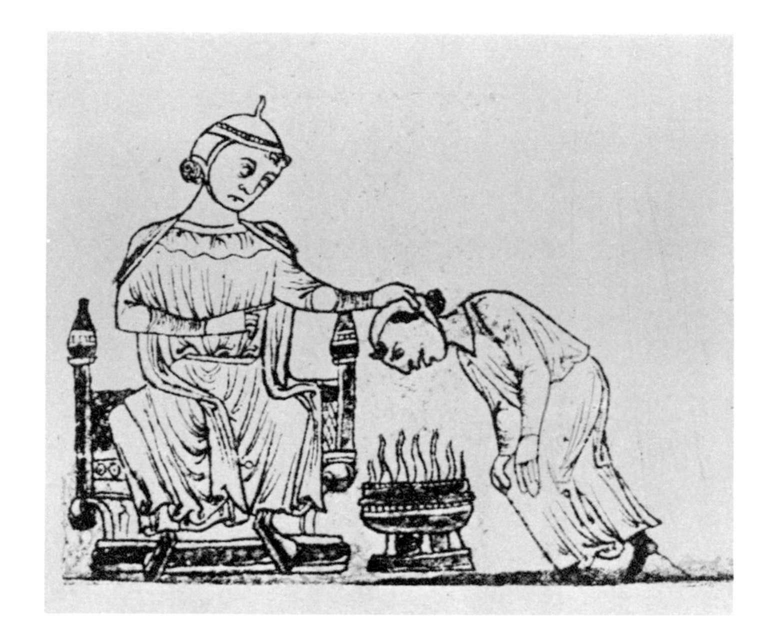

Combating pain in the Middle Ages. The vapors of heated henbane were inhaled against toothache. Miniature from a French edition of "Practica Chirurgiae" by Roger of Salerno (13th century). Trinity College, Cambridge.

From Natural to Synthetic Drugs: Analgesics and Antipyretics. From ancient times pain has been alleviated in two ways: by psychic means ranging from ritual to the "animal magnetism" of Mesmer, or by the use of narcotic drugs such as mandrake, henbane *(Hyoscyamus niger* L.*)*, or poppy. Once medicine had become permeated by the ideas of natural science, it was bound to avail itself of the second method more and more.
In 1799 Humphry Davy, then director of the "pneumatics laboratory" in Bristol, demonstrated in experiments on his own person the anesthetic effect of nitrous oxide, later termed laughing gas. Then, in 1818, his pupil Michael Faraday observed ether fumes to possess a similar property. Both men proposed that their discoveries be utilized for alleviating pain in surgical operations. Decades passed, however, before the effects of ether and laughing gas were turned to any more constructive purpose than the amusement of country fair crowds.

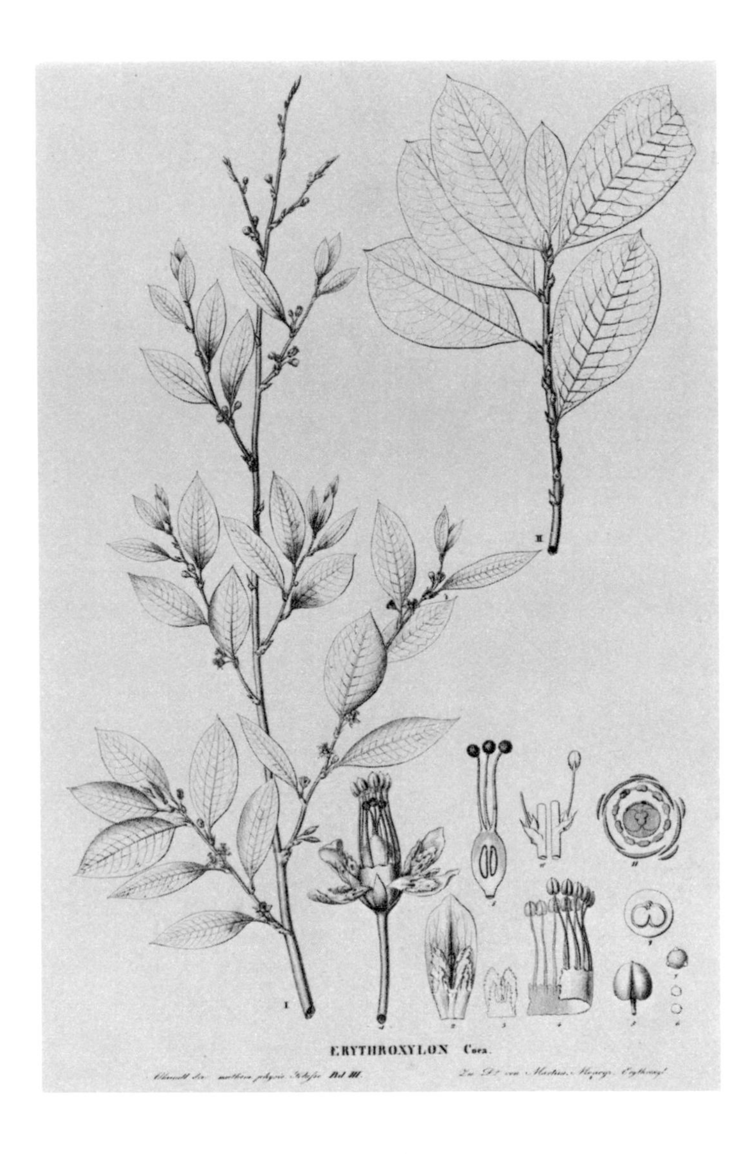

From the leaves of the coca tree, long known to the Indians of Peru as a stimulant and pain-killer, the alkaloid cocaine was isolated in 1860.
Left: A depiction of Erythroxylon coca Lam., which furnishes coca leaves, from a work on the subject by Carl Friedrich Philipp von Martius; Munich, 1843.
Right: Coca leaves, containing about 1% cocaine.

Only towards mid-century did the two substances find entry into respectable medical practice. In 1846 W. T. G. Morton gave the first public demonstration of anesthesia, using ether during a surgical operation in Boston. A year later chloroform anesthesia was introduced. The use of this readily prepared chemical marked the beginning of modern anesthetic science. Together with antiseptic surgery, which was coming to the fore at the same time, it made possible tremendous strides forward in the realm of surgery.

Anesthetic technique was further improved by the method of local anesthesia, introduced in 1884 by Hepburn and Knapp in the United States. By injecting cocaine solution they made the field of operation insensible to pain. Cocaine is an alkaloid from the leaves of the coca plant *(Erythroxylon coca* Lam.*)*; its constitutional formula was elucidated in 1898.

Cocaine

In 1905 Professor Alfred Einhorn of Munich succeeded in synthesizing *Novocaine* (Hoechst), a local anesthetic ten times less toxic than cocaine. After this discovery cocaine declined in importance.

Novocaine

In 1929 CIBA Basle developed *Nupercaine,* a local anesthetic ten times as effective as cocaine.

Nupercaine

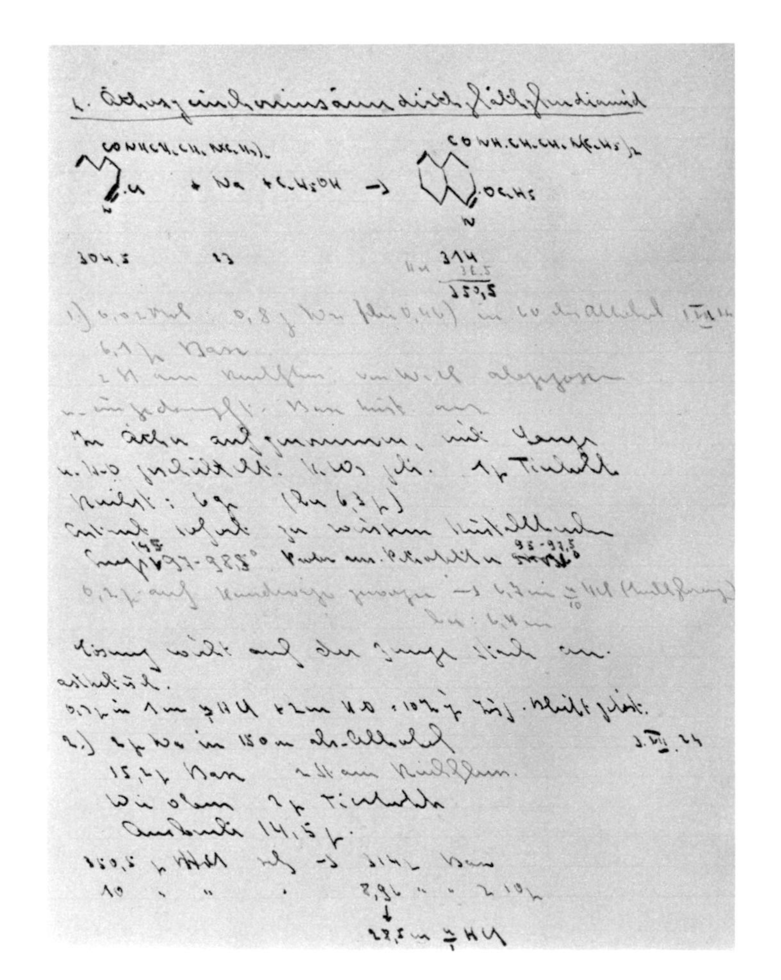

A page of Karl Miescher's laboratory journal dated 1924, describing the synthesis of the local anesthetic *Nupercaine.*

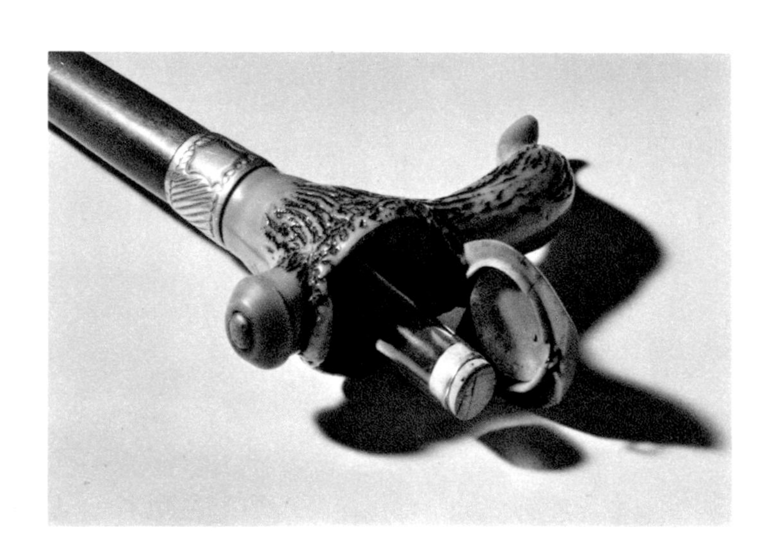

Niche in the pommel of a walking-stick where the physician of yore kept his opiates ready to hand. Swiss Museum of Pharmaceutical History, Basle.

Up to the middle of the last century doctors were in the habit of always carrying a drug around with them. They took the pommel of their sword or, later on, the handle of their walking-stick as a portable container for opium, ready for use. Opium, the inspissated juice of poppy-heads, was given the patient for the alleviation of unbearable pains.
Morphine, the active substance of opium, was isolated on a commercial scale in the early 19th century and, since it could be more accurately dosed than the natural drug, became a part of the pharmaceutical armamentarium.

Morphine developed similarly to cocaine. Synthetic products possessing both greater efficacy and less toxicity came to replace the natural substance in medicine. In 1940, with *Dolantin,* the Hoechst Dyeworks created the first synthetic with morphine-like action. Other highly active analgesics with the structural characteristics of their natural counterparts came out of the Basle research laboratories in 1949: *Cliradon* (CIBA) and *Dromoran* (Roche).

Morphine — Cliradon — Dromoran

Quinine, long the only known effective antipyretic, had been used since the 17th century against malaria, which is still the world's commonest disease. Fever chart of a patient from "Malaria" by Bernhard Nocht and Martin Mayer; Berlin, 1936.

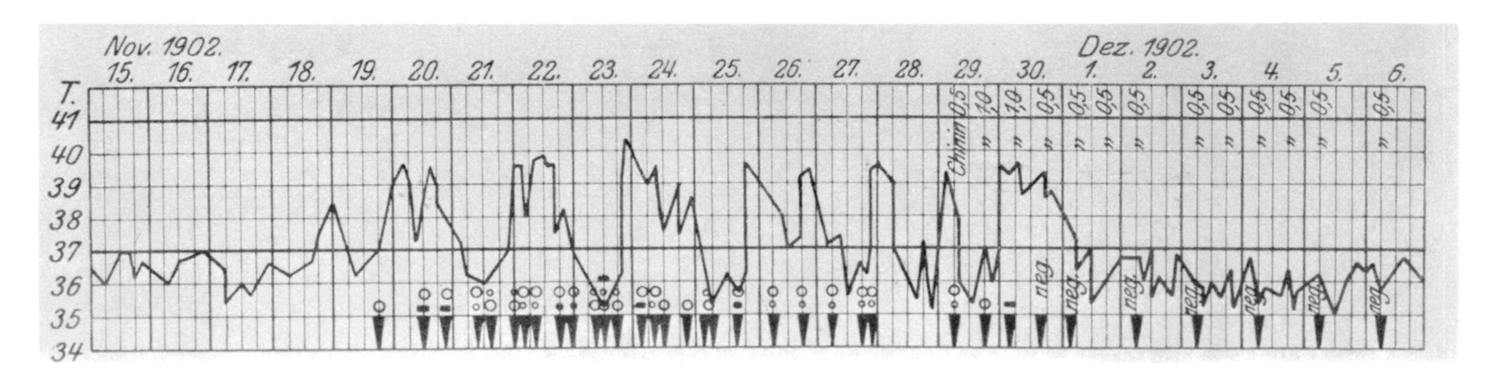

Since the time of the Thirty Years War Peruvian, or cinchona, bark had been the medicine generally used as an antipyretic. In 1820 it was succeeded by quinine, the alkaloid extracted from the cinchona bark.

Quinine

The 1880s saw the structural clarification, in various university laboratories, of quinoline, a fragment of the quinine molecule. At the same time it was recognized that quinoline was identical with "leukol", which had been isolated from coal tar fifty years previously. This information brought quinoline into the province of industrial chemistry. Derivatives of it were synthesized and tested for their antipyretic efficacy. From these efforts there resulted, in 1883, *Antipyrine,* synthesized by Ludwig Knorr, Emil Fischer's assistant in Erlangen, and submitted to pharmacological tests in the Hoechst Dyeworks. The surprising outcome here, subsequently revealed, was that Antipyrine, far from being a quinoline derivative, is chemically derived from pyrazolone. *Pyramidon,* a more effective febrifuge based on Antipyrine, came out in 1896. Another half-century elapsed before Geigy chemists and physiologists found an efficacious third member of this series, the antiphlogistic *Butazolidin.*

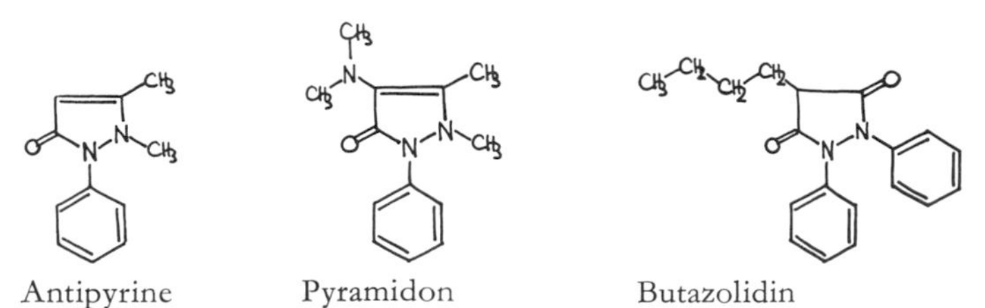

Antipyrine Pyramidon Butazolidin

All these pyrazolone derivatives act not only as febrifuges, but also have anti-inflammatory and analgesic properties.

Fever thermometer, 17th century depiction. Woodcut from a commentary on the works of Avicenna the Arabian by Santorio Santorio; Venice, 1646.

Sleep: a woodcut entitled "Pharaoh's Dream" by Hans Holbein the Younger. From "Historiarum Veteris Instrumenti Icones"; Lyons, 1538.

Success of a Rational Working Hypothesis: Modern Somnifacients.

"Give me to drink mandragora...
That I might sleep out this great gap of time
My Antony is away",
cries Shakespeare's Cleopatra. Mandrake, poppy-seed, and valerian, the most ancient medicines against insomnia, all owed the explanation of how they acted to views colored by mysticism and magic. The attitude which led Oskar Liebreich, Virchow's assistant in Berlin, to the discovery of chloral hydrate in 1869, however, was neither mystical nor magical, but scientific. In alkaline solution chloral hydrate separates off chloroform, which is narcotic. This reaction, so Liebreich suspected, may also occur in the blood of the living organism, reacting as an alkaline medium. Chloral hydrate did in fact prove to be a potent somnifacient – a remarkable coincidence, since Liebreich's working hypothesis was actually incorrect.

The discovery of the somnifacient action of chloral hydrate was the starting gun for industrial research in the field of hypnotics and sedatives. In the course of numerous experiments certain empirical rules took shape. To groupings such as are contained in the molecules of alcohol and urea was ascribed responsibility for the sedative effect. On the basis of these rules the physician Joseph von Mering suggested the synthesis of diethyl barbituric acid, and in 1903 Emil Fischer, professor of chemistry at the University of Berlin, carried it out. As anticipated, this substance proved to be an excellent hypnotic. Marketed as *Veronal* – after Verona, the North Italian town where Mering spent his holidays – it was manufactured by Merck in Darmstadt and Bayer in Leverkusen.

Veronal

By varying the substituents on the barbituric acid ring the action of the drug can be modified considerably. Everywhere in the years that followed sedatives were built up on this principle. In 1912, for example, Bayer patented the phenyl-ethyl barbituric acid, *Luminal.*

Dial was realized by CIBA in 1913. Like other barbituric acid derivatives developed in Basle research laboratories, it is still in use today.

Dial

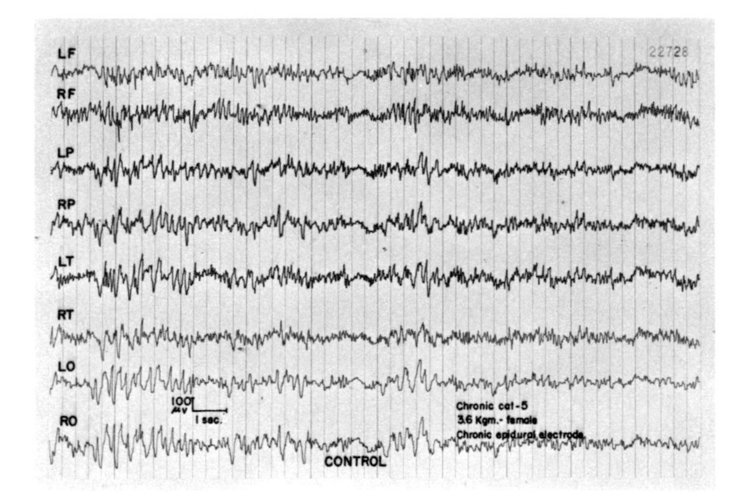

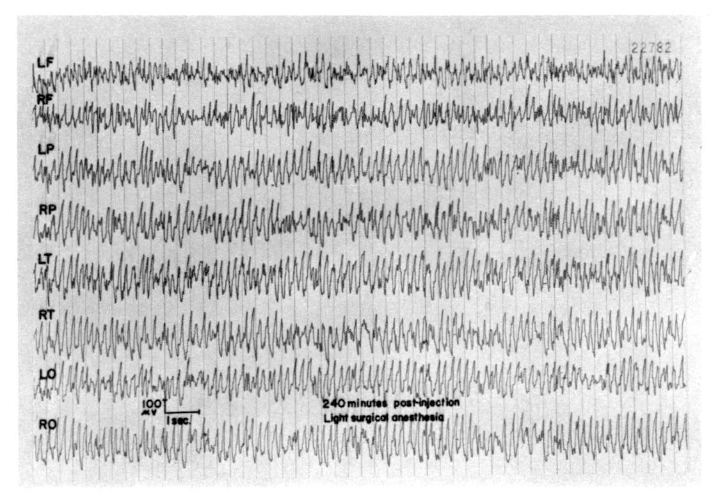

Dial, a long-time CIBA sedative, causes a change in electric potentials in the brain which can be chartered by means of electroencephalographs. Typical measurements taken on a cat asleep; left: before and, right: after injection of Dial.

In 1955 CIBA and Roche launched somnifacients synthesized according to new principles, independent of the barbituric acid structure: *Doriden,* a glutarimide derivative, and *Noludar,* a piperidine derivative. Doriden is a mild hypnotic which, unlike barbituric acid preparations, neither produces hangover nor causes habituation.

Very slight alterations in a molecule can modify its biological activity. In 1958 CIBA released *Aturbane,* an antiparkinson drug based on the same structural principle as the glutarimide Doriden. Aturbane is indicated in autonomic nervous symptoms and in disturbances of motor function such as occur in Parkinson's syndrome as sequelae of arteriosclerosis and encephalitis.

Doriden

Noludar

Aturbane

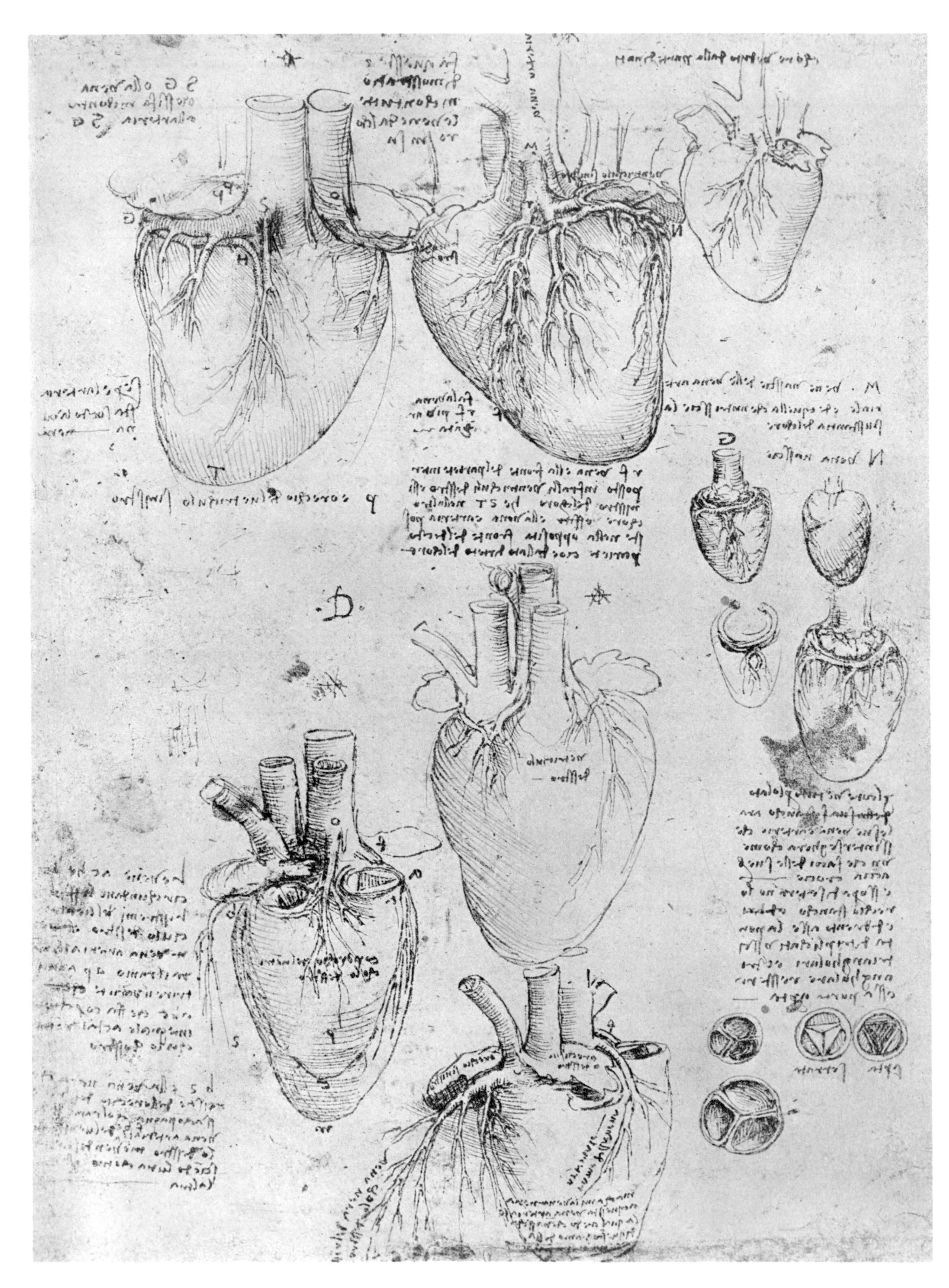

Opposite: The human heart. Drawings by Leonardo da Vinci in the "Quaderni d'Anatomia", Vol. II. Published under the editorship of Ove C. L. Vangensten and others in Oslo, 1912.

The foxglove plant. Digitalis, prepared from its dried leaves, is a cardiant. Colored copper engraving from the first edition of "An Account of the Foxglove, and some of its Medical Uses" by William Withering; Birmingham, 1785.

Popular and Proper Medicine: Digitalis Extracts Inaugurate New Cardiovascular Therapy. In 1785 the English physician William Withering subjected certain popular remedies to a critical analysis. In pursuing these investigations he discovered the tonic effect on the heart of foxglove leaves *(Digitalis purpurea* L.*)*. Eighty-four years passed, however, before the French pharmacist Nativelle isolated one of the active principles of this vegetable drug: crystalline digitalin. In 1884 digitalin, a potent cardiac stimulant, was accepted into the French pharmacopoeia. Once again a purified extract had supplanted the crude drug; once again rational therapy took the place of popular medicine.

Digitalis therapy experienced a decisive impetus thanks to Max Cloëtta, professor of pharmacology at the University of Zurich, who isolated digitoxin from digitalis leaves in 1904. This soluble glycoside, approximately 1000 times as active as the natural drug, was made available for treatment of heart disease in the same year by Hoffmann-La Roche under the label *Digalen.*

In the course of the brilliant development that ensued, Prof. Tadeus Reichstein at the University of Basle and a research group at Sandoz, the Basle chemical firm, elucidated the constitutional formula of further cardioactive substances occurring in nature.

From the Middle Ages to quite modern times rye blighted by the fungus disease ergot had caused pestilential epidemics among the peoples. In especially wet summers the harvest would contain up to ten percent of grain attacked by an Ascomycete *(Claviceps purpurea* Tul. ex Fries*)*. The symptoms of poisoning from ergotized grain were horrible; circulatory disturbances were followed by spasmodic states (ergotism or "St. Anthony's fire") ending often in death. Towards the end of the 11th century a nursing order, the Antonites, was founded expressly for the purpose of caring for the victims of erysipelas. It established a number of infirmaries, among them one at the St. Johann-vorstadt in Basle and another on the Lesser Basle side

Rye attacked by ergot causes serious poisoning if eaten.
Left: Ergotism was called "St. Anthony's fire" after the much-tempted first Christian monk; a visit to his shrine was believed to allay the affliction. Woodcut by Hans Weiditz, first half of 16th century.
Below: The humane order of the Antonites, founded in France, cared for sufferers from ergot poisoning. In this detail of a plan of Basle by Matthew Merian, done in 1615, the Antonite establishment in Lesser Basle is just this side of the fountain.

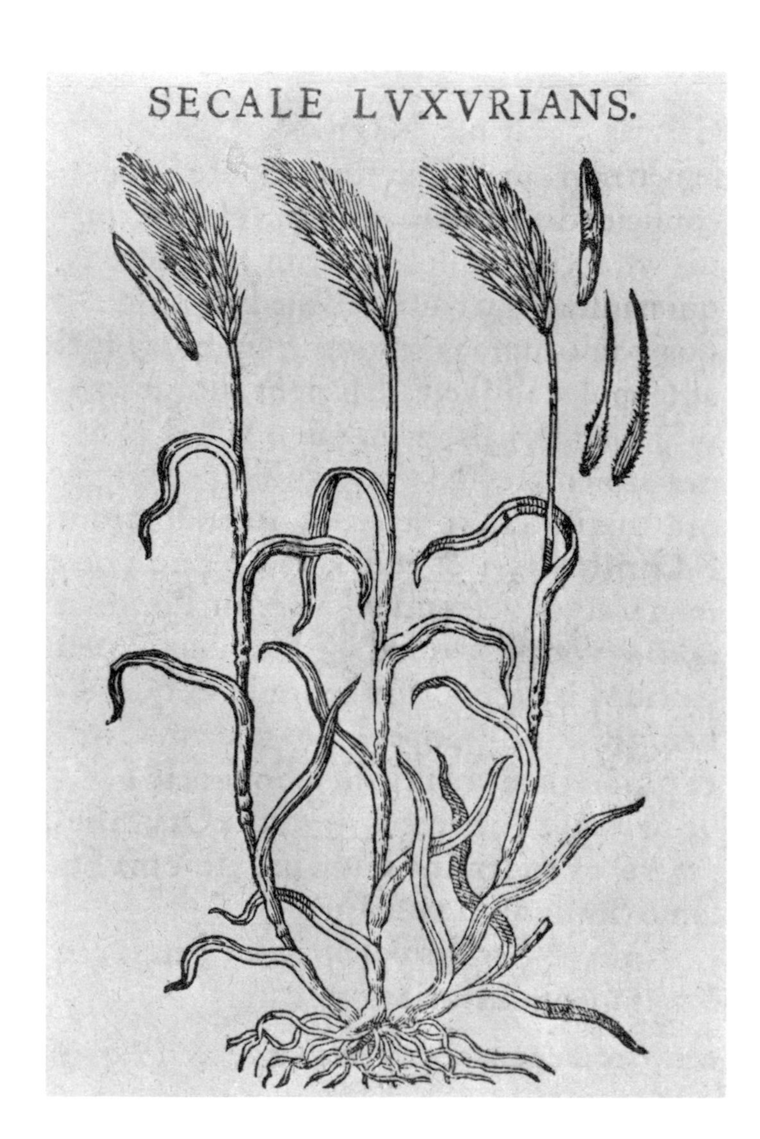

The first drawing of ergotized grain. Woodcut from the "Theatri Botanici" of the systematist Caspar Bauhin; Basle, 1658.

of the Rhine, both mentioned in ancient documents dated 1304 and 1462, respectively.
The use of small amounts of ergot for medicinal purposes, too, was known at an early date. It is first mentioned as an obstetrical drug in the 1582 edition of the Book of Herbs by Adam Lonitzer, the municipal physician of Frankfurt. Of its haemostatic effect, Theodore Zwinger of Basle wrote in his "New Compleat Book of Herbs" in 1696: "Ofte one findes long black little grains. In some several places they are known as death's-heads and are misfashionings like the blight. Held under the tongue, they stanch bleeding."

The enormous toxicity of the ergot drug precluded its widespread use in medicine. The obvious step was to extract the active substances in order to make more exact dosage possible. Christian Tanret, a pharmacist of Troyes, was the first to isolate and crystallize an alkaloid preparation (ergotinine) in 1875. During the succeeding decades further constituent substances were isolated at various places.
These extracts having been made available, it was now possible to undertake systematic study of their pharmacological action. They were found to have a stimulant effect on the smooth muscles. This is seen in uterine contractions, for example, where the blood vessels which pass through the uterine wall are mechanically occluded.
The early extracts, however, did not capture a place in medicine, for their side-effects were too dangerous. To Sandoz, which performed first-class research in the chemical and medical fields, goes the credit for making ergot the starting material for valuable medicines; in 1918 its research workers succeeded in isolating ergotamine intact.
Known by the trade-name of *Gynergen,* the tartaric acid salt is used to stop bleeding in obstetrics. Its hypotensive action and its vasodilator effect on the brain make it possible to combat certain forms of hypertension and migraine.

Ergotamine heralded a period of successful research in the field of ergot preparations. Further constituent substances were isolated and, by chemical modification, new biological compounds showing pharmacological activity produced.

Protocol recording the isolation of ergotamine, the hemostatic active alkaloid of ergot. Page from the laboratory journal of Arthur Stoll, the Sandoz chemist, dated 1918. Works Archive of Sandoz Ltd.

Max Hartmann, the CIBA chemist, created the first synthetic cardiovascular drug. By the chemical modification of nicotine, he arrived in 1918 at the circulatory and respiratory stimulant *Coramine,* technical designation pyridine-β-carboxylic acid diethylamide.

Coramine

In 1924 Coramine began to be used for the treatment of circulatory disorders. Since that time it has become an indispensable remedy in the treatment of collapse, anesthetic emergencies, poisoning, the resuscitation of victims of drowning, and so on.

Coramine, developed by Max Hartmann, has long maintained its reputation as a highly effective and safe circulatory, respiratory, and central nervous stimulant.
Opposite: Extracts from minutes taken by Hartmann which throw light on the obstacles that the introduction of Coramine had to contend with.
Below: Soot spirogram showing respiratory stimulation under anesthesia.

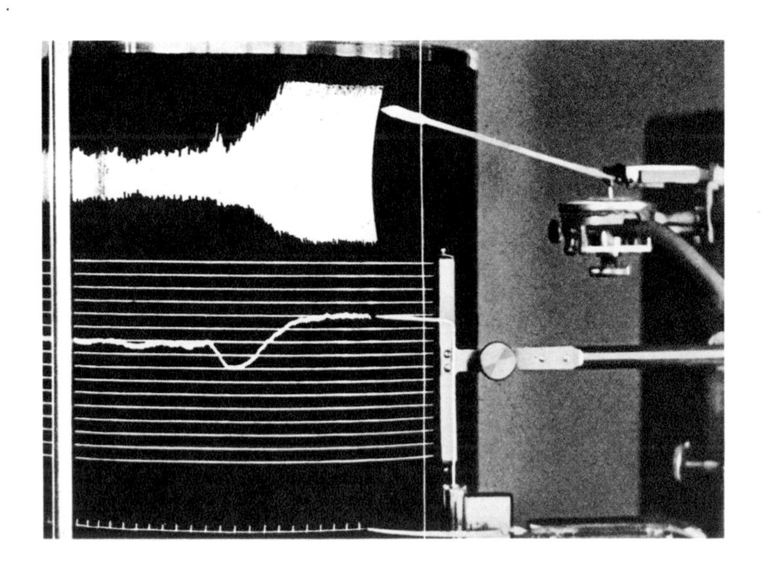

B.C.

Besprechung über Präparate 497 F & 562.

Dr Gams verliest ~~ein~~ Schreiben von Prof. Faust vom 28 VI. 25. das Dr Engi mit ~~dem~~ z ~~Bericht~~ Mitteilung über die definitive Stellungnahme beantwortet wünscht.

Dr Gams teilt auf Anfrage Dr Beck mit dass die heutige Sitzung ~~dem Zweck~~ als Vorbesprechung zu dienen soll, zur Äusserung der Ansicht der einzelnen Herren. Ein Kollektivantrag des Komitees sei nicht beabsichtigt.

Dr Beck kommt auf den Fragebogen zurück. Eine so detaillierte Beantwortung sei den Prüfern nicht möglich gewesen, da die (wie sie in dem Fragebogen gewünscht wurde) Prüfer unmöglich so ~~specialisiert~~ eingehend untersuchen konnten, sondern nur auf allgemeinere Eindrücke abstellen mussten. Auch bei der Zusammenstellung der Herren Beck & Uhlmann war es nicht möglich bis ins kleinste Detail specificierte Angaben auszugeben. Speciell schwierig zu bewerten war der Einfluss auf das Zentralnervensystem. Der zentrale Einfluss wird z. Teil an Blutdruck & Atmung gemessen & ~~Sekretion~~ d unter diesen Stichwörtern wieder. Eine Komplikation (psychomotorischer Effekt) ~~erscheint~~ z. T. den Prüfern als unerwünscht, im Gegenteil wäre ~~eher~~ nach Ansicht dieser Herren eher eine sedative Komponente vorzuziehen. Dr B. ~~stellt den Antrag~~ konstatiert dass ihm die Informationsreise Gelegenheit gegeben habe, das Problem in einer Weise kennen zu lernen die nicht nur für den gegenwärtigen Entscheid sondern auch für die spätere Bearbeitung. Er stellt den Antrag, es möchte sich zuerst Herr Mundorff zur Sache äussern.

Physiological chemistry pointed the way to other medicines acting on the cardiovascular system. It was recognized that two substances produced by the organism itself act to regulate circulation: adrenaline constricts the blood vessels and increases the blood pressure; histamine, among its other effects, dilates the capillaries and lowers the blood pressure.

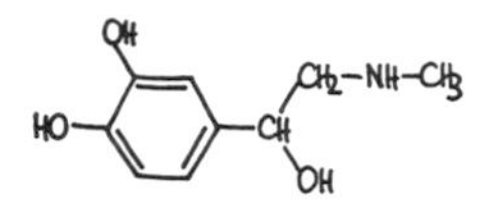

Adrenaline

Histamine

In 1939, by combining the chemical structural elements of adrenaline and histamine, CIBA research teams synthesized the vasodilator *Priscol,* and the vasoconstrictor *Privine*. This was followed in 1948 by *Regitine,* which helps to promote peripheral circulation.

Priscol

Privine

Regitine

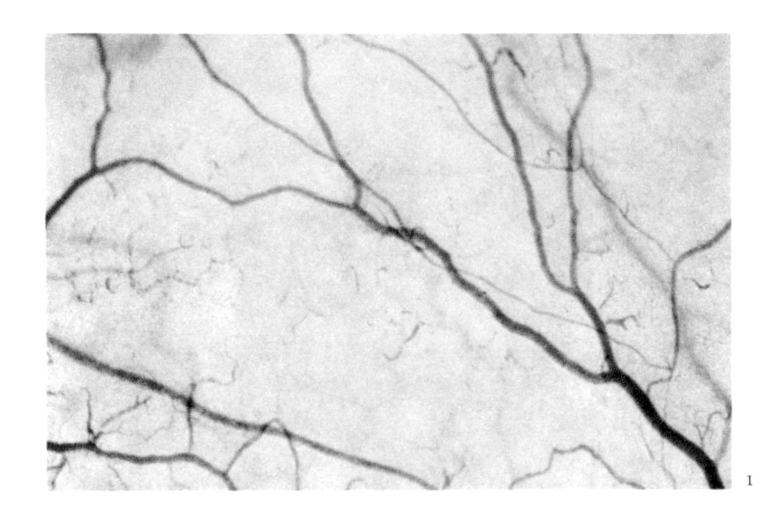

1

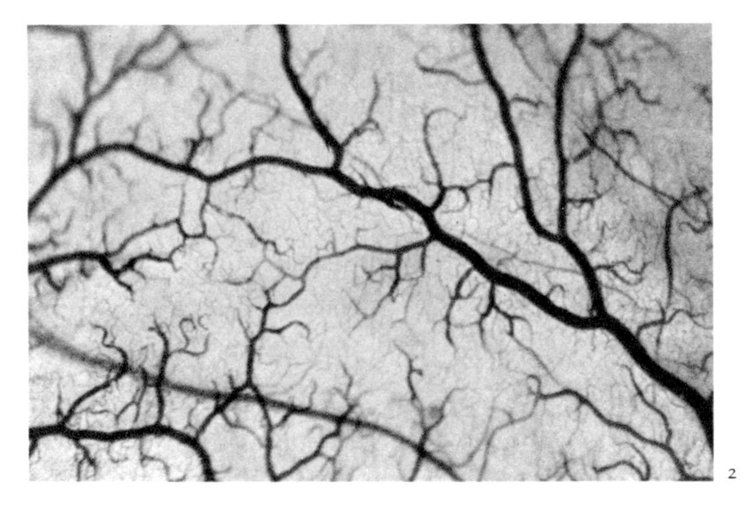

2

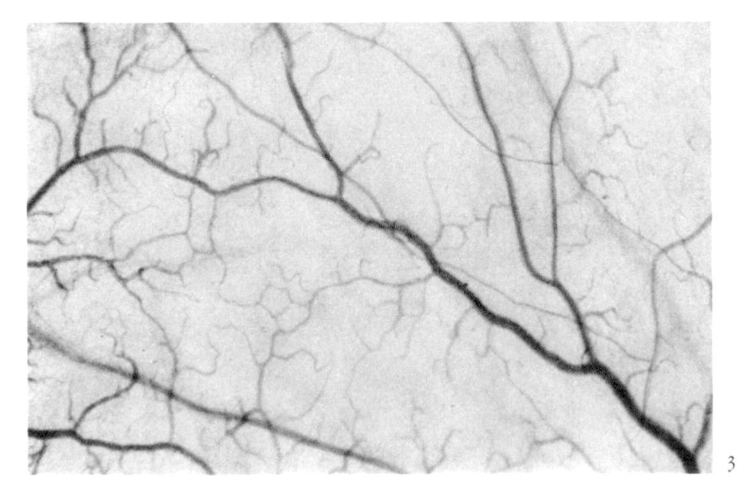

3

With vasoactive substances the blood vessels can be widened or narrowed. Reflected light photos of the conjunctiva of the rabbit's eye taken before the experiment (1), after administration of *Priscol* drops (2), and after termination of the effect with *Privine* (3). Magnification x 250.

By chemical modification, as stated, Coramine had been derived from nicotine. Nicotine was also the starting point for another group of cardiovascular drugs: the ganglionic blocking agents. The study of the toxic effect of nicotine and, later, that of muscarine, a component of poisonous mushrooms, enabled an explanation of how stimuli are transmitted in the organism. The impulse path is located in the nervous system, with the ganglia representing important relay points. The material basis of their function are carrier substances such as acetylcholine and noradrenaline.

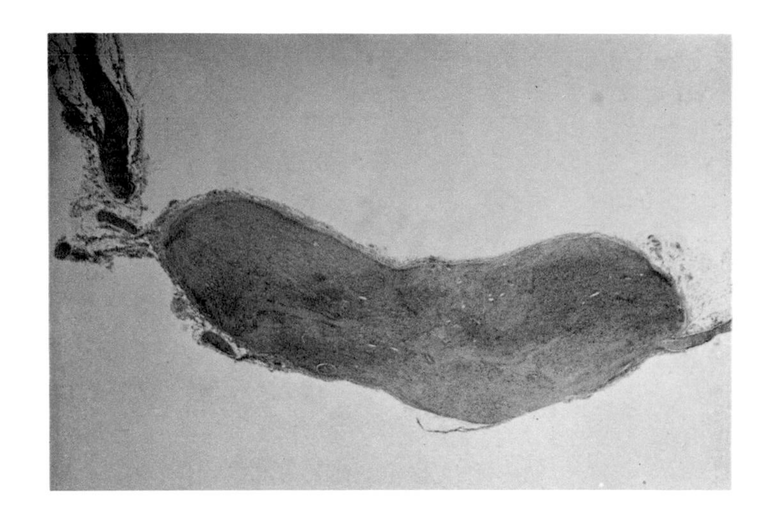

Ganglia are masses of nerve cells which act as relay centres in the neural pathways. Stained section of a human cervical ganglion, magnification x 6. From the Pathological Institute of the University of Zurich.

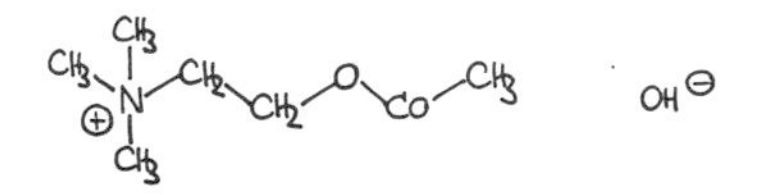

Acetylcholine

Noradrenaline

With this well-ordered picture of how impulses are relayed, pharmaceutical research had the background it needed to consider in what way the system of impulse transmission might be influenced by means of medicaments. When the carrier substances are modified, substances are formed which cancel out the effect of the carrier in the relay points; such antagonists intercept impulse transmission. The neural relay points of the sympathetic nervous system possess a blood pressure regulating function, exercised by influencing the calibre of the vessels. From 1946 to 1948 Anglo-American research groups discovered the ganglionic blocking – and thus at the same time the blood pressure lowering-effect of tetra-ethyl ammonium bromide and of hexamethylene-bis-trimethyl ammonium bromide.

Within a short time this discovery was converted to industrial use. In 1951 CIBA introduced *Pendiomide,* which regulates circulation and is an antispasmodic, and in 1956 *Ecolid,* a ganglionic blocker which lowers blood pressure, into medical practice.

Pendiomide (CIBA Basle)

Ecolid (CIBA Summit)

At almost the same time as the ganglionic blockers were being explored, new territory was discovered by Basle researchers in the area of antihypertensive agents. In hydrazine derivatives of the phthalazines, CIBA chemists found compounds distinguished by their gradual and protracted hypotensive action, and with surprisingly little toxicity. In 1952 *Apresoline* was introduced and a year thereafter, *Nepresol.*

Apresoline

Nepresol

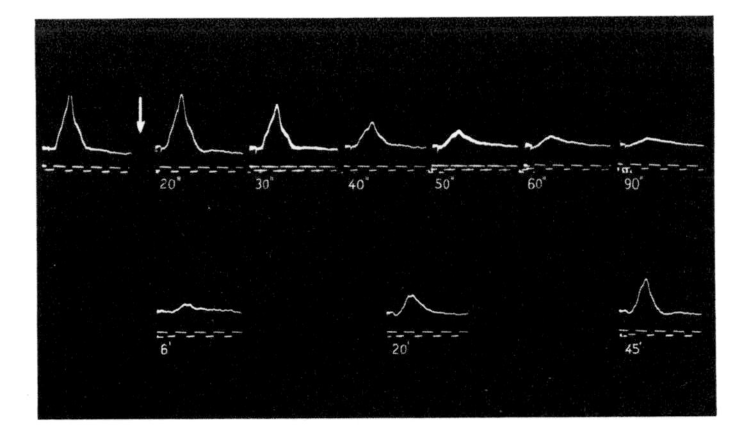

These drugs occupy a special position among the antihypertensive agents, promoting as they do the blood flow through the kidneys. Recent opinion views these pharmaceuticals as antagonists of enzyme systems which raise the blood pressure and have a heavy metallic content. By intercepting and removing the heavy metals as complexes, they inactivate the enzyme.
We have seen how the modern treatment of circulatory disorders began with the introduction of extracts of the digitalis drug long known in folk medicine. Seventy years later traditional medical lore was again to become a source of rationally utilized knowledge. In 1952 CIBA scientists reported the isolation of reserpine, the hypotensive alkaloid crystallized from the root of *Rauwolfia serpentina* Benth. The following year reserpine was placed in the hands of the medical profession under the trade name of *Serpasil.*

Serpasil

Today, Serpasil is used not only as a remedy for lowering blood pressure, but also as a tranquilizing agent in psychotherapy.

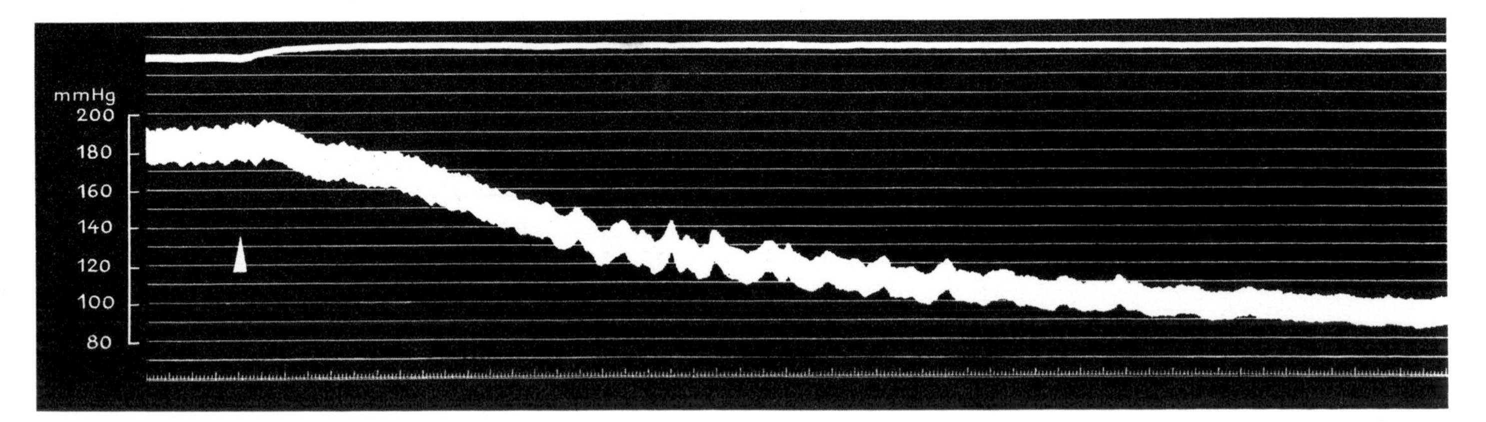

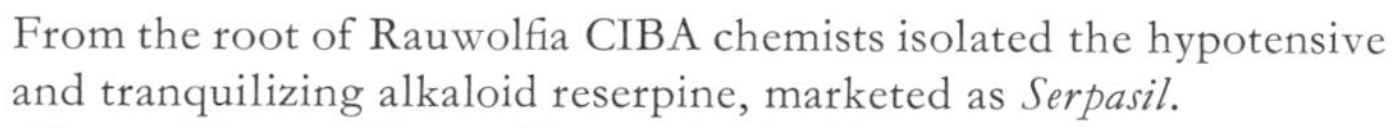

From the root of Rauwolfia CIBA chemists isolated the hypotensive and tranquilizing alkaloid reserpine, marketed as *Serpasil.*
Above: Pieces of Rauwolfia vomitoria Afz. root.
Above right: Reserpine crystals in polarized light, magnification x 100.
Right: Methodical data on the extraction, from the laboratory journal of Johannes M. Mueller.

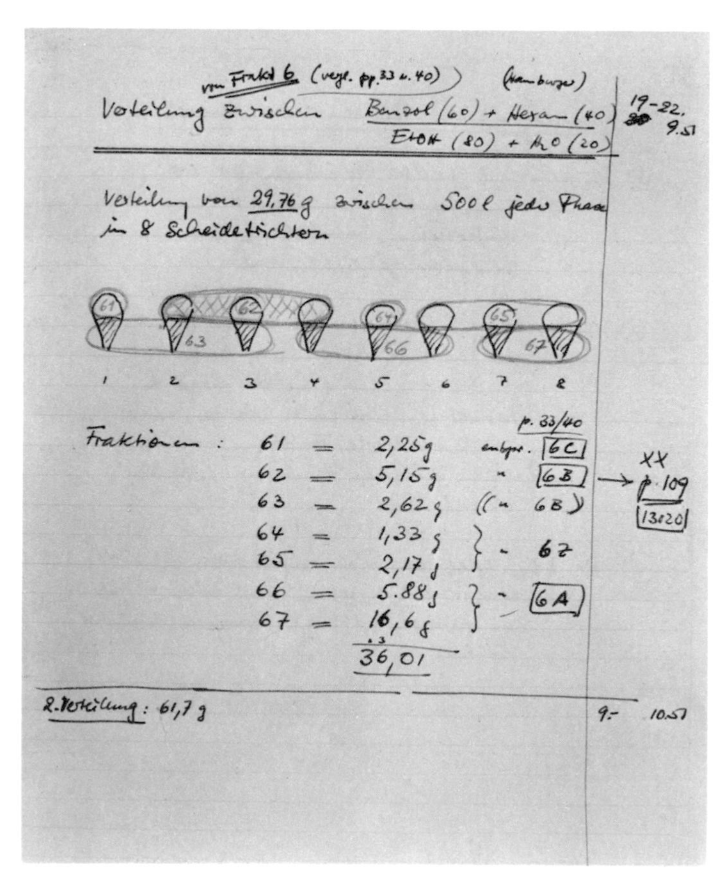

Above left opposite: Ganglionic blockers interrupt the transmission of impulses at the relay points of the sympathetic nervous system. In the cat, *Pendiomide* (arrow) reduces the nervous potentials characteristic of intact neural transmission.
Opposite: After injection of *Apresoline* (arrow), high blood pressure is gradually reduced, with lasting effect. Blood pressure curve of an anesthetized cat.

Diseases Diagnosed as Pathological Deficiency: Vitamins and Hormones. Scurvy was at one time a much-feared disease, one which wrought its worst ravages among sailors and prisoners. Its external symptoms were hemorrhages of the gums and of the muscles. Increased susceptibility to infectious diseases was the peculiar danger to which scurvy exposed its victim.

The means for curing scurvy were known even at an early date: green vegetables and, above all, citrus fruit. Theodore Zwinger, for instance, writing in 1696, noted that "a crew of sailors, as soon as they touch upon a shore at a place where limens and oranges do grow, can, by eating of these fruits, drive away the scurvy forthwith and return fresh and healthy to their work".

A satisfactory explanation of this disease, however, came only later. Studies on the physiology of nutrition carried out at the beginning of the 20th century showed scurvy to be a "deficiency disease". A diet consisting of carbohydrates, protein, fat and mineral salts does not suffice to cover the body's needs. Small quantities of additional "accessory" nutritive substances are vitally necessary; they play a regulative role in the bodily economy. If these are lacking, deficiency diseases make their appearance, as the American physiologist Casimir Funk reported in 1912, the chief ones being scurvy, beriberi, and pellagra. He termed these vital substances "vitamins", in the opinion – subsequently seen to have been ill-founded – that chemically speaking they were all amines.

Funk's work inaugurated a period of intensive research in this newly disclosed field. Between 1913 and 1948 no less than a dozen vitamins were isolated, elucidated in their chemical structure, and synthetically reproduced.

Basle's share in the research work on vitamins was an essential one. In 1933 Tadeus Reichstein – then an assistant at the Swiss Federal Institute of Technology – synthesized the anti-scurvy vitamin C (L-ascorbic acid) from grape sugar, or dextrose. Two years later,

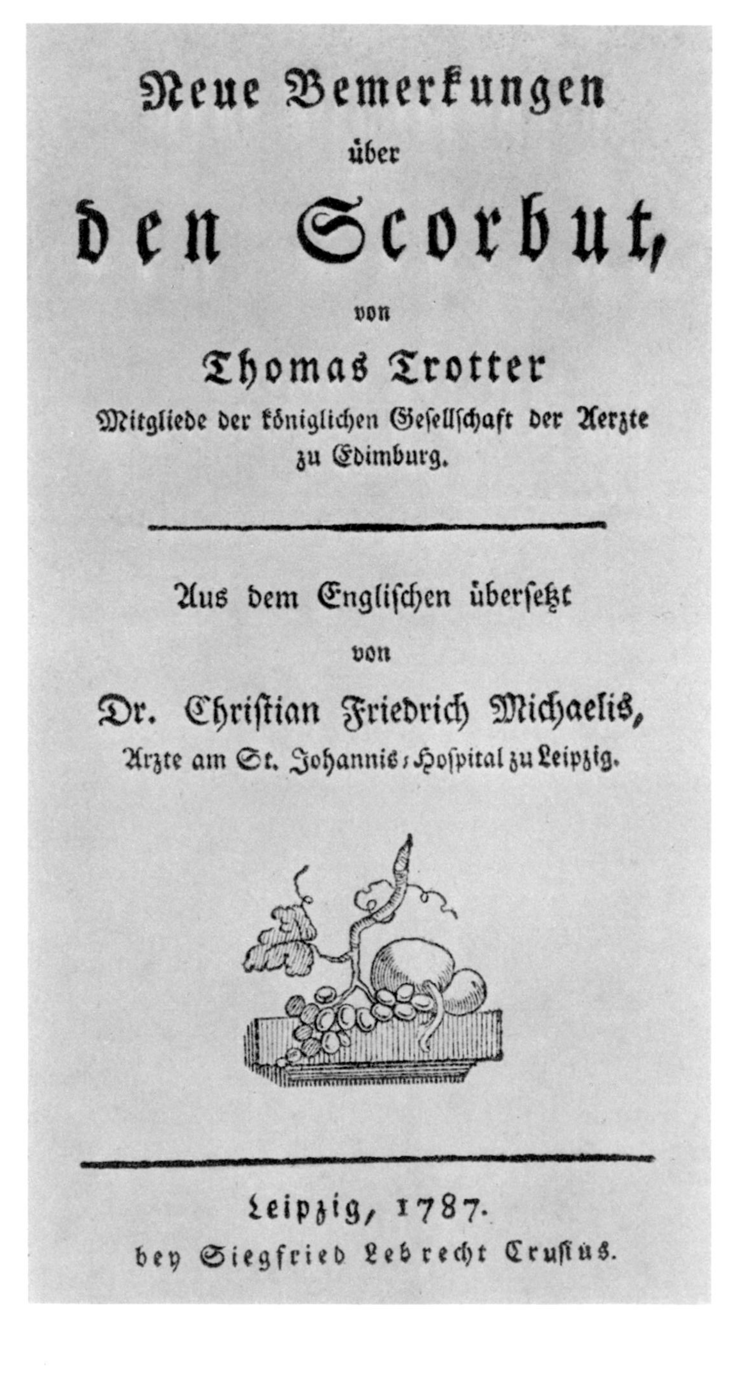
Neue Bemerkungen
über
den Scorbut,
von
Thomas Trotter
Mitgliede der königlichen Gesellschaft der Aerzte
zu Edimburg.

Aus dem Englischen übersetzt
von
Dr. Christian Friedrich Michaelis,
Arzte am St. Johannis-Hospital zu Leipzig.

Leipzig, 1787.
bey Siegfried Lebrecht Crusius.

One of the most important publications on scurvy was written by Thomas Trotter of the Royal Society of Physicians in Edinburgh. Although Trotter still attributed the disease to salty sea air, he did spot the possibility of curing it with fresh vegetables.

after working out a technically practicable process, Hoffmann-La Roche began manufacturing this nutrient.
In 1945 the same firm discovered a technically viable synthesis of vitamin A, which protects the epithelial tissue, on the basis of which industrial production was begun shortly afterwards.

Vitamin C

Vitamin A

Here again we note the same movement as in color and plastics chemistry: the chemical factory takes the place of the natural "manufacturing installation". Vitamins, which had previously been built up only by plants and animals, were now produced synthetically by chemists.

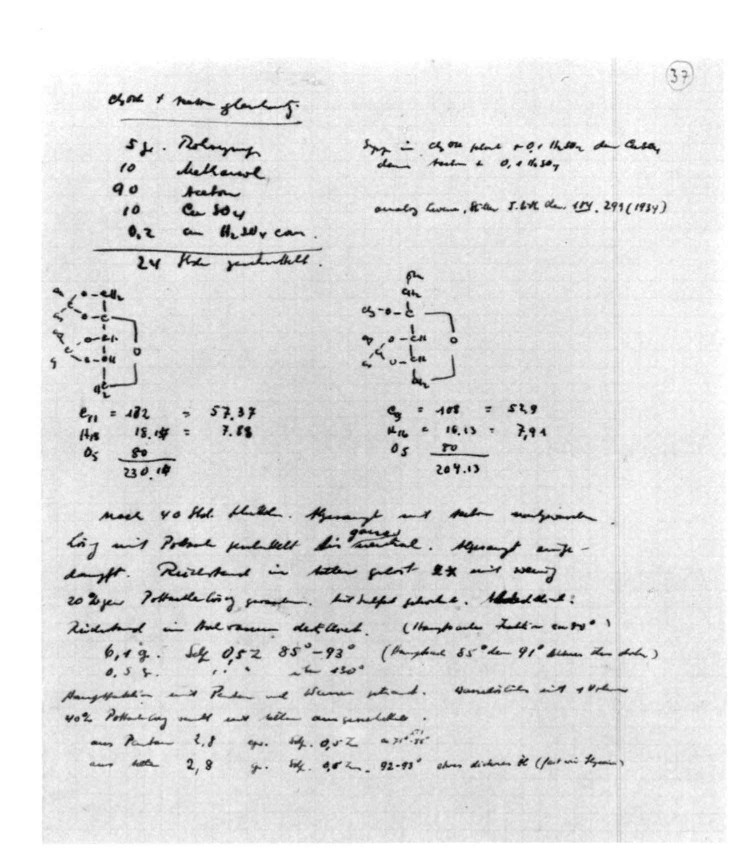

Above: Laboratory notes dated 1934 on work concerning sugars by Tadeus Reichstein, who synthesized Vitamin C from grape sugar, or dextrose.
Right: The Hoffmann-La Roche firm accomplished the industrial synthesis of Vitamin A. This microphoto was the first to be taken of the crystals at the Roche works.

In an earlier chapter the magic notions have been described which long ago led men to consume animal organs such as the brain, heart, or testicles. Qualities assumed to reside in these organs were supposed to be conveyed to him who ate them. These ancient notions gave way to more tenable ideas in the last century. In 1889 the Parisian physician Brown-Séquard extracted substances from animal testes with which he was able to bring about a rejuvenating effect in himself. Magic ritual was again superseded by modern therapy, using active substances from glandular secretions.

To these substances the English physiologist E. H. Starling gave the name "hormones" in 1905, a word which he took from the Greek and which is equivalent to "excite" or "arouse". Hormones, it was recognized, are emitted from internal glands into the blood and lymph and serve to regulate important life processes. Objective biological testing techniques had to be developed in order to make real research work on hormones possible. The cock's comb test was worked out around 1920. Male sex hormones are injected into castrated cocks, and the effect of the hormone is measured by the growth of the comb.

In 1932 Adolf Windaus, a professor in Goettingen, elucidated the structure of cholesterol, which is the basic steroid type. Nineteen years later Prof. Robert B. Woodward of Harvard University built up this substance by a total synthesis.

HO

Cholesterol

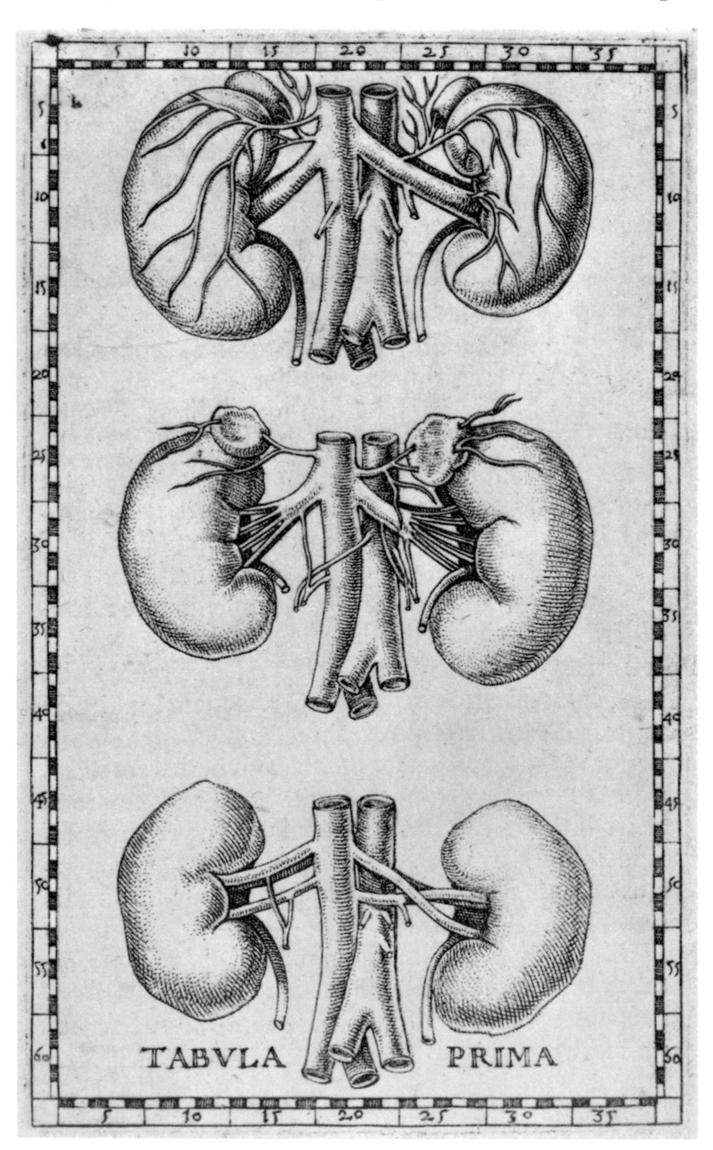

Earliest depiction of the adrenal glands, a copper engraving after a drawing by Bartolomeo Eustachi, from the first edition of his "Opuscula Anatomica"; Venice, 1563/64. This endocrine organ, situated on the top of each kidney, secretes the vital hormones adrenalin (medulla) and cortisone (cortex).

In the two decades which passed between the constitutional elucidation and the total synthesis of cholesterol, an enormous amount of work had to be accomplished in the university and industrial laboratories of Europe and America. Elaborate chemical and biological methods were developed in order to isolate the steroid hormones of the reproductive glands and the adrenal cortex, found in minute amounts only in the body, and to elucidate their structure, and finally to synthesize them.

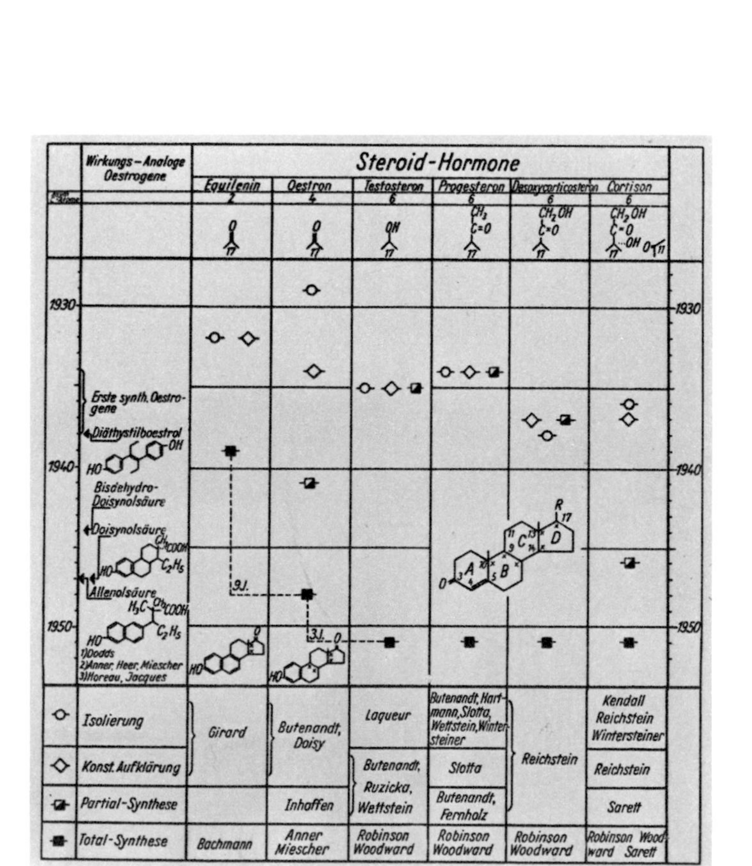

		Equilenin	Oestron	Testosteron	Progesteron	Desoxycorticosteron	Cortison
○	Isolierung	Girard	Butenandt, Doisy	Laqueur	Butenandt, Hartmann, Slotta, Wettstein, Wintersteiner	Reichstein	Kendall Reichstein Wintersteiner
◇	Konst. Aufklärung			Butenandt, Ruzicka, Wettstein	Slotta		Reichstein
◪	Partial-Synthese		Inhoffen		Butenandt, Fernholz		Sarett
■	Total-Synthese	Bachmann	Anner Miescher	Robinson Woodward	Robinson Woodward	Robinson Woodward	Robinson Woodward Sarett

Above: Schematic presentation of the gonads, their relationship to the pituitary, and the influence of hormonal secretions on the genitalia. From Vol. II of "The CIBA Collection of Medical Illustrations", drawings by Frank H. Netter; Summit, N. J., 1954.
Left: Chronological table of research on steroid hormones, from "Drugs in the Advance of Science" in *Angewandte Chemie 65*, 273 by Karl Miescher. The most important achievement since this publication appeared in 1953 has been the isolation and synthesis of aldosterone.

Verseifung von Androstenon-(3)-ol-acetat
zum Androstenon-(3)-ol (Testosteron ?)

80 mg der Spitzenfraktion vom Acetat sowie deren Mutterlauge + 100 mg Acetat-Mutterlaugen-Produkt vom Fp. 128-34° unk.
zusammen also ca 180 mg Acetat wurden mit 10 cc 1%iger methylalkoholischer Kalilauge (= 80 mg KOH) 1 Stde am Wasserbad unter Rückfluss zum Sieden erhitzt. [Corpus luteum-Hormon-Krystallisate werden beim Erwärmen mit 2%iger Alkalilauge auf 70° nicht zerstört; s. Butenandt etc. Hoppe-Seyler 227, 91 (34)]. Das Verseifungsgemisch goss man in 100 cc Wasser, ätherte erschöpfend aus^x, wusch die Ätherlösung mit gesätt. wässr. Natr.bic.-Lsg, ganz verdünnter HCl + Wasser bis zur Neutralität + dampfte sie im Vac. ein. Es resultierte ein völlig fester, in Hexan schwerlöslicher (w. Diol) Rückstand. Man trennte ihn aus: I. mit 20 cc Hexan. Das aus dieser Lösung zuerst Auskrystallisierende gab man zu II. Der Rest wurde nochmals umkrystallisiert + dabei wieder ein kleiner Anteil schwerlöslichen Teil verworfen.

II. mit 20 cc Hexan. Dazu die schwerlöslichen Anteile von I.

x nach Ansäuern, um Schichtentrennung zu erreichen

III. Fraktion. Der nicht in den ersten 40 cc Hexan lösliche Anteil löste sich sehr leicht in Methanol. Man gab ca 50% Wasser zu.

Die obigen 3 Fraktionen zeigten (ohne Hochvakuumtrocknung) folgende Schmelzpunkte:

I. nach kurzem Sintern bei 149°:
150-152° unk.; 153-155° korr.
II 151-152,5° unk.; 154-155,5° korr.
III 151-152,5° unk.; 154-155,5° korr.

Sie sind also von ganz bemerkenswerter Konstanz. Eine Trennung mit dem über 25° höher schmelzenden Diol erscheint ausgeschlossen, auch weil obige Substanz gar keine Tendenz zum Zurückhalten von Lösungsmitteln zeigt.

Alle 3 Fraktionen wurden also, da sie offensichtlich identisch sind, zusammen nochmals aus Hexan umkrystallisiert. Ausb. 106 mg. Trocknung 15 Stdn an Hochvacuum bei 95°.
Fp. 151-152,5° unk.; 154-155,5° korr. also konstant!!

Analyse: W54
Dr. Gysel: 3,592 mg Subst. gaben 10,43 mg CO_2 + 3,15 mg H_2O
Gef. C 79,19% H 9,81%
$C_{19}H_{28}O_2$ (288,22) Ber C 79,11% H 9,79%

The first partial synthesis of testosterone, the male sex hormone, was carried out at CIBA. From the laboratory journal of Albert Wettstein, 1935.

In this world-wide effort concentrated on hormones, CIBA scientists, working together with a research team of the Federal Institute of Technology, succeeded in 1934 in isolating the hormone of the corpus luteum, progesterone. In 1935 came the elucidation of the constitutional formula and the partial synthesis of the male sex hormone, testosterone, and in 1948 the total synthesis of estrone, the metabolic product of the ovarian hormone, estradiol.

Pathological deficiencies are remedied in men with testosterone, and in women with estradiol. With progesterone, impending miscarriage can be prevented.

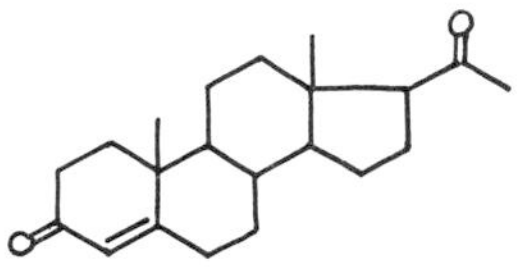

Progesterone

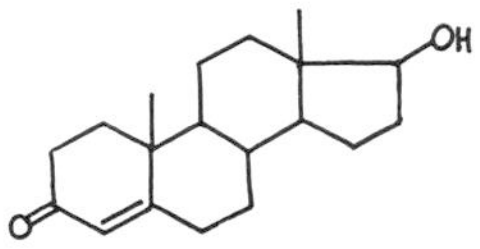

Testosterone

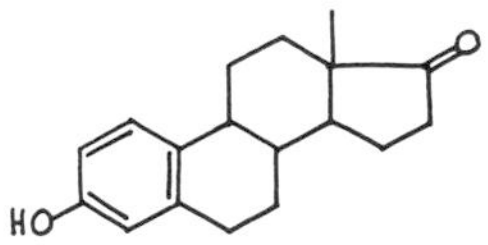

Estrone

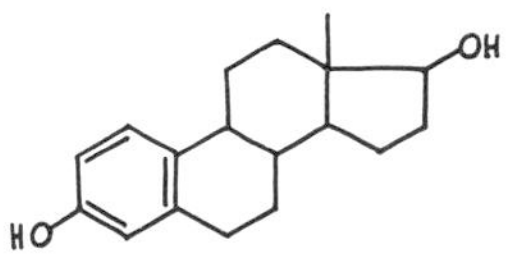

Estradiol

On the basis of these projects CIBA created a range of therapeutically valuable preparations. In 1936 a market form of testosterone, *Perandren,* was introduced. Between 1938 and 1946 it was followed, first, by the progesterone preparation *Lutocyclin,* and then by the estrogen preparations *Ovocyclin, Eticyclin,* and *Fenocyclin.*

Simultaneously with work on the sex hormones, CIBA research groups, in close collaboration with Professor Reichstein, were devoting their attention to the hormones of the adrenal cortex. Reichstein's work resulted in the years 1936/37 in the isolation and constitutional elucidation of cortisone. CIBA subsequently made an important contribution to its technical synthesis by developing an ingenious technique based on the decomposition of bile acid. In 1937 and 1938 there ensued research which led to the first technical preparation of desoxycorticosterone.

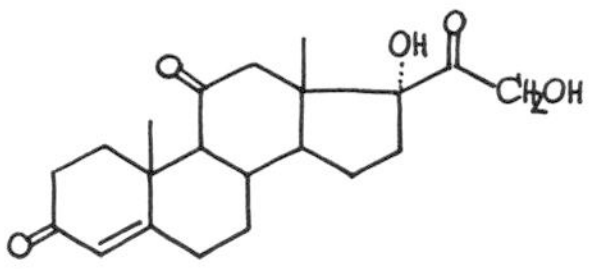

Cortisone

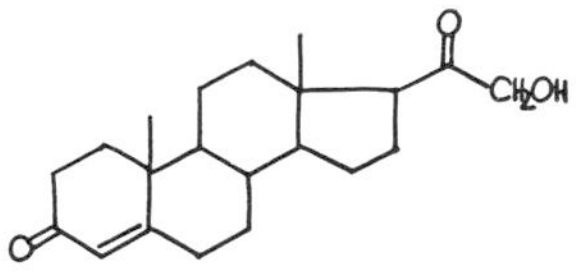

Desoxycorticosterone

The adrenocortical hormones influence protein and carbohydrate metabolism and regulate the balance or salts and water in the body. Their anti-inflammatory properties are utilized, among other indications, in the treatment of arthritis.

During these last years, too, CIBA has scored gratifying success in the hormone field. 1956 brought the total synthesis of the highly active adrenocortical hormone aldosterone, three years after its isolation from the adrenal glands of cattle had been achieved in collaboration with research groups of the University of Basle and the Middlesex Hospital in London. In 1958 there followed the isolation, constitutional elucidation and synthesis of a new and potent principle which regulates the physiologically important excretion of salt (sodium chloride) from the organism.

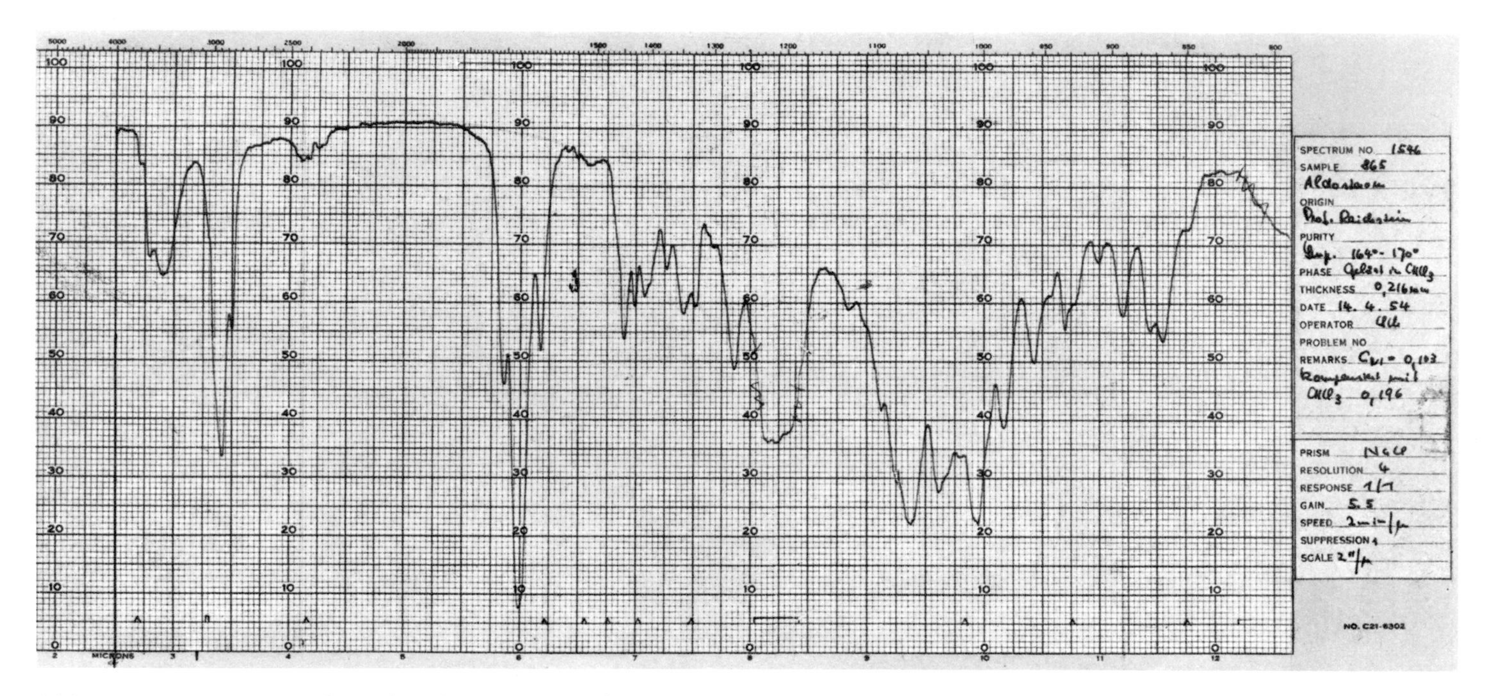

Aldosterone, the hormone of the adrenal cortex, was isolated by Tadeus Reichstein and synthesized at CIBA. The infrared curves of the product isolated (above) and of the product synthesized (below) show the chemical correspondence between the two compounds. From the laboratory journal of Julius Schmidlin.

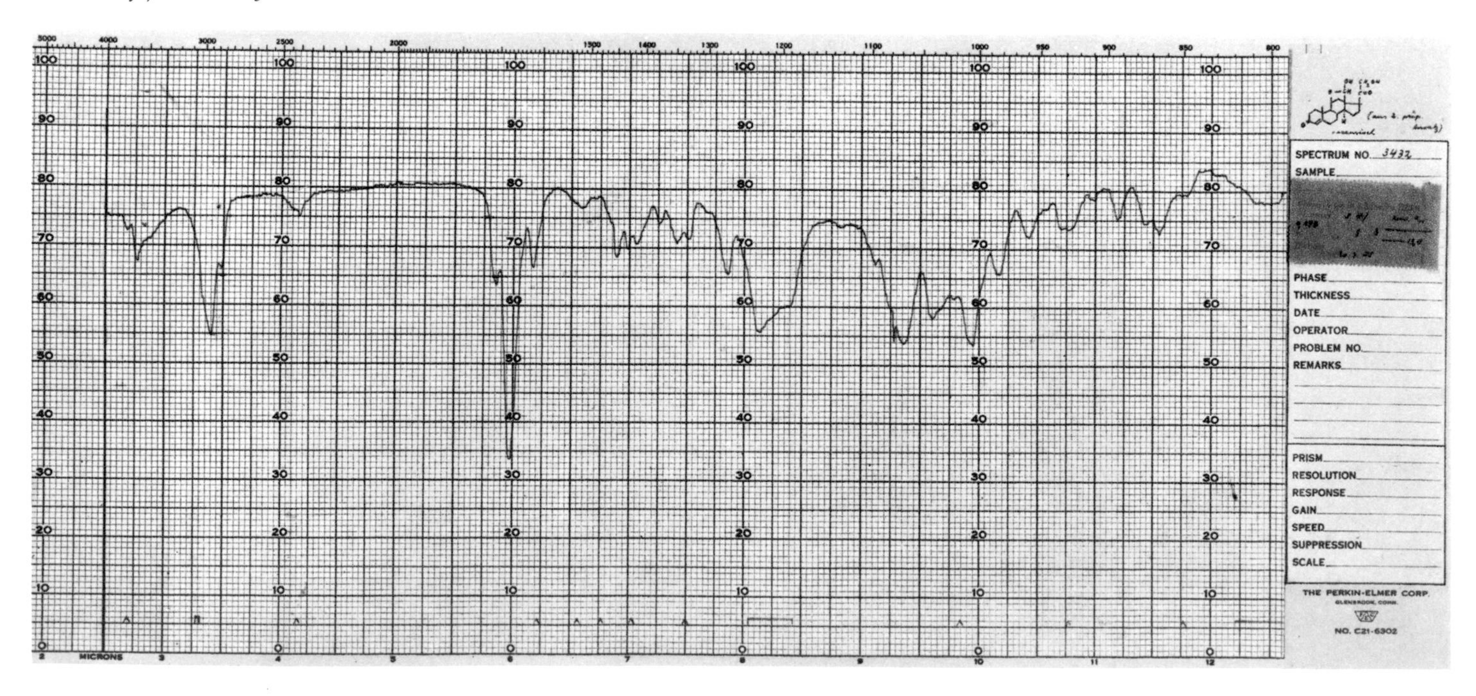

The Foundations of Pharmaceutical Research: Pharmacology and Physiology. Two main pillars support the edifice of pharmaceutical research: a knowledge of drugs and how they act (pharmacognosy), and a knowledge of the functions and metabolism of the parts of the body (physiology).
From drugs whose effects are known, the chemist isolates the active substances and inquires into how they are built up. By ringing chemical changes on them, he seeks to enhance the therapeutic effects desired and to reduce undesirable side effects.
Physiology gives a coherent picture of life processes by tracing biological functions back to chemical reactions. Once these mechanisms are understood, it is possible to influence them through medicinal intervention. Physiology also governs the working methods of the pharmacologist who tests the preparations that come from the chemical laboratories – isolated natural substances and synthetic products – for their effectiveness and suitability as medicaments.

Three examples may serve to illuminate once again the way that leads from the disciplines of pharmacology and physiology to a remedy against disease. Antispasmodics are an outgrowth of pharmacology, while physiology pointed the way to the antiallergics and to psychoactive pharmaceuticals.

When the botanist Carl Linnaeus gave the scientific name "Atropa belladonna" to the deadly nightshade, he was alluding to two effects of the juice from its fruit, leaves, and roots, namely, its toxicity and the cosmetic effect obtained by dilation of the pupils. In the world of Graeco-Roman mythology, Atropos was the goddess of Fate who severs the thread of life. The plant bears "the name Donna bella forasmuch as the ladie of Italie doth ofte lave her face with the juyce prest from it", according to the 17th century Basle scholar Theodore Zwinger, of whom we have heard before.
In 1833 atropine, the substance which causes the pupils to dilate, was isolated. Later it was recognized that

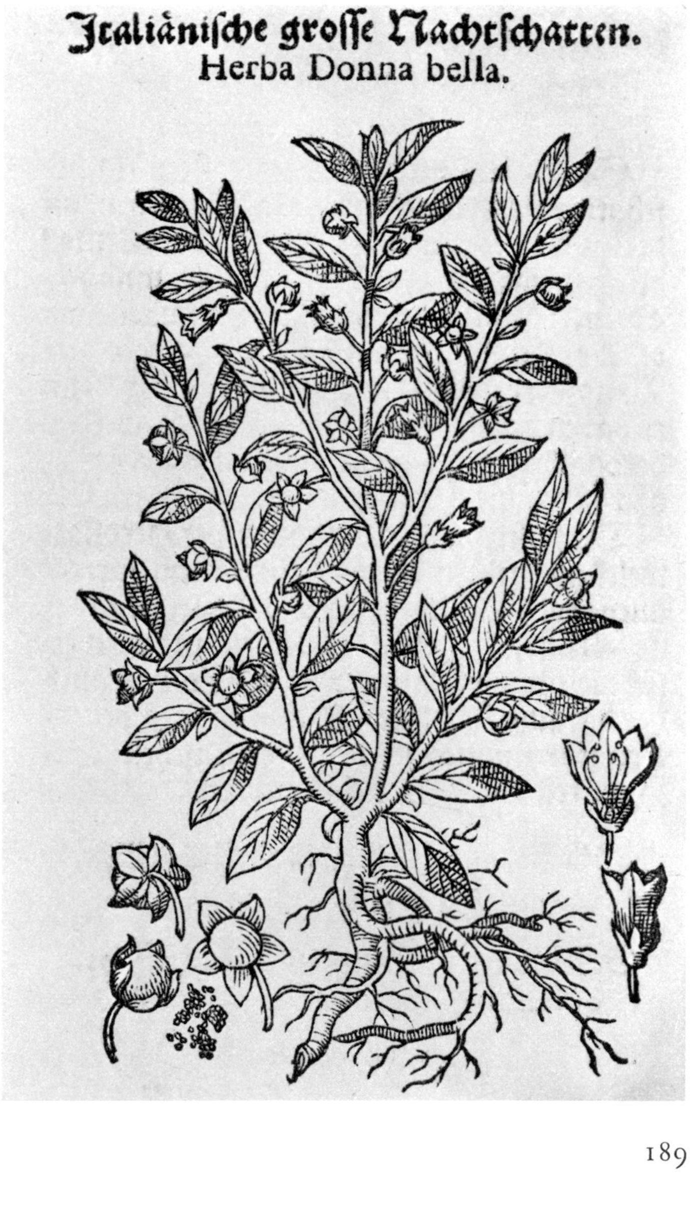

Italiänische grosse Nachtschatten.
Herba Donna bella.

Atropine, an antispasmodic substance which dilates the pupils, was isolated from the leaves and roots of the deadly nightshade. Drugs prepared from this plant were used at an early date in folk medicine. Woodcut from Theodore Zwinger's Book of Herbs; Basle, 1696.

atropine does not act on the muscles which control the pupils alone, but also has a relaxing or antispasmodic effect, above all via the parasympathetic nerves, on all of the involuntary muscular organs.

Any doubts about its structure were cleared up through the synthesis in 1901 by Richard Willstaetter, an assistant of Baeyer in Munich and later professor at the Swiss Federal Institute of Technology in Zurich.

Taking atropine as a basis, research groups in the Basle chemical industry worked with great success in the field of antispasmodics. Their goal was medicaments which, surpassing atropine, would be capable of relieving as many kinds of spasm as possible. In the train of these efforts *Syntropan* (Roche) in 1932, *Trasentin* (CIBA) in 1934, and *Antrenyl* (CIBA) in 1952 were added to the pharmaceutical armamentary.

Atropine

Trasentin

Antrenyl

Spasms of the smooth muscle cause severe pains in the gastro-intestinal tract. The anticholinergic *Antrenyl,* by selectively inhibiting gastric motility and secretion, resolves spasms of the stomach and intestine.
Left: Large movement range of the stomach before administration of Antrenyl.
Right: Reduction of stomach peristalsis after treatment with Antrenyl.
Radiokymogram of the stomach after H. Reinecke. *Klinische Wochenschrift 31,* 465 (1953).

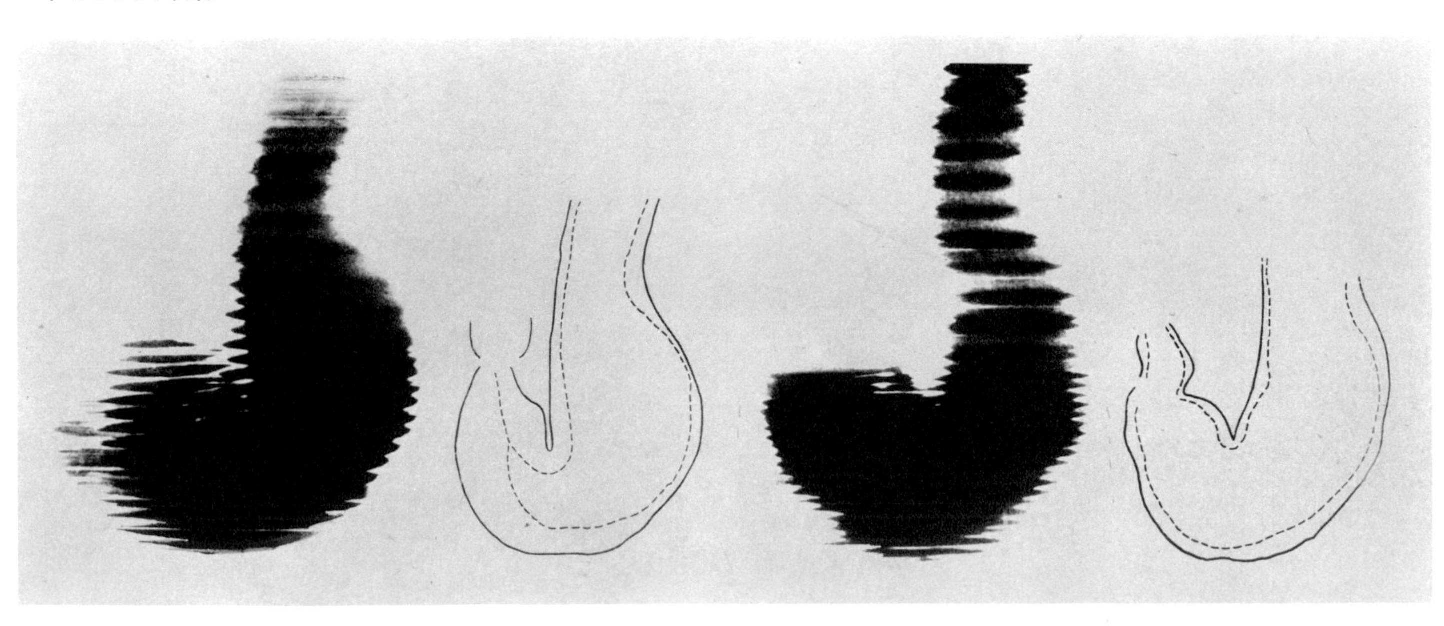

As a protective measure against harmful foreign substances which have penetrated into the body, the organism forms defensive substances, the so-called antibodies. These antibodies react with the foreign substances and help to eliminate them from the organism. But the reaction can, in certain cases, be accompanied by unpleasant side effects in the form of allergies: hay fever, hives, hypersensitivity to drugs. Medical research recognized that such side effects may often be attributed to the liberation of histamine.

Histamine

In 1937 Daniel Bovet, working at the Pasteur Institute, found that substances with an ethylenediamine grouping in the molecule cancel the effect of histamine and thus relieve the allergy.
This discovery was turned to industrial use when, in 1942, the Rhône Poulenc chemical factory created *Antergan,* the first antiallergic able to be employed in medicine. In 1946 CIBA Summit followed with *Pyribenzamine* and CIBA Basle with *Antistine.*

Pyribenzamine

Antistine

Psychoactive pharmaceuticals represent the newest group of drugs. They are used, as their name suggests, for the treatment of psychic disorders.
Descartes postulated that only the corporeal world is accessible to rational observation, but not the spiritual world. In penetrating the human psyche, experimental medicine made this postulate subject to revision. In

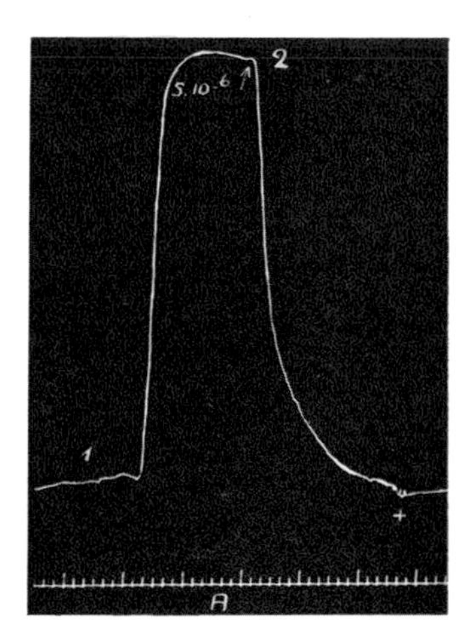

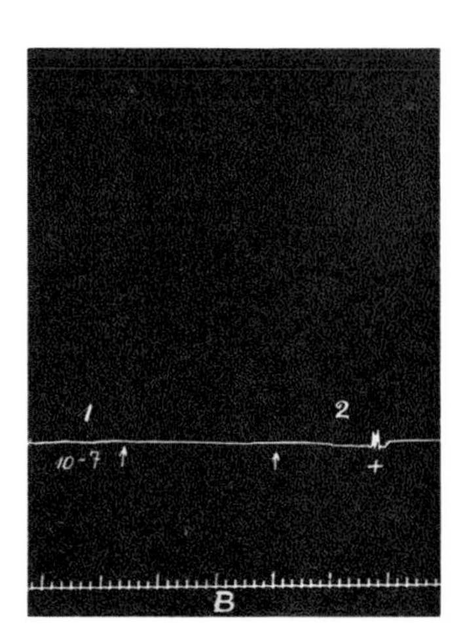

Sensitized smooth muscular organs react with an antibody (antigen) by contracting violently (A). The antiallergic *Antistine* forestalls this reaction (B). The Schultz-Dale test.

actual fact, however, the breakthrough is an apparent one only, for the "psyche" as science conceives of it does not coincide with our supra-rational idea of the "soul". Psychical processes are understood as the subtly exercised functions of the brain and as the consequences of chemical reactions. In this manner, mental disorders are placed upon the same level as other diseases and, like the latter, considered to be amenable to treatment with medicaments.
Physiological investigations commenced in the early 1950s show that impulse transmission in the junctions and receptors of the central nervous system is the function of endogenous carriers of stimuli, the neurohormones. Some researchers assume that psychosis and neurosis are due to a disturbance of the neurohormonal equilibrium. The presence of acetylcholine, serotonin, adrenaline, and noradrenaline has been ascertained in the brain substance; they may possibly be the carriers of stimuli.

Serotonin

Noradrenaline

The final effect of psychoactive pharmaceuticals, drugs which soothe or stimulate the central nervous system, may be attributed to a process which is frequently complex: for example, the biochemical and pharmacodynamic regulation of the neurohormone content or effect, or a change in the reactivity of central nervous substrates. Among its other effects, Serpasil lowers the noradrenaline content in the central nervous system and other organs, while *Largactil* (Rhône Poulenc) inhibits the action of this amine. Acting as "tranquilizers", both are prescribed for schizophrenic and hyperactive patients. The "energizers" *Ritalin* (CIBA) and *Marsilid* (Roche) have the opposite effect (but in a way which qualitatively can be clearly distinguished) and are used for patients suffering from depressive states.

Other realms of medicine are ripe for illumination by rational scientific knowledge. In research laboratories and institutes throughout the world, the virus and cancer problem is being tackled with new working hypotheses. The internal relation between virus and cancer has become an object of thorough examination. With investigations using new experimental methods on the origin of arteriosclerosis now in progress, the foundation for treatment of this chronic affliction is being laid. Close collaboration between higher centres of learning and industry marks the study being devoted to the physiology of ageing, which promises new possibilities of coping with geriatric troubles by pharmaceutical means.

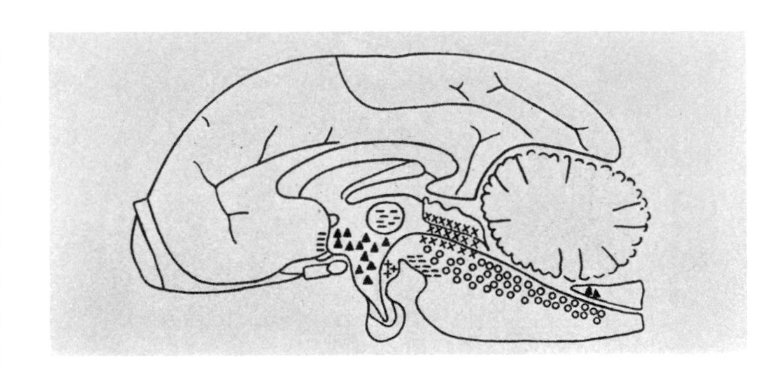

Neurohormones regulate the function of the brain. This is a diagram of a medial sagittal section of a dog's brain, showing the distribution of noradrenaline in the various regions.
▲ $= 1.0\mu g/g$; $+ = >0.4<1.0\mu g/g$; $o = >0.3<0.4\mu g/g$; $- = >0.2<0.3\mu g/g$. After Marthe Vogt, *Journal of Physiology 123*, 451 (1954).

Pages 193–195: Electron microscopy enables morphological investigation of viruses and tumors due to carcinogens. Information gathered from such experiments points more and more clearly to a close connection between the problem of virus and cancer research.
Opposite: Cancer cell from a spontaneous tumor of the mammary glands of a mouse. At right below is the cell nucleus; in the cytoplasm located above it numerous viruses are visible as inclusion bodies. Maturing forms of the same viruses can be seen in the intercellular space at top left; quite probably they correspond to the milk factor of Bittner. Magnification x 40 800.
Below: Psychoactive drugs serve to soothe or to stimulate the central nervous system. Central psychomotor stimulation, produced for experimental purposes by caffeine (1, 2), is modified by *Serpasil* (3, 4). These charts record the spontaneous activity of mice in the jiggle cage. 1–3: direct kinesimetric record. 2–4: totalizer's record (each mark corresponds to 100 movements).

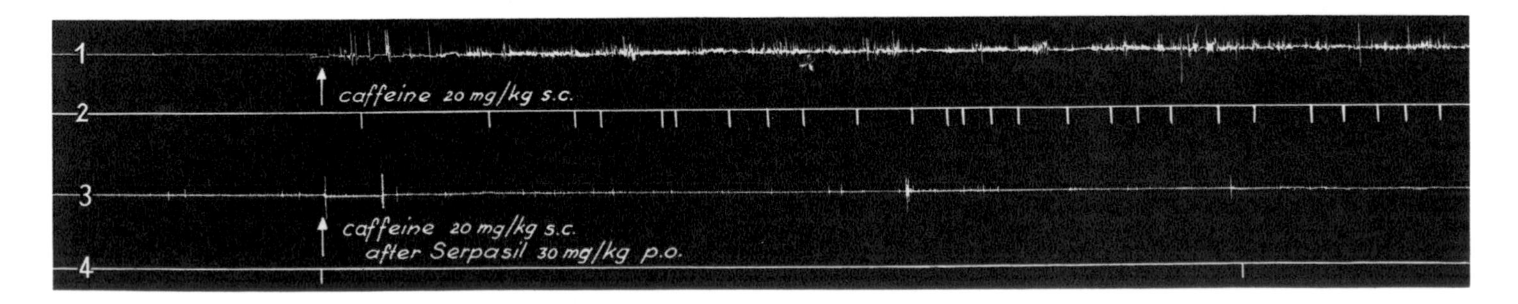

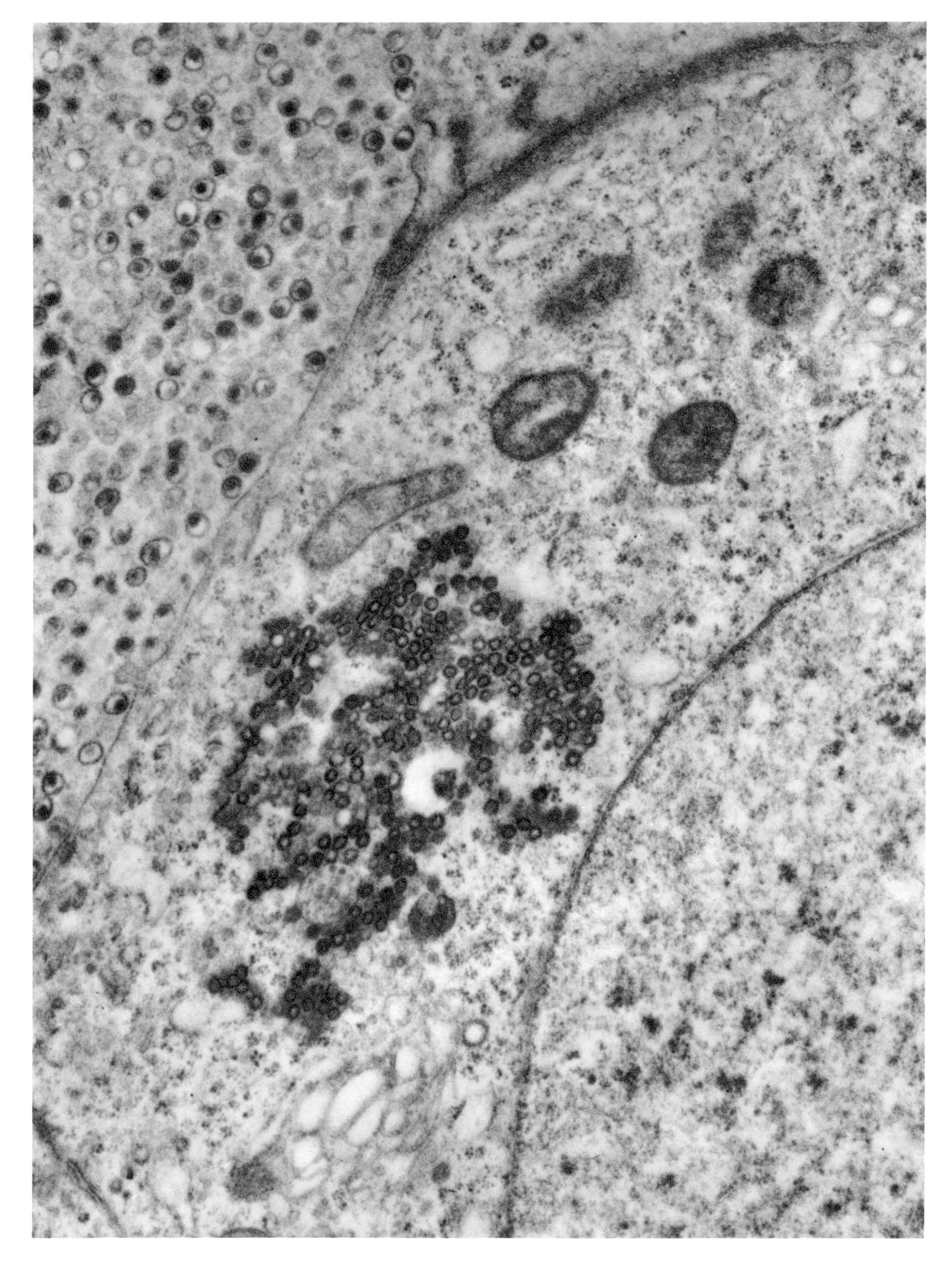

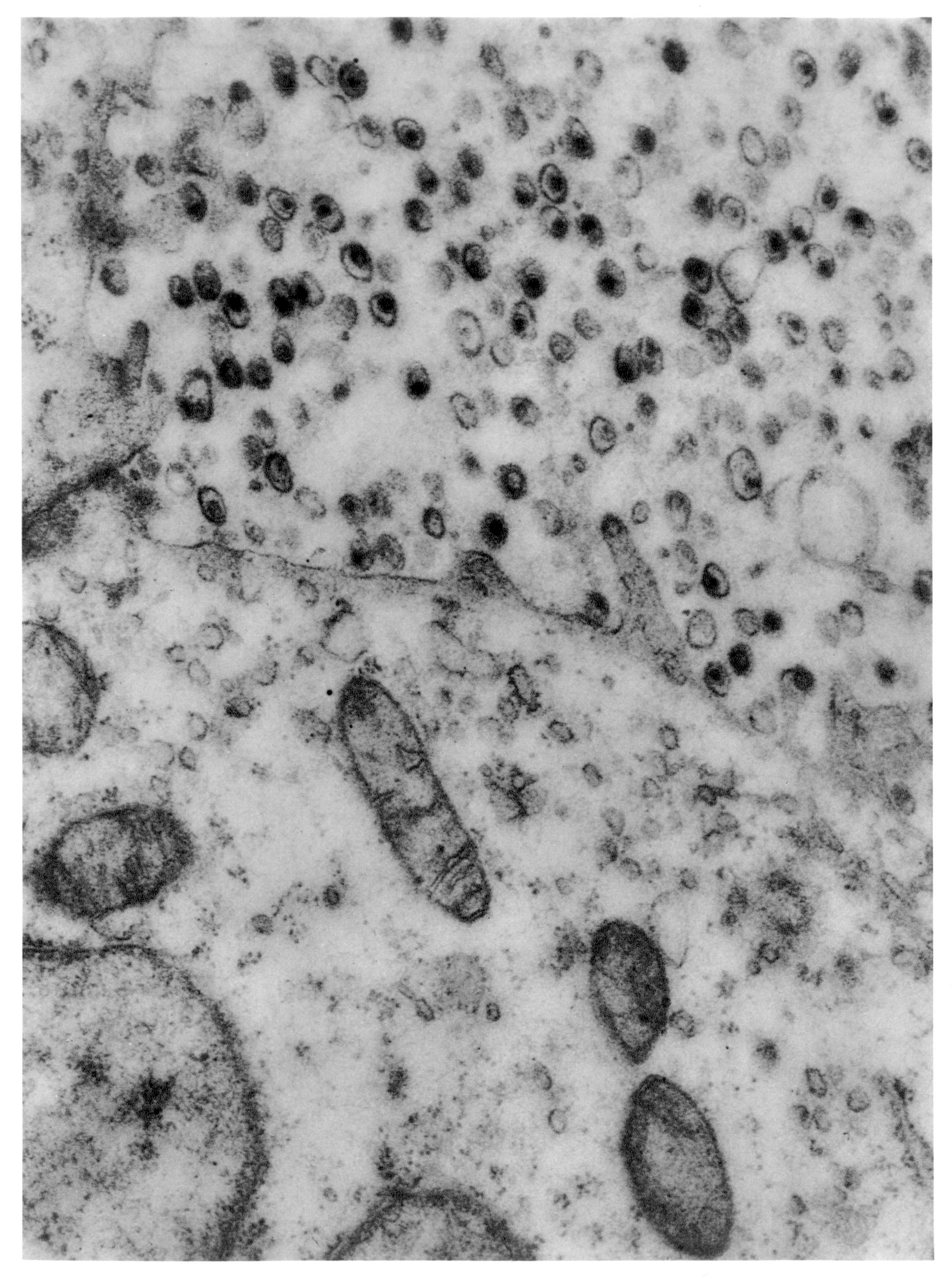

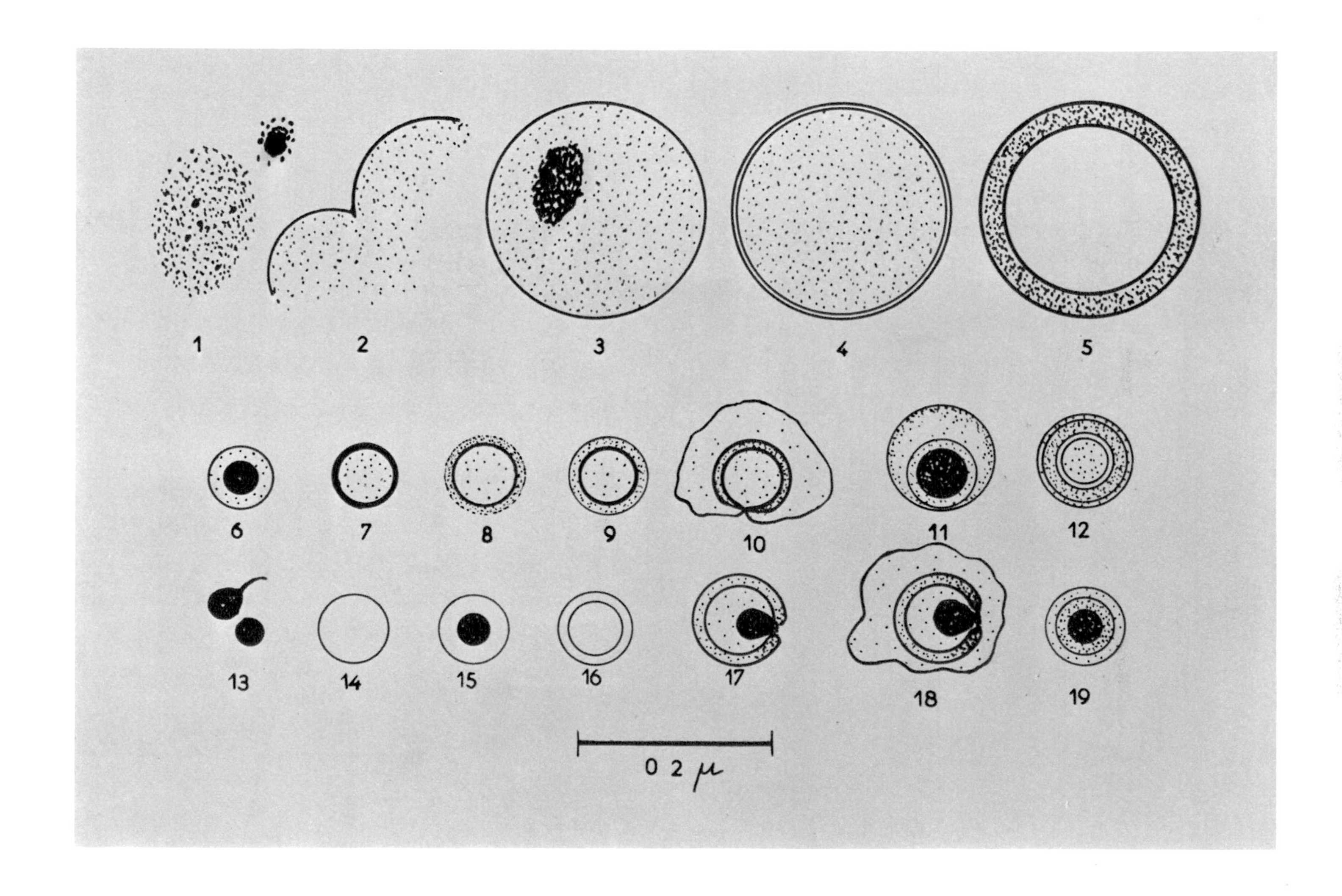

Opposite: In a cancer cell with mitochondria (small granules or rod-shaped structures) in its cytoplasm, likewise taken from a spontaneous tumor in the breast of a mouse, numerous virus particles may be found in the intercellular space (above) in well-advanced stages of maturation. Magnification x 50000.
The electron microphotos and the diagram are by Dr. W. Bernhard, Institut de Recherches sur le Cancer Gustave Roussy in Villejuif/Seine.

Above: Schematic presentation of tumor viruses photographed with the electron microscope. 1–5: Developmental stages of fibromatous virus in the rabbit and of the virus causing Molluscum contagiosum in man. 6–12: Developmental stages of the Bittner milk factor, the cause of mammary cancer in the mouse. 13–18: Different forms of Lucké's virus, the cause of a renal cancer in the frog. 19: A virus recurring in all forms of malignant tumor and leukaemia of the hen.

Among the first substances which man the materialist turned to use were clay for ceramic articles and certain metals.
Above: A small vase from the Bronze Age with the design scratched into the clay. Found at Muntelier near Fribourg. Anthropological Museum, Basle.
Below: Double-edged knife from the late Bronze Age (Hallstatt civilization). Found at the Kleinhueningen Rhine port. Anthropological Museum, Basle.

Plastics

The "material cause" of technology is, quite patently, the material which it employs. Houses have required wood and stone for as long as houses have been built; textile technology uses vegetable and animal fibres; and the smith works on metals. Nature provides man with two kinds of materials: inorganic ones from the mineral realm, ranging from homely stone to noble gold, and organic ones from the plant and animal realm such as wood and wool.
The effort to create new materials goes far back in time. As it advanced, technology inevitably came to have need of materials with properties which were better adapted to the use intended.
Very early in history inorganic natural materials were complemented by man-made products. It has been shown that as far back as 5000 B.C. ceramic articles such as vases, bricks, or figurines were made by baking clay. In the fourth millenium before the Christian era, the Egyptians obtained glass as a reaction product from sand, lime, and soda. The metals smelted from ores have given whole eras their names; the Stone Age was succeeded first by the Bronze Age and then the Iron Age.
The reason why inorganically created materials were discovered so early lies in the technical simplicity of

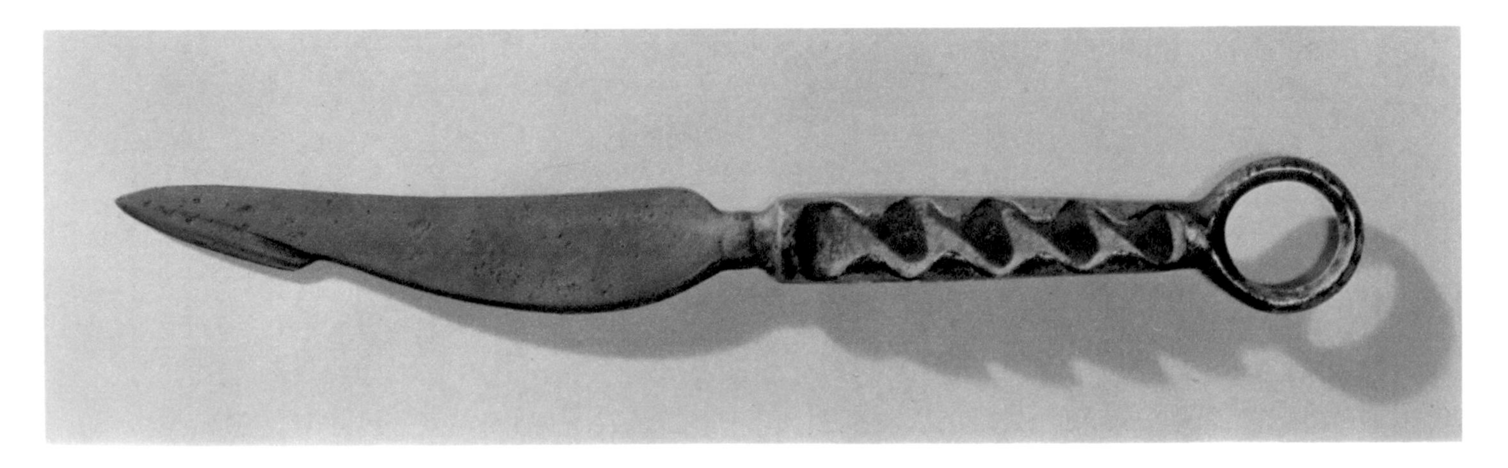

The smelting of ores containing sulfur and bitumen, and the making of the earthenware vessels required for this process. Woodcut from Agricola, 1556.

the procedures used to prepare them; the raw materials are caused to react under the influence of heat. And it was the construction of ovens for generating the heat required which constituted the main problem here.
With organic materials, it was not possible to progress beyond the natural products until the middle of the 19th century. Just as with dyestuffs and pharmaceuticals, this evolution began so late because vegetable and animal substances became chemicals, as the chemist understands this term, only when – thanks to Friedrich Woehler, the pioneer in ureic synthesis – the irrational idea of the "vital force" had been shelved.

The way in which organic materials developed, as well as the beginning of the new period, coincides with the advent and development of dyes and pharmaceutical chemistry. In the initial phase, natural products were modified; later on, synthetic materials were created. The term "plastics" has come to be applied universally to such materials.

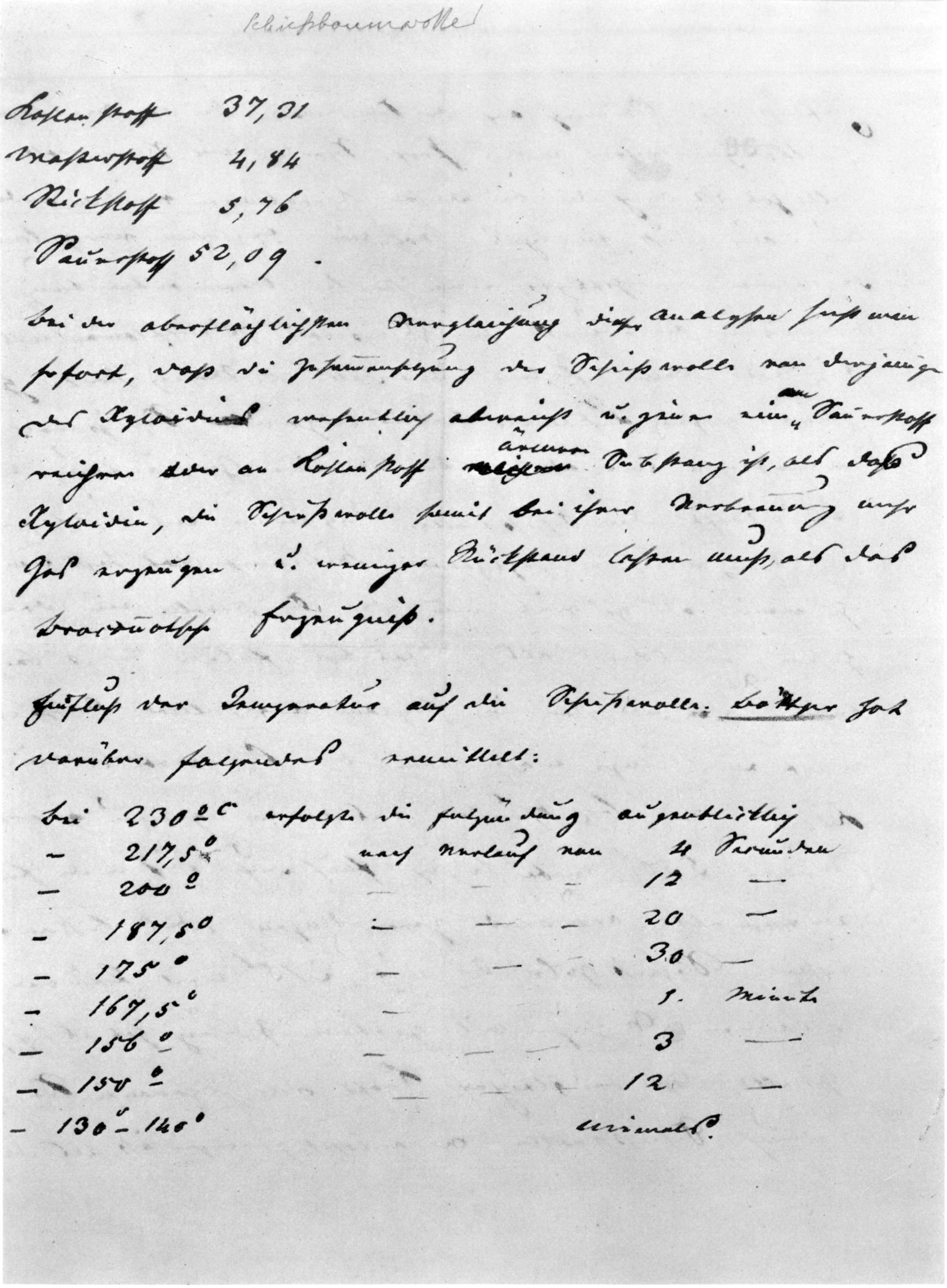

Schießbaumwolle

Kohlenstoff 37,31
Wasserstoff 4,84
Stickstoff 5,76
Sauerstoff 52,09.

bei der oberflächlichsten Vergleichung dieser Analysen sieht man sofort, daß die Zusammensetzung der Schießwolle von derjenigen des Xyloidins wesentlich abweicht u. zwar eine an Sauerstoff reichere oder an Kohlenstoff ärmere Substanz ist, als das Xyloidin, die Schießwolle somit bei ihrer Verbrennung mehr Gas erzeugen u. weniger Rückstand lassen muß, als das Baumwolle hinterläßt.

Einfluß der Temperatur auf die Schießwolle. Böttger hat darüber Folgendes ermittelt:

bei	230° C	erfolgte die Entzündung augenblicklich		
–	217,5°	nach Verlauf von	4	Sekunden
–	200°	— — —	12	—
–	187,5°	— — —	20	—
–	175°	— — —	30	—
–	167,5°	—	1	Minute
–	156°	—	3	—
–	150°	— —	12	—
–	130°–140°		niemals.	

Because of its extremely rapid combustibility, Schoenbein termed the mixture of cellulose nitrates which he had discovered "guncotton". As an explosive cellulose nitrate failed to make a career, although Sir F. A. Abel later showed how to make it stable by pulping. As a starting material for celluloid, however, Schoenbein's discovery was a harbinger of the plastics era.
Opposite: Laboratory note recorded by Schoenbein in November 1846 on the analysis and inflammation temperature of guncotton. University Library, Basle.
Right: Nitrocellulose at the moment of ignition.

The epoch of turning natural materials into man-made ones had its beginning in Basle. In 1845/46 Christian Friedrich Schoenbein, professor at the University of Basle, investigated the effect of a mixture of sulfuric acid and aqua regia (nitric acid) on various substances. He noticed that cotton underwent a chemical transformation while retaining its fibre structure: the cellulose of the fibre became cellulose nitrate. The reaction product he named "guncotton" which, because of its high inflammability, he suggested might be used as a propellant for rifle bullets. To Faraday he also submitted the idea that collodion cotton, because of its toughness and resistance to water, might be used for the manufacture of banknotes.
Schoenbein's guncotton became the starting material for a plastic. About ten years after his discovery J. A. Cutting found that cellulose nitrate – in contrast to cellulose itself – would, if combined with camphor, dissolve into an easily mouldable mass. This discovery was turned to industrial use in 1869, when J.W.Hyatt established, in Albany, New York, the Billiard Ball Company for the manufacture of objects made from the mixture of guncotton and camphor. This plastic he called "celluloid".
Cellulose nitrate was also the starting material for the first artificial silk. In 1855 Audemars dissolved the compound in a mixture of alcohol and ether; while evaporating the solvent he spun silk-like threads from it. Its ready inflammability prevented this first artificial silk from being used to any extent, however. Only after Count Hilaire de Chardonnet had managed to perform the "denitration" of the cellulose nitrate filament, regenerating it to difficultly flammable cellulose, did it become possible to proceed with the large-scale manufacture of "artificial silk". This inventor founded a company for the manufacture of Chardonnet silk at Besançon in 1884. Although the product is no longer of economic significance, its historic importance is beyond question. For it paved the way for the development of textile raw materials on a cellulose basis – such as viscose, copper, and acetate rayon – which are indispensable today.

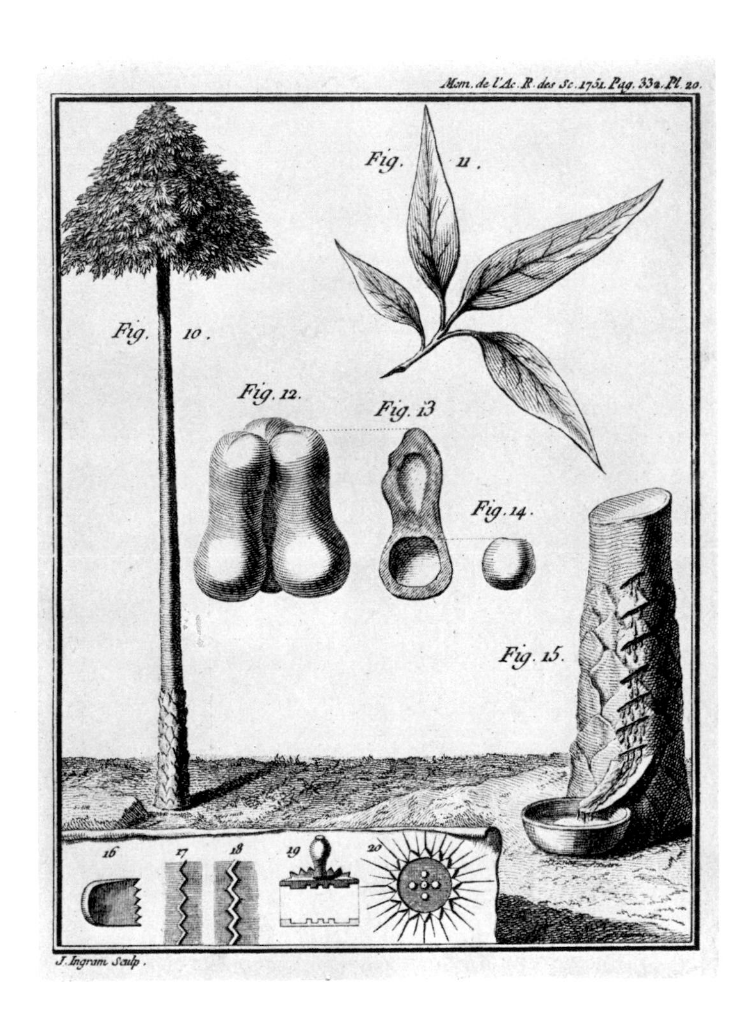

The first drawing of the Hevea brasiliensis tree, source of rubber, together with its leaves and fruit, as well as the method of tapping. Copper engraving from the "Description de divers arbres de la Guiane", a paper by François Fresneau which appeared in the Memoirs of the Royal Academy of Sciences; Paris, 1751.

It is not just by chance that cellulose became a raw material for the industrial manufacture of plastics. As a skeletal substance, i.e. one whose atoms are arranged in a three-dimensional framework, cellulose leads all others in quantity in the plant realm. And a similar law governed the ascendancy of proteins – the class of substances occurring most frequently in the animal realm – as a starting material for plastics. In 1897 Krische and Spitteler applied for German patent protection for a plastic material made of milk protein (casein) and hardened with formaldehyde. This material is still manufactured in large quantities today under the name of "Galalith" or "artificial horn".

As had been the case with cellulose nitrate, technology seized upon formaldehyde-hardened casein as a material for textile fibres. The experiments of the Dessau chemist Todtenhaupt had to wait thirty years for their industrial realization when, in 1935, the first artificial albuminoid fibres appeared on the market.

"Crude rubber" is the name given to the coagulated milky juice or latex of many plants, the most important of which is *Hevea brasiliensis* Muell. Arg., a native of the Amazon region. Crude rubber became an essential raw material for elastic and such with the discovery of "hot vulcanization" by the American Charles Goodyear in 1839; in this process the thermal and plastic qualities of raw rubber were improved by heating it in the presence of sulfur.
Not unsurprisingly, crude rubber became an attractive subject of chemical investigations. In 1860 the English chemist Williams found a substance in the distillate of crude rubber which was to prove important in the synthesis later on: isoprene. The idea that it might be the basic unit of the rubber molecule was advanced by the Frenchman Bouchardat in 1875. From the decomposition product of rubber – isoprene – he was able, by treating it with hydrochloric acid, to build up rubber-like masses again.

Isoprene is a basic unit of many natural substances such as perfume materials, natural dyestuffs, and vitamins. In 1884 the English chemist W. A. Tilden managed to obtain good yields of isoprene from turpentine oil. And it was Tilden who apprehended the chemical structure of isoprene:

$$CH_2{=}C(CH_3){-}CH{=}CH_2$$

Isoprene

With this work achieved, the scientific aspect of the rubber problem was cleared up sufficiently to bring the technical realization of rubber synthesis within striking distance. The turn of the century saw a number of chemists preoccupied with this challenge. In 1909 Fritz Hofmann, a chemist with the Bayer Dyeworks in Elberfeld, submitted a viable synthesis for patenting, and four years later the first synthetic rubber came on to the market.

This primary synthesis was but the beginning of developments. It was soon found that isoprene could be replaced by more easily available and thus cheaper starting materials, for example by butadiene, dimethylbutadiene, and chloro-butadiene. The vigorous research work carried on in the late 1920s resulted in *Buna* at I. G. Farben in Germany and in *Neoprene* at Du Pont de Nemours in the United States.

Left: The gathering of latex from the rubber tree in the Amazon region. Xylography done in the 1870s, from Louis Figuier's "Marvels of Industry".
Below: With the upsurge of the automotive industry, rubber became an indispensable material. Our car-age civilization rolls on rubber-tired wheels.

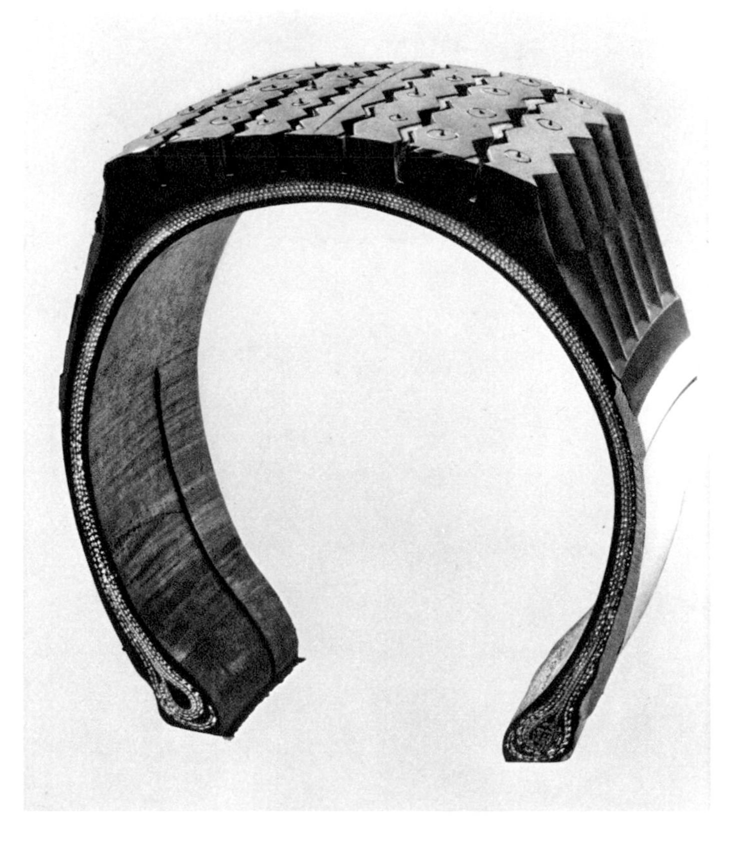

The first synthetically constructed plastic without a prototype in nature was created by C.H. Baekeland, a Belgian chemist residing in America. In 1907 he had a process patented for the condensation of phenols from coal tar with formaldehyde. The new thermohardening plastic he named *Bakelite,* and production of it was soon taken up all over the world. All of a sudden resinous substances such as often result from organic chemical experimentation ceased to be bothersome by-products and began to be examined for their suitability as plastic materials. It was in this period that a number of products – urea-formaldehyde resins, polyvinyl chloride and acetate, polystyrene – entered the industrial scene.

Such initial successes were isolated discoveries, for the chemistry of polymers was still in its empirical stage. An insight into the architecture of the molecules of synthetic substances was provided by the theory of macromolecules, which came along at an amazingly late date in the history of organic chemistry. At the beginning of the 1920s H. Staudinger, then professor at the Federal Institute of Technology, recognized that macromolecules are built up according to the same laws as organic combinations of low molecular weight. It had long been known that cellulose treated with hot diluted acids decomposes into glucose. The new – and at first sharply assailed – view of Staudinger's school was that the glucose units in cellulose do not form agglomerates, as had been supposed, but rather are joined in long chains by chemical linkage as Kekulé understood this term. It was now possible to research the plastics field systematically.

Der Naturkautschuk ist darnach ein echter hoch-
molekularer Kohlenwasserstoff mit vielen Aethylenbindungen, und das chemische Verhalten
entspricht auch völlig dieser Auffassung. Die
Aethylenbindungen können teilweise oder ganz
durch Anlagerung abgesättigt werden, ohne dass
die kolloiden Eigenschaften sich ändern, also ohne
dass die „Makromolekel" zerfällt. ...

Staudinger later improved on his conception of macromolecular structure by distinguishing between linear, branched, and cross-linked types:

Linear Macromolecule

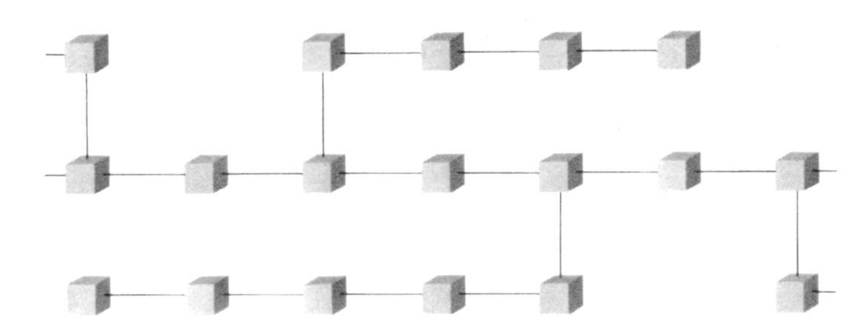

Branched Macromolecule

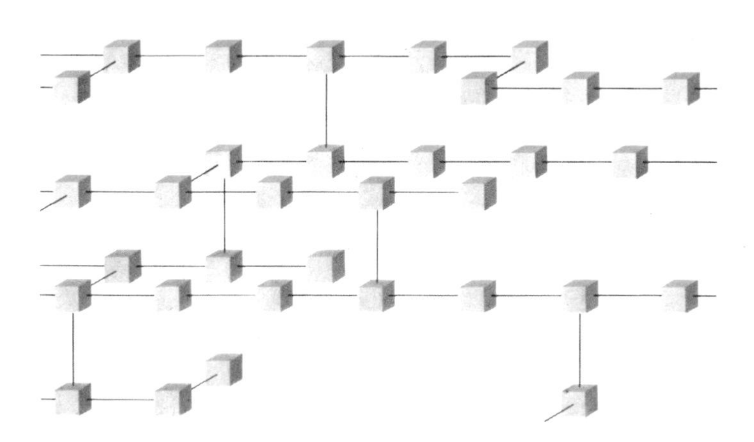

Cross-linked Macromolecule

Opposite: Recent transcription, in the author's own handwriting, of a passage from a paper published in 1922 by H. Staudinger and co-workers on the constitution of rubber.
Right: The fused mass of linear, high-polymer substances, such as the thermosoftening polyethylene shown here, can be drawn out into thread-like shapes. Magnification x 2.

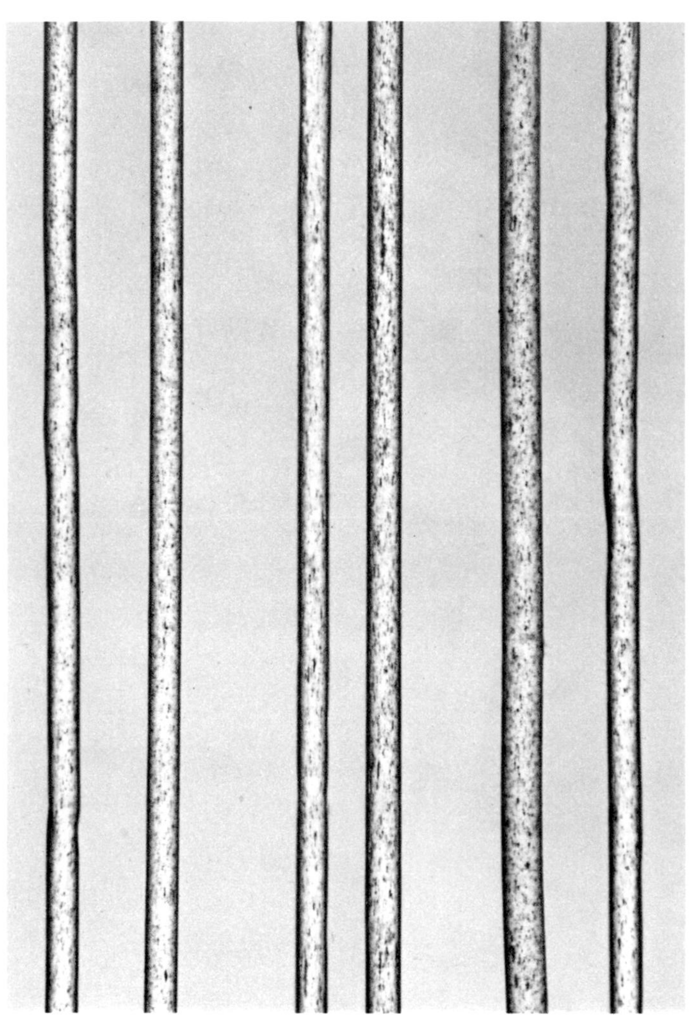

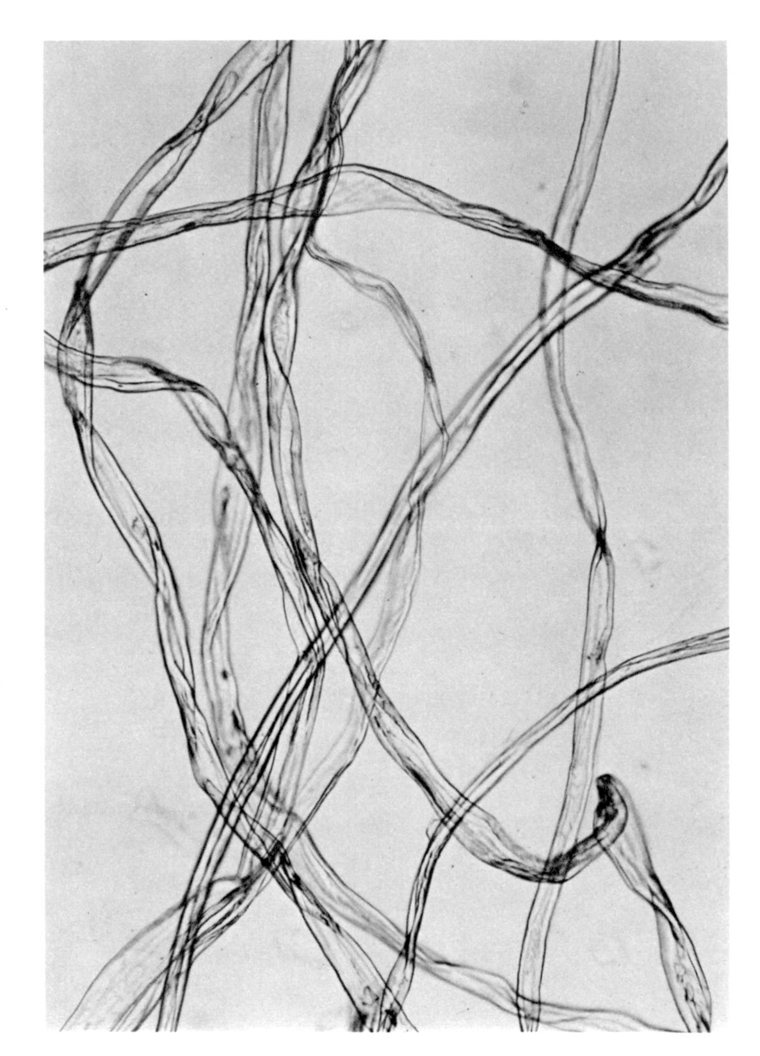

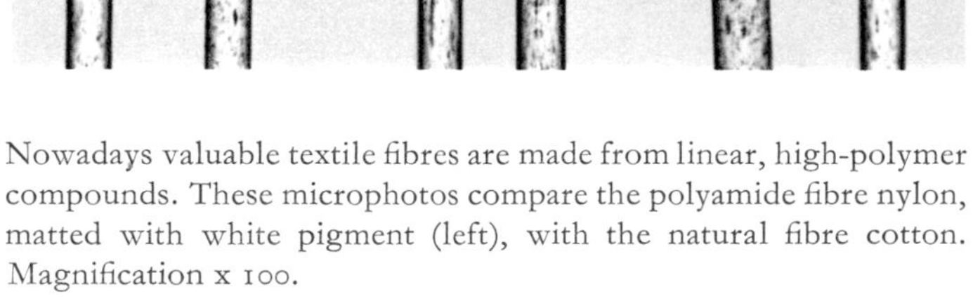

Nowadays valuable textile fibres are made from linear, high-polymer compounds. These microphotos compare the polyamide fibre nylon, matted with white pigment (left), with the natural fibre cotton. Magnification x 100.

Ingenious and systematic experiments carried out by the American W. H. Carothers in the Du Pont laboratories from 1929 to 1937 illuminated the field of linear macromolecules. Within a short time the conversion to technical utilization on a gigantic scale became possible. During the brief period between 1938 and 1953 the chemical industry in America, Germany and England introduced polyamide, polyester and polyacrylnitrile synthetic textile fibres to the market.

In the field of cross-linked macromolecules, scientific work on isocyanates (Bayer) and epoxydes (CIBA) bore fruit in products for a broad market.

Plastics have permeated every facet of modern life. We wear cloths made of synthetic fibres, walk on floors surfaced with plastic tiles, and sit on furniture covered with plastic film. Edibles are sold in plastic wrappers and often even served on plastic dinnerware. Handbags and suitcases, writing instruments and telephones, eyeglass frames and tooth fillings – all are made of

plastic materials nowadays. The output of synthetic organic materials has already overtaken the quantity of non-ferrous metals used.
Plastics make possible new solutions to technical problems. A high degree of non-conductibility and good dielectric properties make them indispensable as materials for electrical apparatus. Their mechanical properties are utilized in the construction of machinery and motor-car bodies, and as bonding agents for wood

Everywhere the eye turns, it is confronted with familiar articles made of plastics. The telephone and cups are of melamine resin moulding preparations, while the bottle stoppers are mass-produced from urea-formaldehyde condensates.

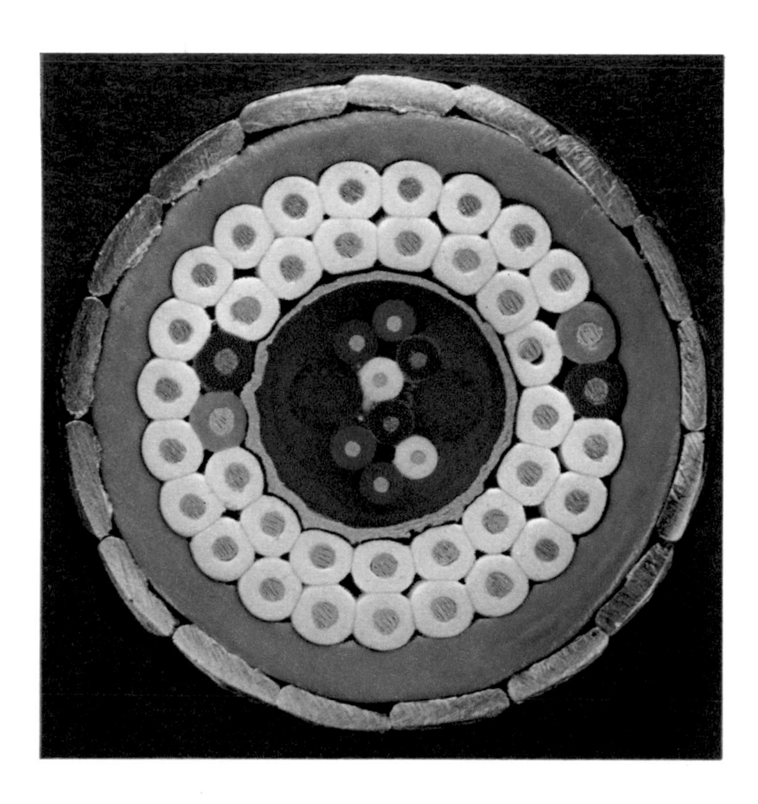

Technology, too, has found new possibilities in plastic substances.
Opposite: Electric discharge on a pin insulator made of *Araldite*. High mechanical stability and electrical quality make possible novel design.
Above left: Cross-section of a telephone cable insulated with plastics. Cables constructed in this fashion are much lighter and more resistant to corrosion than lead ones insulated with paper, which have been standard hitherto.
Left: In the construction of apparatus, not only the housing but important functional components as well are made of artificial resin moulding compounds. These are switch props with parts manufactured from *Melopas*.
Above: Construction of a stratified laminate, with an overlay, a decorative sheet, and a barrier sheet which are dip-coated with melamine resin and pressed together at high temperature.

and metal they are important materials in modern construction. They can be formed by compression moulding under heat, calandering, and injection moulding, and this property of plasticity has made them a class of commodities which is typical of our time: the mass-produced article.

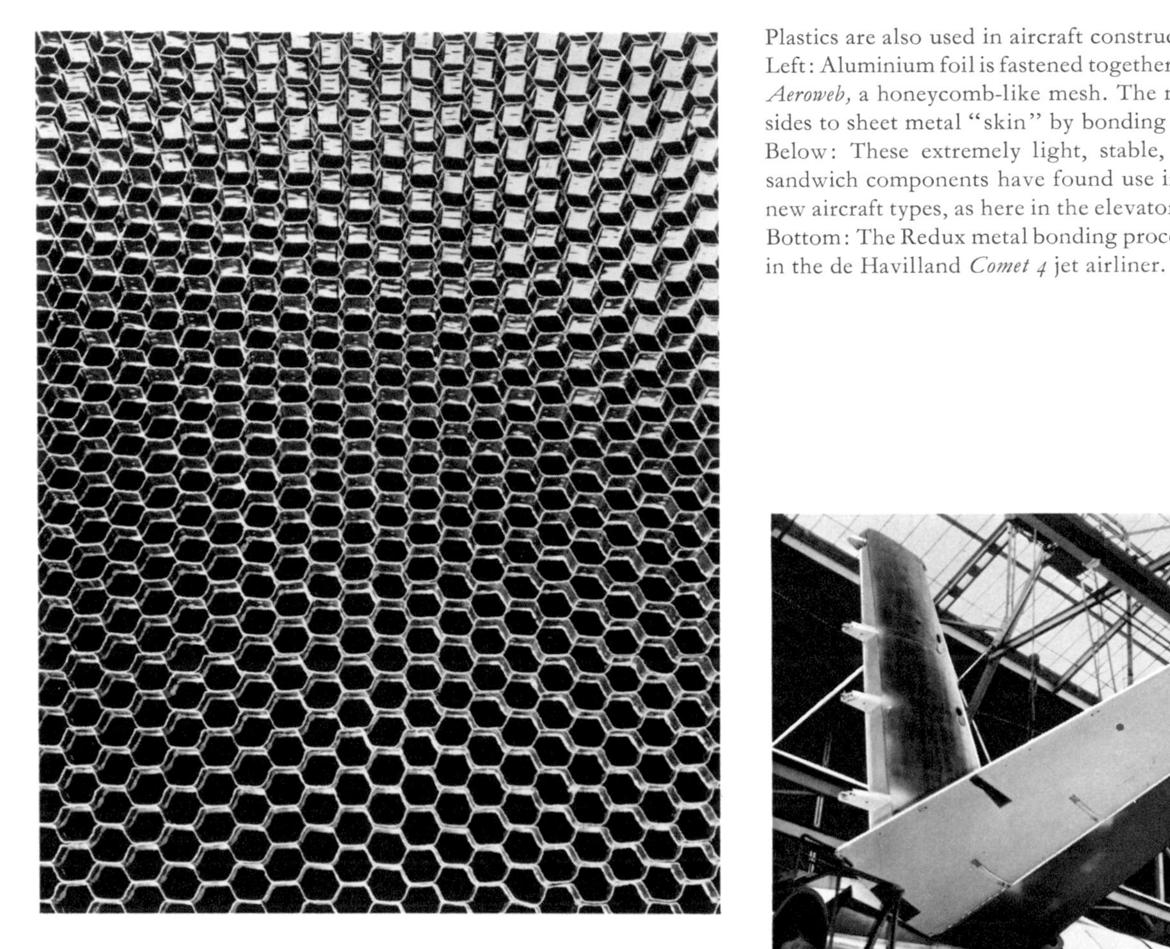

Plastics are also used in aircraft construction.
Left: Aluminium foil is fastened together with *Araldite* to form (left): *Aeroweb,* a honeycomb-like mesh. The mesh is then joined on both sides to sheet metal "skin" by bonding with *Redux* adhesive foil.
Below: These extremely light, stable, and mechanically resistant sandwich components have found use in the fuselage and wings of new aircraft types, as here in the elevator of the Vickers *Vanguard.*
Bottom: The Redux metal bonding process has been used extensively in the de Havilland *Comet 4* jet airliner.

In Basle industrial research in the field of plastics began at quite an early date. In 1920 Staudinger published his views on polymerization products of high molecular weight. In the very next year experiments of a scientific and technical nature were being conducted in the CIBA laboratories, with a view to working out Staudinger's ideas. In the course of the 20s these studies led to the colorless and light-fast urea-formaldehyde resins *(Cibanoid, Melocol H)*. These hardenable aminoplasts found use in electrotechnology, in the manufacture of household utensils, and as wood glue in the making of plywood and furniture.

The stability to heat and water possessed by the melamine-formaldehyde condensates worked out in the 1930s excited considerable interest. In developing the raw material base melamine from a scientific laboratory preparation into a large-scale industrial product, CIBA chemists performed a technological feat of the first order. Moulding compositions, wood adhesives, textile application products, coating and laminating resins *(Melopas, Melocol M, Cibamin)*—these are the forms in which the melamine-formaldehyde condensates are applied.

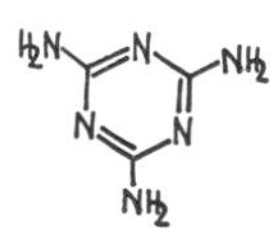

Melamine

The 1940s saw the creation of the epoxy resins. CIBA was the first firm to produce this class of synthetic resins on an industrial scale, marketing them under the name of *Araldite*. The basic product – manufactured, say, from epichlorohydrin and dihydroxide diphenyl propane – makes possible intermolecular etherifications and can also be made to undergo a series of further conversions. Thus the properties of this group of synthetic resins may be varied within

Melamine crystals under the magnifying glass. Developed at CIBA into a large-scale product, melamines are the raw material basis of a whole class of plastics. Magnification x 25.

With artificial resin glues, new kinds of laminated wood construction are possible. The half-domed pavilion of the Federation of the Belgian Timber Industries at the 1958 international exhibition in Brussels incorporated CIBA urea-formaldehyde *Aerolite* resins. Illustration from *Wood* magazine, Oct. 1958.

wide limits and adapted to whatever use is intended. Products made on such a basis are applied as casting resins. In the making of electrical apparatus, for instance, sensitive parts are potted in Araldite. Protected in this way from mechanical effects and moisture absorption, their perfect electrical constancy is guaranteed. Ethoxyline resins, as the class has also been termed, are valuable bonding agents for most materials in industrial use, particularly metals. In the construction of vehicles and aircraft, they serve to bond metal parts firmly, replacing riveting, soldering, and welding. Coatings of epoxies and glass fibre have excellent dimensional stability; they fulfil the requirements demanded of measuring and assembly jigs.

Textile Application Products

The process of working up loose fibre material to textiles ready for use is an involved one. Since a long time back it has required a whole series of substances, either as auxiliaries or as finishing agents.
Wool has to be scoured before being spun. Until well into the 18th century, alkaline solutions – for example, aqueous extracts of beechwood ash, which contains potassium carbonate, or solutions of soda found in nature – were used as the main expedients in scouring raw wool. In addition, fuller's earth, ox gall, and decoctions of saponin-containing plants such as the soapwort *(Saponaria officinalis* L.) were made use of for the same purpose, although more rarely.
The same materials also served as auxiliaries in milling, or fulling. Under the powerful blows of the fulling hammer, saturated wool fabric shrank and became compact and resistant, its uniform surface showing scarcely any traces of the weave structure.
Until the 18th century soap was too dear to be utilized to any great extent in textile processing. Being a luxury article, its use was limited to keeping body and apparel clean. In the course of the Industrial Revolution, however, this situation changed; cheaper sources of raw materials for soap manufacture were opened up. The use of inexpensive oils and above all the replacement of wood ashes and barilla – the soda ash from saltwort – by soda, for the preparation of which Nicolas Leblanc found a cheap process from common salt in 1789, reduced the price of soap so sharply that it began to be used in textile processing. As an auxiliary in scouring and milling it supplanted all other animal, vegetable, and mineral adjuvants.
But textile processing did not require scouring and milling auxiliaries alone. The weaver coated the threads of the warp with sizing agents, usually starch or glue, in order to protect them better against damage from the heald shafts and shuttles. With the same substances, often mixed with fillers such as talc or calcium

The soapwort. Its very lathery decoction was already employed in ancient times as a washing agent for textiles. Copper engraving from "Hortus Eystettensis", a sumptuous volume dealing with the plants which were cultivated in the botanical gardens of the princely bishops of Eichstädt. Nuremberg, 1613.

L'INDUSTRIE DES SAVONS. 425
Fig. 286. — Vue générale de la salle des chaudières d'une savonnerie de Marseille.
Opération de l'*empâtage*.

Soap manufacture in the latter part of the 19th century. Plate illustrating the thickening operation from Louis Figuier's "Marvels of Industry".

sulfate, he dressed his linen and cotton fabric to heighten its appeal to the critical buyer. The saturation of fabrics with oil imparted water-repellent properties to them. Textiles such as fishing nets which were dipped in tannin solutions and then dried, showed superior resistance to rotting when stored damp. Nor had natural colors and dyes alone ever sufficed for the dyer's needs either. He used auxiliaries like metallic salts and oils as mordants, tanning principles, tartar, and soap, in order to enhance the brilliance of the dyeing or to lend it better stability to sunlight and laundering.

Even these few examples of auxiliaries employed in textile processing before the industrial age are enough to suggest the classification which distinguishes between textile auxiliary agents and textile finishing products.

Thanks to textile auxiliaries, textile operations can be carried out rapidly and reliably. Such agents are then removed from the textile material, as is soap after washing, for instance.

Textile finishing agents are a different case, for they stay on the textile material. In this way they bestow upon it the wished-for properties which are aimed at in finishing.

Textile Auxiliaries. In 1823 Michel-Eugène Chevreul, a professor at the Jardin des Plantes in Paris, published the results of thirteen years of personal research. This work, which bore the title "Recherches chimiques sur les corps gras d'origine animale", was to prove a pioneer one, of fundamental importance for theoretical organic chemistry. It not only illuminated the structural principles of fatty substances, but also shed the first light on the chemistry of soap manufacture.

In soap boiling, i.e. when fats or oils are boiled down with strongly alkaline solutions, the fatty substances split up into glycerin and fatty acids. The latter – isolated by Chevreul and termed margaric, stearic, and ellaic acid – combine with alkali to form sodium and potassium salts: soaps.

With the chemical structure of soap thus explained in principle, it could claim to be a well-defined chemical, as the chemist understands this term; and the soap boiler's art became a scientifically well-grounded branch of chemical technology. The result was quickly apparent, for the method of producing soap was made both simpler and less expensive. In addition, it was now possible to modify the soap molecule chemically, changing its properties along the lines sought.

Friedlieb Ferdinand Runge, a chemist of Oranienburg, was the first to effect a chemical modification of soap in the year 1834. While attempting to saponify olive oil with sulfuric acid rather than with alkali, he obtained the first representative of the sulfated oils, a group which has since become voluminous in range. Runge also perceived how this product might be used. As "Turkey red oil" it replaced "rancid olive oil" in red madder dyeing, the latter being an aqueous emulsion

RECHERCHES CHIMIQUES

SUR

LES CORPS GRAS

D'ORIGINE ANIMALE,

PAR M. E. CHEVREUL.

On doit tendre avec effort à l'infaillibilité sans y prétendre.
MALEBRANCHE.

A PARIS,

CHEZ F. G. LEVRAULT, LIBRAIRE-ÉDITEUR,
RUE DE M. LE PRINCE, Nº 31;
ET A STRASBOURG, RUE DES JUIFS, Nº 33.

1823.

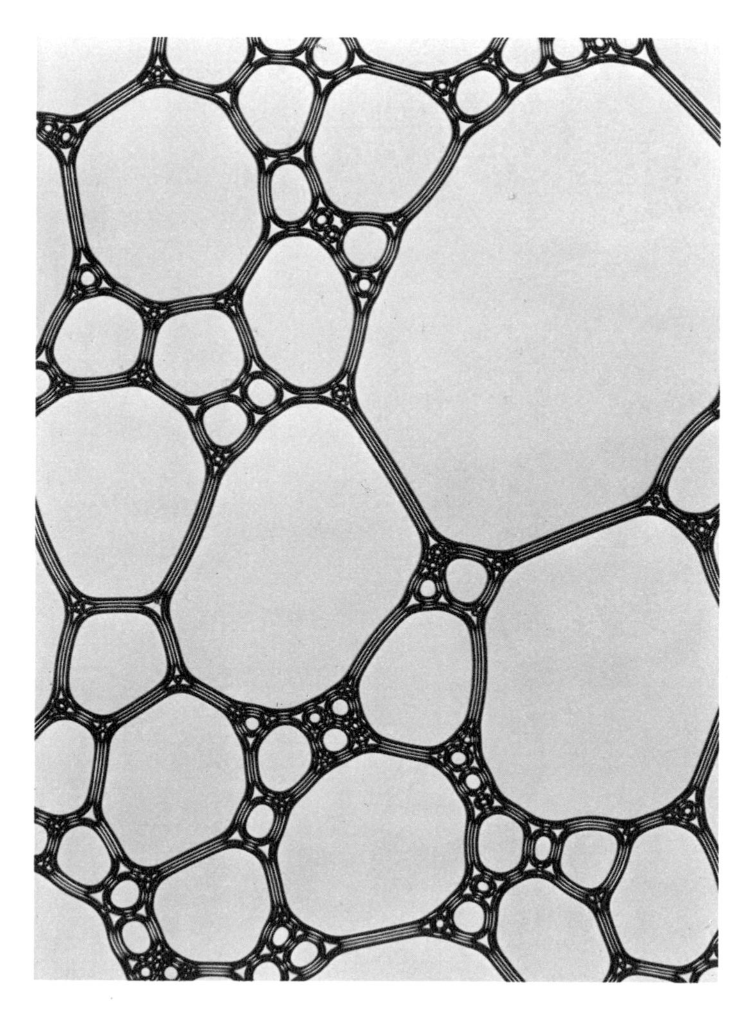

Left: The motto from Malebranche which graces Chevreul's work on animal fats is modest enough. His researches showed fats to be compounds of glycerol and fatty acids, and in this publication he explained the principles of soap chemistry. Above: Soapsuds, magnification x 20.

How wetting agents act. In the rear beaker, wool yarn in water containing alkylnaphthalene sulfonate *(Invadine BL conc.)* is rapidly wetted. But without this auxiliary the textile material swims for hours on the surface of the liquid.

of rank olive oil used as a mordant. Turkey red oil was not made on a large scale, however, until the Scottish industrialist Walter Crum took cheap castor oil as the starting material. That was in 1864. Although brilliant Turkey red is no longer used as a color, Turkey red oil has survived the process which gave it its name. It is effective as a wetting agent, and its presence in the bath guarantees speedy and uniform penetration of the textile material.

A knowledge of the chemistry of soap and of Turkey red oil, then, had been added to the domain of textile auxiliary chemistry by the middle of the 19th century, and it was an acquisition of basic importance. But the industrial development of this branch of chemistry did not really start until seventy years later, though then with a vengeance.

The beginning of modern textile auxiliary chemistry was marked by the discovery of the wetting and cleansing action of alkylnaphthalene sulfonates. In 1917 F. Guenther, a chemist of I. G. Farben, observed that the reaction product from naphthalene, isopropyl alcohol, and sulfuric acid foams like soap and, besides a cleansing action which is not particularly marked, shows an outstanding wetting effect. The product termed *Nekal,* similar to soap in its effect, could thus be manufactured without fat as a starting material. Since fatty substances were among those in short supply during the first World War, the interest of industry in this product was self-explanatory. Nekal type textile auxiliary products are still used in large amounts as wetting and emulsifying agents.

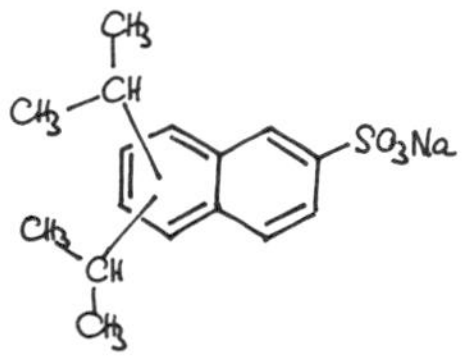

CH_3 CH CH_3 SO_3Na CH_3 CH CH_3

Nekal A
Sodium diisopropyl naphthalene sulfonate

chemical structure of soap be meaningfully connected with its effect. In 1917 the American chemists Langmuir and Harkins published their theory describing emulsion formation, derived from a conception of surface films as being composed of oriented detergent molecules. In its carbohydrate chain soap possesses a fat-soluble, or lipophilic, part and in its carboxyl group a water-soluble, or hydrophilic, one.

Soap:

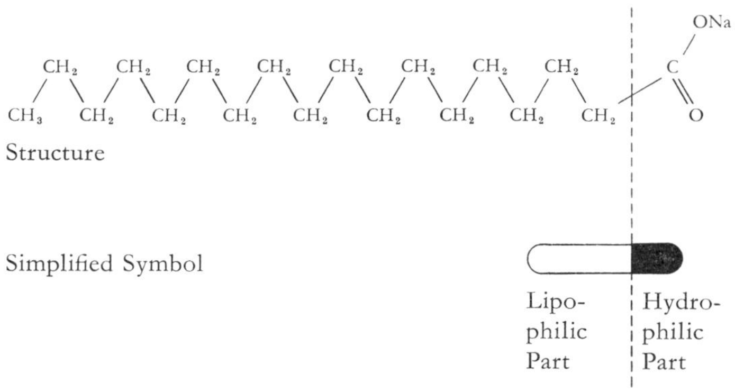

CH_2 CH_2 CH_2 CH_2 CH_2 CH_2 CH_2 CH_2 ONa C
CH_3 CH_2 CH_2 CH_2 CH_2 CH_2 CH_2 CH_2 CH_2 O

Structure

Simplified Symbol

Lipophilic Part | Hydrophilic Part

The empiric discovery of Nekal did not, however, provide the only impulse for further scientific and technical work on textile auxiliary products. This field was opened to exhaustive and systematic treatment only after chemists had succeeded in projecting a rational picture of how such agents act and in clearing up the relation between the chemical structure of a textile auxiliary product and its cleansing and wetting effect.

The washing theory of Berzelius, dating from the beginning of the last century, ascribed this effect to the alkaline reaction of the soap exclusively. One incorrect and therefore fruitless conclusion drawn from this theory was that stronger alkalis, in so far as they did not harm the textile material, would surpass soap as washing agents. Not until a hundred years later could a clear idea of the washing process be gained and the

In the washing process the soap molecules are concentrated around the fat-containing dirt, whilst the fat-soluble groups act to remove impurities. Aided and abetted by mechanical treatment, or elbow grease, the dirt particles, enveloped by soap molecules, separate off from the textile and are held in suspension in the washtub.

The molecules of the washing agent not only concentrate on the fat/water surface of contact, however, but on others as well, for example air/water and textile/water. In this way the surface tension of the water is diminished: the solution penetrates the textile material more speedily and uniformly; and the soap also acts as a "wetting agent". With the idea of what happens thus visualized, it was now possible for the chemist to build up specialized wetting and washing agents systematically.

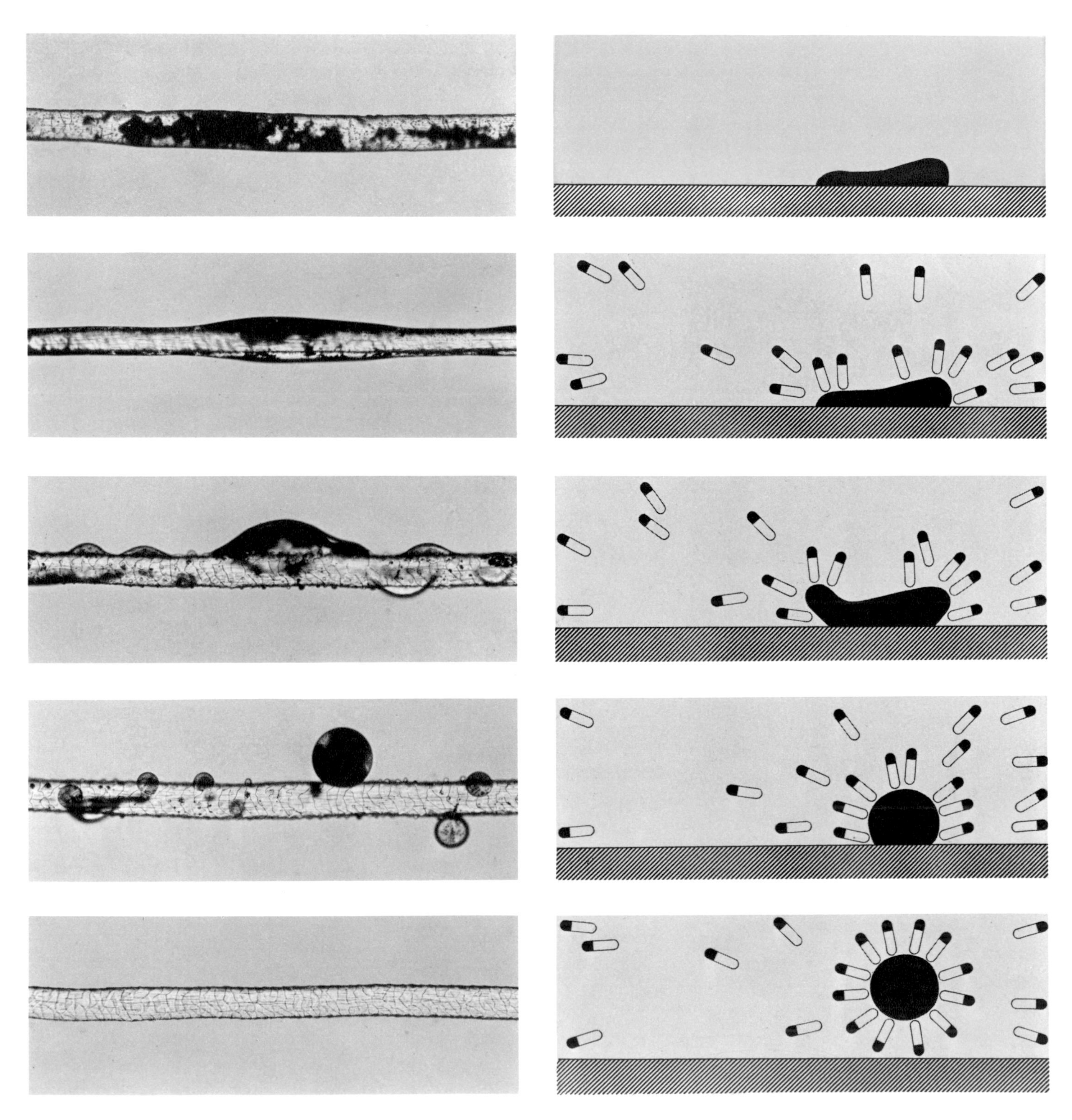

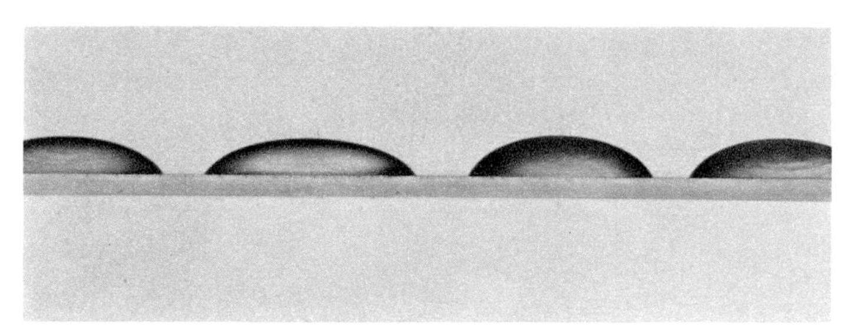

Opposite: The washing process under the microscope and in schematic representation. The dirt, which is made up of olive oil and soot, is removed from the wool hair when acted upon by the washing agent. Magnification x 150.
Above: Wetting agents reduce surface tension. Drops of water on a paraffined glass plate tend to take on a globular shape because of the high surface tension (top). Note that the surface of contact is small. Drops containing a wetting agent, on the other hand, flatten out (bottom), spreading over a larger surface. Magnification x 2.

Soap, the basic type of the textile auxiliary agents, has its drawbacks as well as its advantages. Insoluble lime soap is formed in hard water, and it is not only ineffective but also downright annoying, for in acid solution free fatty acid is deposited. Chemically, this disadvantageous behavior may be ascribed to the carboxyl group of the soap molecule. The goal of the chemist was clear to see. He had to modify the carboxyl group in such a way as to keep it from reacting sensitively to hard water and acid.

In the field of surface-active textile auxiliary agents, Basle was the scene of a pathfinding success achieved in 1927. Chemists in the Pharmaceutical Division of CIBA condensed oleic acid with diethyl-ethylene diamine. As expected, this condensation product was found to be strongly wetting and emulsifying. Salts of the substance were marketed under the brand name of *Sapamines*.

$$C_{17}H_{33}-CO-NH-CH_2-CH_2-\overset{\oplus}{N}(C_2H_5)_2-H \quad Cl^{\ominus}$$

Sapamine CH, Monooleyl-diethylene-diamine hydrochloride

In aqueous solution the active part of the molecule is not, as in ordinary soap, Turkey red oils, and Nekal, electrically negative. Rather, it is positively charged as a cation. In contrast to ordinary soap, these cationic detergents develop their effectiveness in strongly acid solution, too, which makes them suitable as wetting agents in carbonizing solutions. Cationic textile application products proved to be a group capable of extension and development. Compounds of this series – for instance Sapamine KW, synthesized in 1931 – are absorbed on to cellulose fibres substantively and, as textile finishing agents, give the material a soft handle. Sapamine also served as a model for the synthesis of products for improving the wet fastness properties of substantive dyeings. By forming salt, they block on the fibre the solubilizing action of the sulfo groups in the dye.

Invert soaps further gained importance as pharmaceuticals. Their wetting action and their lethal effect against pathogenic organisms are turned to use in antiseptics such as *Zephirol* (Bayer), *Desogen* (Geigy), and *Bradosol* (CIBA) (see page 160).

Oleyl-S-Base.

$(C_2H_5)_2$ N-CH_2-CH_2-NH-CO-$C_{17}H_{33}$. Mgw = 380.

1.) 20 g Ölsäure wurden mit 4 g (bei 0,1 g) PCl_3 auf dem W.B. bis zur
18.VI.23. Beendigung der Reaktion erwärmt. Dann wurde i/V. Luft durchgesaugt zur Entfernung der HCl. Das gebildete Chlorid wurde in etwas Aether gelöst und unter Eiskühlung & Rühren zu einer Lsg. von 16,6 g S-Base in 150 cm³ abs. Aether zufliessen gelassen. Nach vollendeter Umsetzung wurde mit Wasser versetzt & die abgehobene Aetherschicht über Na_2SO_4 getrocknet. Der Aetherrückstand wurde i/V. auf W.B. von flüchtigen Körpern befreit & dann mit der berechn. Menge n HCl auf eine 10%ige Lsg gelöst. Klare stark schäumende Flüssigkeit. Bei etwas alkalischer Reaktion dickflüssig wie eine conc. Gummi arab.-Lsg. Ein 20%ige Lsg erstarrt zu einer Gallerte.

In 1923 the first cationic detergent was synthesized by CIBA researchers. These laboratory notes of Hans Kaegi describe the preparation of the Sapamine base, called the oleyl-S base at that time.

In 1929 I.G. Farben filed a patent application in which a further method of blocking the carboxyl group was described. The fatty acids which are the bases of soaps sensitive to hard water and acid were condensed with oxyethane sulfonic acid. Marketed as washing agents under the trade name of *Igepon,* these products made their way into the textile industry.

$C_{17}H_{33}-CO-O-CH_2-CH_2-SO_3Na$

Igepon A

The same goal, namely the checkmating of the carboxyl group, was reached in Basle by other means. In 1932 research work carried out at CIBA resulted in detergent agents obtained through the condensation of fatty acids with phenylene diamine to derivatives of benzimidazol and subsequent sulfonation. These washing, wetting, and dispersing agents came on to the market in 1934 as *Ultravon* brands W and K.

NaO_3S–[benzimidazole, N–H]–$C_{17}H_{35}$

Ultravon K

The detergent effect of fatty acid condensation products is, in reference to the fatty acid, greater by some bit than that of soap. One gram of fatty acid in soap removes only 2.2 grams of wool fat from the raw fibre, whereas the same amount of acid in Ultravon W dissolves 17.4 grams of wool fat.

The benzimidazol field turned out to have considerable potential also. Based on the same structural principle as the Ultravon brands just described, levelling and penetrating agents possessing dyestuff affinity were obtained. The first specimen of this group, *Albatex PO,* was made available to dyers in 1935 and soon enjoyed deserved world-wide recognition.

Another notable piece of research work was also done by Basle chemists in the field of textile auxiliaries free of fats. With the sulfophthalic acid esters, CIBA found in the year 1930 a new structural principle for highly effective wettingout agents, one which the American Cyanamid Chemical Company took up, using it as a basis for developing the sulfosuccinic acid esters of the *Aerosol* line.

NaO_3S–C_6H_3(–CO–O–CH_2–CH_2–CH_2–CH_2–CH_3)(–CO–O–CH_2–CH_2–CH_2–CH_2–CH_3)

Invadine C
Sodium salt of sulfophthalic acid diamylester

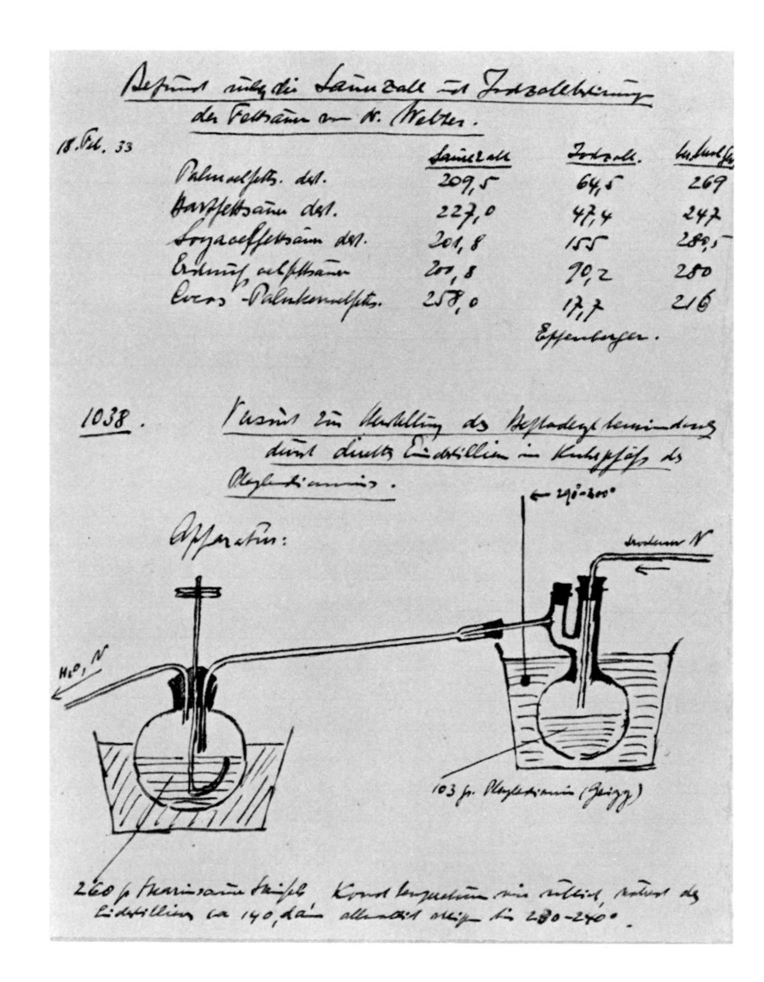

Above: In building up synthetic washing agents, CIBA chemists took as their method the condensation of fatty acids with o-phenylene-diamine. One such condensation experiment is recorded in this page from the laboratory journal of Charles Graenacher.

The molecules of all surface active textile auxiliaries developed up to 1930 split up, in aqueous solution, into particles with opposite electrical charges, i.e. into positively charged cations and negatively charged anions. If the anion is the carrier of the wetting or washing effect, as for instance in soap, we speak of anion-active textile auxiliary products; if however it is the cation which plays this rôle, as for instance in the first Sapamine brands, then such compounds are termed cation-active. The water solubility can be explained by this cleavage into ions.

The synthesis of the non-ionic textile auxiliaries developed by I.G.Farben in the 1930s was both novel and surprising. Their water-solubility is based on a polyethylene ether grouping which, if prepared with ethylene oxide, can easily be introduced into the most

Right: Specially synthesized derivatives of benzimidazol act as levelling agents in vat dyeing. 0.25% *Cibanone Violet F4R* Micro Powder on cotton fabric; left: without levelling agent; right: dyeing done with the addition of *Albatex PO*.

The washing of heavy wool fabrics in the textile industry. The wool is hung on a reel and drawn through the hot washing solution.

diverse organic molecules. Basle followed suit by developing non-ionic textile auxiliaries on this principle. Among them were a number of universally applicable wetting and washing agents such as the non-ionic *Ultravon* (CIBA), *Sandozen* (Sandoz), and *Tinoveten* (Geigy) brands. In the early 1950s CIBA introduced its *Neovadine* brands, conceived as dyeing and printing assistants. By forming a complex, Neovadine intercedes between liquor and fibre in the dyestuff equilibrium during coloring, thus acting (depending on the amount used) as a levelling and stripping agent in wool dyeing.

Textile Finishing Agents. The chemical finishing of textiles alters the properties of natural and man-made fibres. Fabrics are made water-repellent, crease-resistant, rot-resistant, and flameproof – to list but a few of the qualities that can be imparted. Products that confer such properties upon textiles are deposited within the fibre, in contrast to the textile auxiliaries. Strictly speaking, therefore, dyestuffs also belong to the textile finishing agents. The historical development, however, and above their magnitude as a class, justify describing them under a separate heading.
The biggest successes scored in the field of textile finishing were achieved with the help of synthetic resins. Finishes of these products are even resistant to repeated washing. In 1926 chemists of the Tootal Broadhurst & Lee Company in Manchester found an original method for reducing the unpleasant creasing of cellulose textiles. They impregnated the fibre with the precondensate of a synthetic resin which they condensed out onto the fabric by heat treatment.
At the beginning of the 1930s, processes were worked out almost simultaneously in Switzerland, England, and the United States with which fabrics that have been impregnated with synthetic resin precondensates can be furnished with all kinds of surface effects by means of embossing and curing. This was the prelude to the study of synthetic resin finishing agents in the chemical industry.
Since the first process for the full-scale manufacture of melamine had been found in Basle, it is not surprising that melamine was taken as the basic substance in the field of synthetic resin finishings, too. In the 1940s CIBA marketed its *Lyofix* brands, melamine formaldehyde precondensates for preventing swelling and for producing chintz and embossed effects on fabrics made of cellulosic fibre. Interesting finishing effects could be achieved with melamine formaldehyde resin products: flameproofing by the deposition of complex phosphates *(Pyrovatex)*, water-repellency by modifying the resin with fatty acid esters *(Phobotex FT)*, and rot resistance *(Arigal C)*.
CIBA chemists also recognized that cationic compositions similar to synthetic resin and based on dicyandiamidine serve to improve the wet fastness properties of dyeings on cellulose fibres. Such products have been on the market under the names Lyofix SB conc. and Lyofix EW since 1941 and 1953, respectively. The application of polymerization plastics to textile finishing

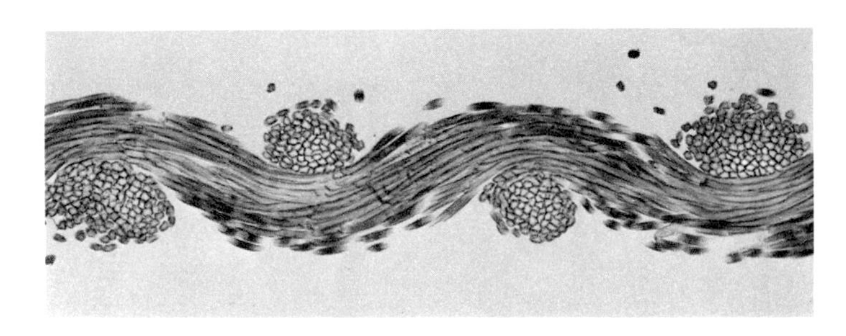

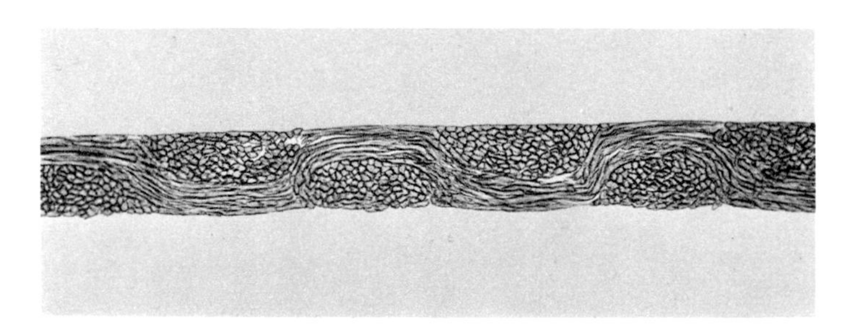

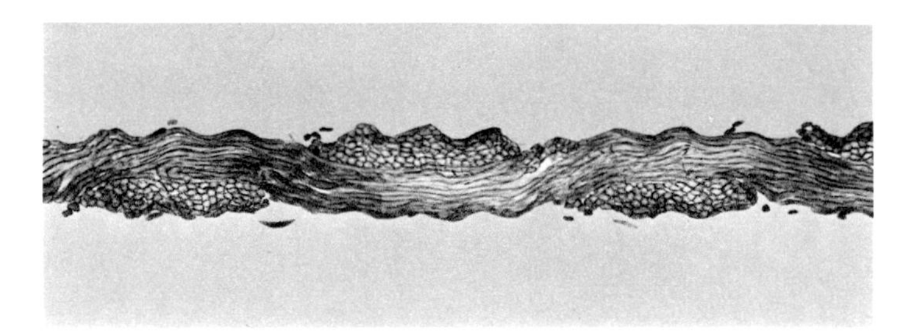

When synthetic resins are deposited in textile fabric, surface effects fast to washing can be obtained. Microphotos taken in cross-section through viscose rayon staple fibre. Top: Non-finished. Centre and bottom: Permanent chintz and embossing effects achieved with the artificial resin precondensate *Lyofix PR*. Magnification x 100.

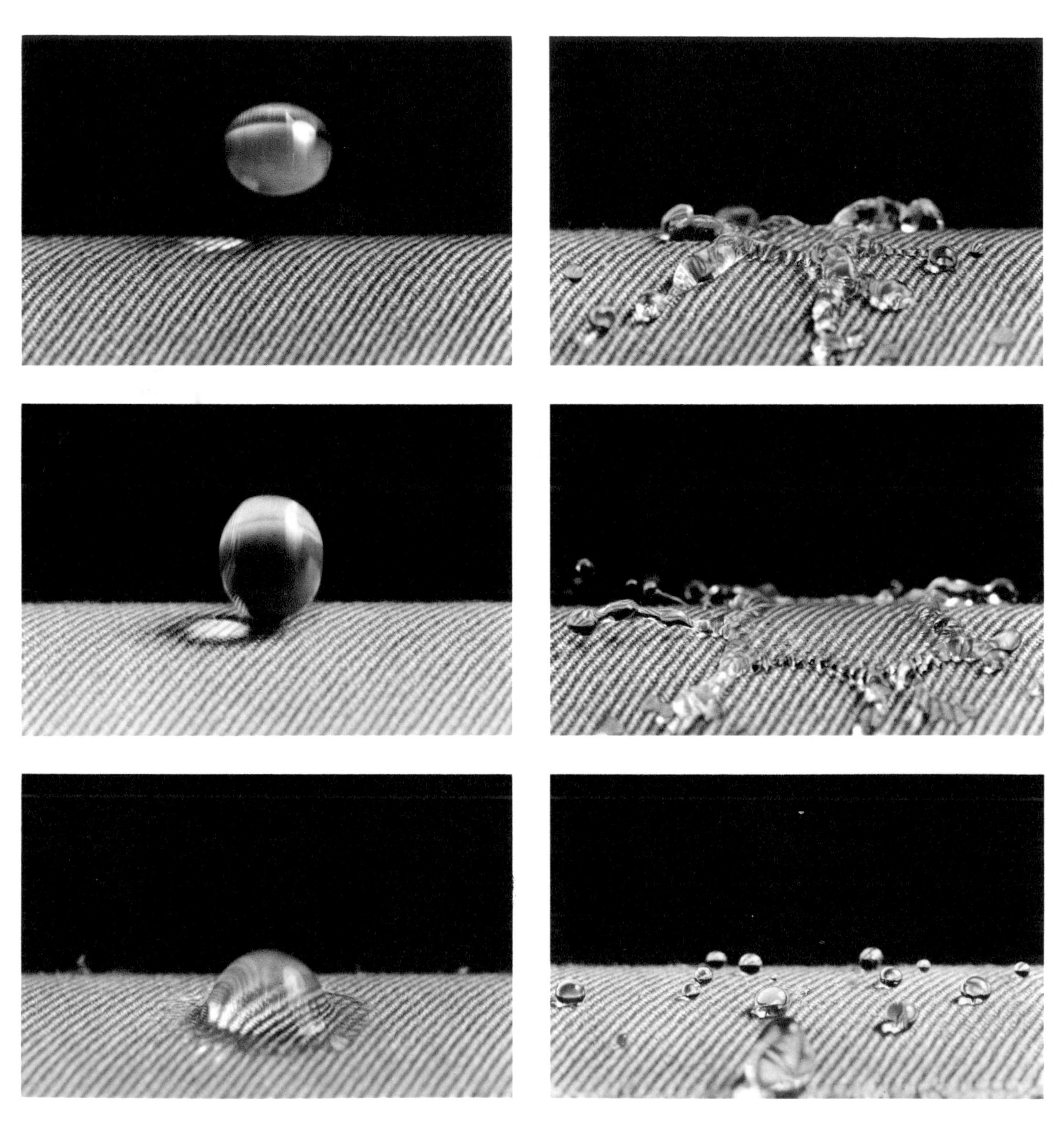

is also being explored in Basle. Since the 1940s, for example, CIBA has been making solutions and dispersions of polyvinyl and polyacryl resins as textile finishing agents for modifying the handle of fabrics as well as for the coating and covering of materials.

Just as in the development of dyes and pharmaceuticals, natural substances also constitute the point of departure in the story of optical whitening agents. In 1929 Krais noted that flax yarn saturated with an aqueous solution of esculin appeared far whiter after drying than before being thus treated. Esculin is obtained from horse chestnuts *(Aesculus Hippocastanum* L.*)*. It contains, fixed to sugar, fluorescent 6,7-dihydroxycoumarin.

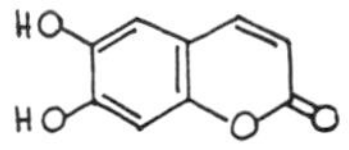

6,7-Dihydroxycoumarin

Esculin has the property of transforming the ultraviolet light of the solar spectrum, which is invisible to the human eye, into visible light: it fluoresces. On textile material, in addition to normally reflected light, fluorescent light is also reflected, and then we speak of the material's being optically brightened. Through the bluish fluorescence, moreover, the yellow tinge of the textile is optically compensated as a complementary color.

Opposite: Photos taken at x 3 magnification of a drop of water as it falls upon cotton gabardine and is dispelled. Finishing of the fabric with *Phobotex FT*, an artificial resin preparation modified by fatty acid parts, prevents the water from penetrating.

The obtaining of esculin on a technological scale is a costly process. Furthermore it cannot be fixed fast to water on to textile fibres. Thus it was obvious that compounds should be sought after which are capable of optically whitening textile materials while improving on the fastness properties of the natural product at the same time. Such products were found. In 1942, I.G.Farben placed derivatives of diaminostilbene disulfonic acid on the market under the name of *Blancophor* B and R.

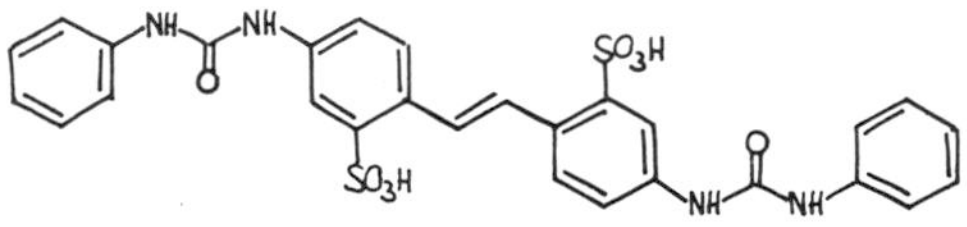

Blancophor R

In 1946, CIBA chemists reverted to coumarin for the synthesis of optical whitening agents. Through the incorporation of amino groups it was possible to increase the fluorescent power; but also, and even more important, in this way such compounds are given the property of being fixed fast to animal fibres such as wool and silk.

New structural principles, too, were worked out. From 1942 on CIBA scientists created a series of optical whiteners on the basis of dibenzimide azoles and similar heterocycles. These agents go on to both cotton and synthetic fibres. Chemists of Geigy gave special attention to the field of the asymmetrical triazole compounds of stilbene. The latest development projects at CIBA have produced whiteners with exceptionally good fastness to light, such as *Uvitex ER*.

Theory and Method

The story of chemistry is illustrative of a precept which has long since been recognized as applying to every branch of natural science. Science progresses, not through the experimental discovery of this or that fact in nature, but rather by dint of the order imposed upon individual observations through formulation of a theory possessing general validity.
In the course of this survey we have heard how René Descartes characterized natural science as "a system of clear and distinct ideas". The molecules which the chemist works with are just such ideas in the Cartesian sense. They are models with the help of which the chemist explains the properties of substances and how they may react, and formulae represent projections by means of which he transcribes these data.

The history of theoretical chemistry is the history of the molecular model. This model, as it becomes more and more refined and complicated, is capable of expressing more and more properties of a substance.
Paralleling the development of the molecular model is the development of scientific method. Theory and method fructify and impel each other. New research methods make it possible to fill in theoretical gaps, while fresh theoretical knowledge is helpful in the working out of new methods.
The chronological change in the concept of the molecule shows an evolution which is continuous and self-consistent. Even the newest views relating to it do not overpass the bounds that Descartes outlined for scientific patterns of thought some three hundred years ago, for they are still constituted by the conceptions of space and motion.

In 1774 Antoine Lavoisier formulated the law of the conservation of matter; in 1808 John Dalton proposed the law of multiple proportions. These two axioms are the foundations of the first rational model enabling us to recognize the kind and quantity of elements making up a substance, i.e. the empirical formula. In 1814 Berzelius devised the technique of recording it which still applies, in the main, today. Setting up empirical formulae required exact measurements. For this reason the working out of a method of quantitative analysis was the main concern of chemists in the first part of the 19th century. In 1826/27 Dumas developed the vapor density method of determining molecular weight, while Liebig had brought combustion analysis to such a point of refinement by 1831 that it was possible to find out the elementary composition of organic substances quickly and reliably.

Towards mid-century many compounds were known which had the same molecular formula but dissimilar properties. Such isomeric substances must also differ in their structure – so much is plainly demanded in any rational view of nature. This requirement led to the spatial depiction of substances. The molecules of two different substances with the same molecular formula – meaning the same number of units of each element involved – necessarily have to contain these units, the atoms, in differing arrangements. In projecting molecules topologically, the concept of valence, introduced into chemistry in 1857, came to be of central importance. The postulate of the quadrivalence of carbon and the representation of bonds by full lines led chemists to assume that chain-like molecules existed.

Chain and ring shaped molecule models took on an added dimension when, in 1874, van't Hoff and Le Bel postulated a tetrahedral model for the carbon atom. The four linkage forces of this atom do not lie in one plane, but rather are arranged regularly in a three-dimensional space, directed towards the vertices of a tetrahedron. In this way the topological formula was transformed into the structural formula that is still used today. With one stroke, three-dimensional molecular models explained the phenomenon of optical isomerism. From the molecular and the linear formula of lactic acid, for example, it is not possible to see why

The conception and formula of the molecule in their historical development, as illustrated by lactic acid. Black stands for carbon atoms, white for hydrogen, red for oxygen.

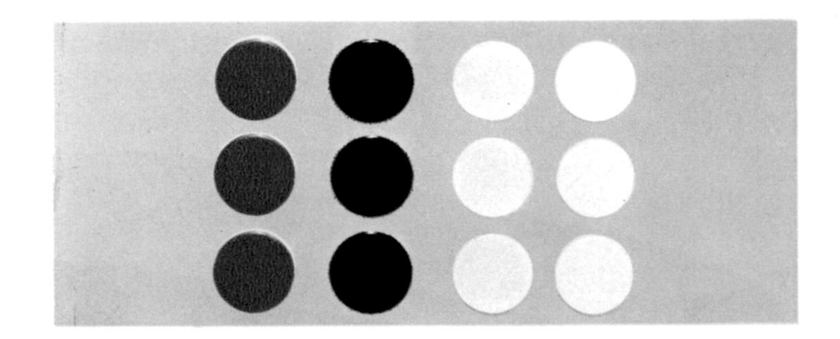

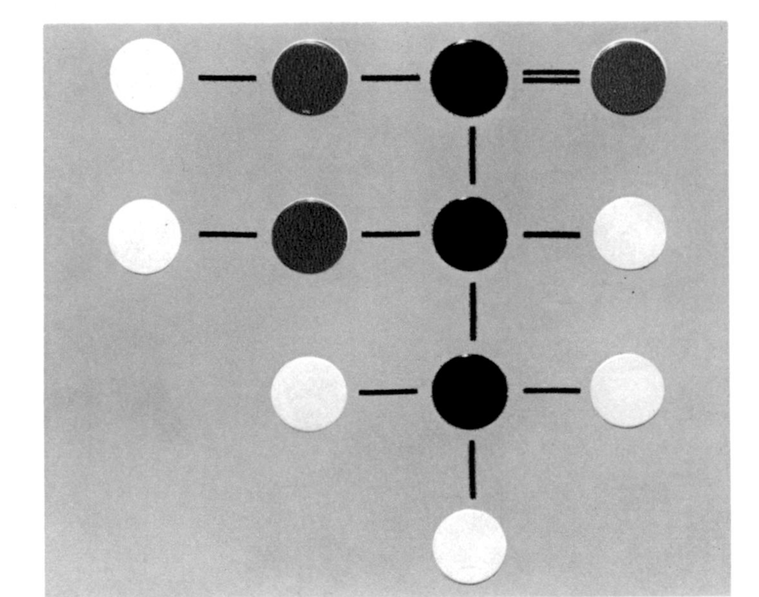

The *empirical formula* (top) only gives information on the kind and number of atoms contained in the molecule.

$C_3H_6O_3$

The *linear formula* (centre) gives an idea of how the atoms join to form the molecule.

$CH_3\,CHOH\,COOH$

The spatially projected *structural formula* (bottom) reveals that two mirror-image forms of lactic acid are possible; one of them rotates the plane of polarized light to the right (dextro-rotatory), and the other to the left (levo-rotatory).

$$\begin{array}{c} COOH \\ | \\ H-C-OH \\ | \\ CH_3 \end{array} \qquad \begin{array}{c} COOH \\ | \\ HO-C-H \\ | \\ CH_3 \end{array}$$

D-Lactic Acid L-Lactic Acid

The two conformational models of cyclohexane, C_6H_{12}. The "chair form" (left) possesses greater thermodynamic stability than does the "boat form".

this compound can exist in isomers which rotate the plane of polarized light to right or left. The structural formula, however, does provide the explanation, i.e. why enantiomorphic, or mirror-image, antipodes, and thus optically isomeric substances, can exist.

The conception of clear structural models provided the basis for a meaningful correlation of physical effects with chemical structural principles. Between 1879 and 1898 the methodical foundations were laid for the measurement of ultraviolet absorption, molar refraction, and infrared absorption of chemical compounds. These physical methods of investigating substances, together with the advent of X-ray spectrography, have become important techniques in elucidating structure.

The study of isomers led to the topological chain and cyclic formula and to the spatially conceived structural formula. The phenomenon of isomerism was to play its part in the development of still another chemical model, that of the conformational structure. In the early 1890s Sachse noted that the cyclohexane ring with its six carbon atoms can be depicted by two models free of strain which take a "chair" or a "boat" form. Molecules of one and the same structure may be found in various spatial conformations which can be interconverted without severing their bonds. In 1936 Kohlrausch found that half of the substituents on the cyclohexane ring are perpendicular to the plane, or "axial", whereas the other half are "equatorial" in it. In the 1940s research workers – conspicuous among them Hassel and Pitzer – were able to ascertain by means of exact physical measurements that varying potential energies may be associated with the various conformations. Thus monochlorocyclohexane, for instance, with its chlorine atom in the equatorial position, has less potential energy and is therefore more stable than the corresponding conformation with the chlorine atom in the axial position. The crux of this theory is the connection which it establishes between the points of view governing stereochemistry and energetics.
Conformational analysis has been developed into a polished instrument of chemical research, particularly in late years. It furnishes the chemist valuable data on the properties of cyclic systems.

Right: Early notations by Lewis, dated 1902, on the arrangement of electrons around the atomic nucleus.
Below: Atomic models of the inert rare gas argon, as projected by Lewis and Kossel. 18 electrons are arranged around the atomic nucleus: three-dimensionally by Lewis, in one plane by Kossel. Illustrations from "Valence and the Structure of Atoms and Molecules" by G. N. Lewis; New York, 1923.

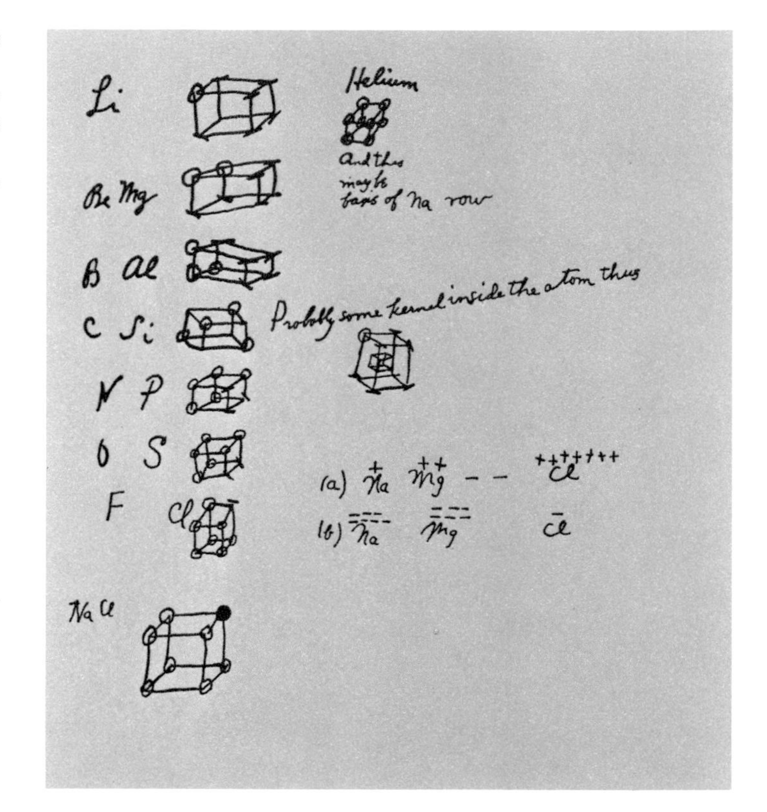

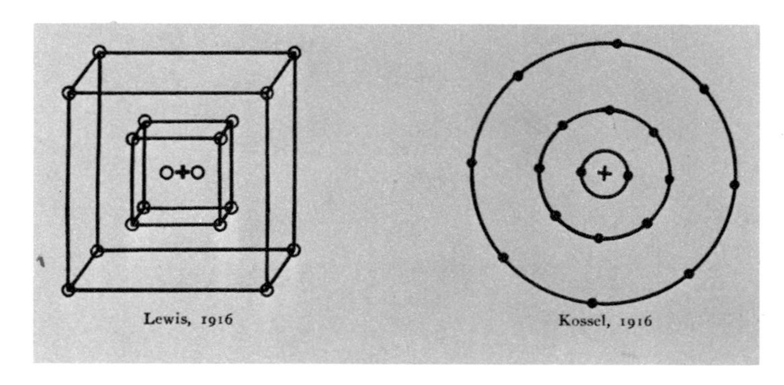

Although the structural formula does give information on the spatial disposition of atoms, it fails to tell us how they are linked to one another. The development of conceptions concerning chemical linkage, expressed in the concrete form of models, took place in two stages. The first step was taken in 1887 by Arrhenius, with his theory of electrolytic dissociation. He noted that solutions of sodium chloride contain positively charged sodium cations (Na^+) and negative chlorine anions (Cl^-). He recognised that the attractive force between the ions was of an electrostatic nature and in so doing outlined the first rational view of ionic relation.

In 1916 Lewis and Kossel independently accounted for the second step by transferring conceptions regarding atomic structure, worked out principally by the physicists Bohr, Sommerfeld and Pauli, to the molecule. Ions are created by the addition or removal of electrons, the negatively charged particles of atomic shells. The covalent bond, which has been symbolized since 1861 by a full line in the pictorial representation of chemical formulae, signifies that two atoms have two electrons in common. The explanation, thermodynamic in nature, given for the formation of ions and covalent bonds is that atoms tend to fill up the outermost shell. This is the octet rule.
In the 1920s Arndt, Robinson and Ingold proceeded to construct a qualitative "electron theory", basing their work on Lewis models. From the insight that atoms attempt to fill up their outermost, or "valence",

electron shell, and assuming ions and free radicals to represent intermediate states in chemical reactions, concepts were evolved which make it possible to appraise the reactive behavior of compounds.

Ideas concerning chemical valence opened up new vistas for chemical synthesis on the one hand and simplified the structure of chemical theory on the other. Working methods, too, were influenced by the theory of chemical union. Electrochemical techniques were necessary for studying electrolytic dissociation, and the investigation of reaction kinetics demanded improved methods of analysis.

Summary of the models and basic calculations pertaining to butadiene by Edgar Heilbronner; left, on the basis of the valence bond theory and, right, of the molecular orbital theory. Both theories are based on quantum mechanics.

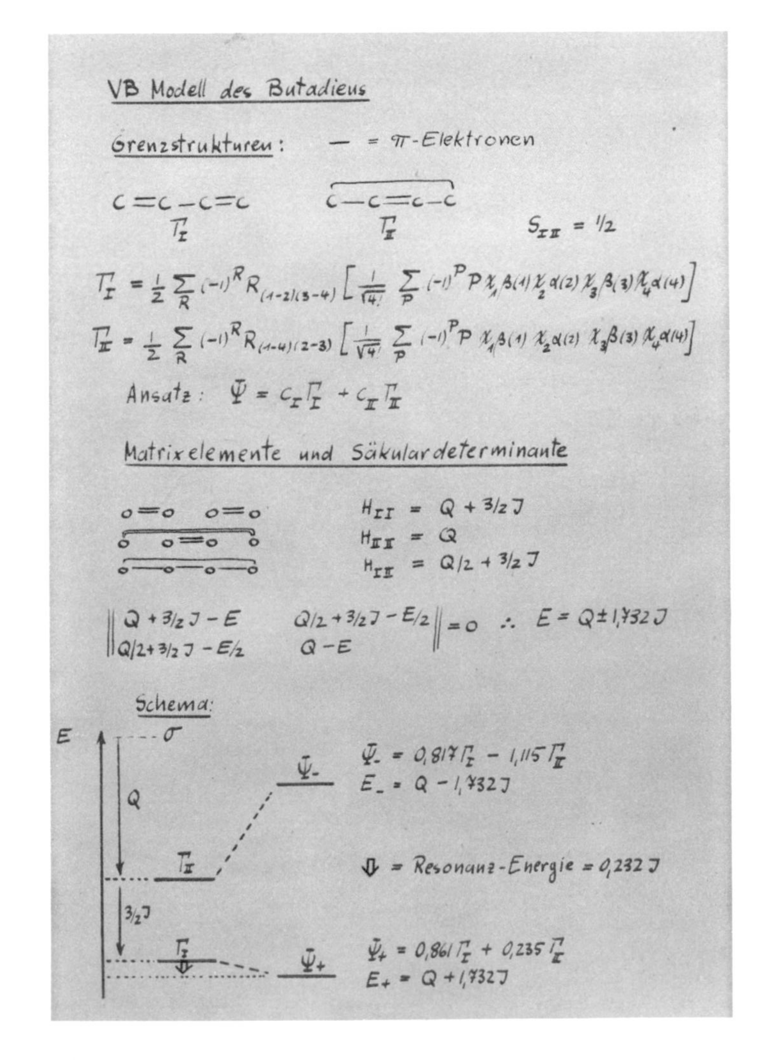

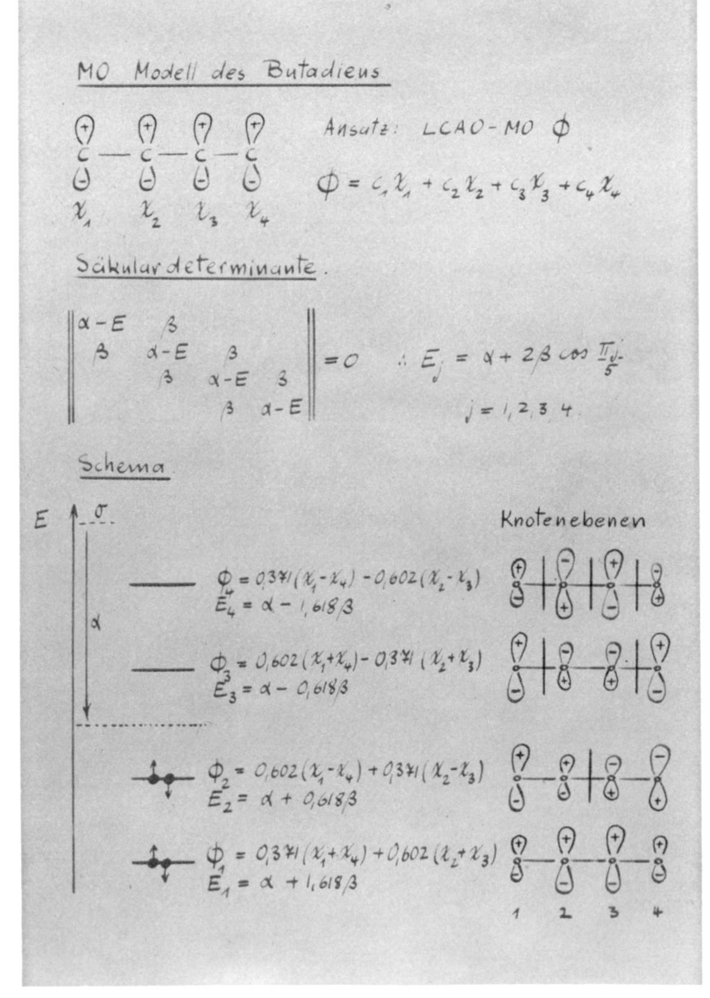

Bredt's Rule states that the valences of the carbon atom are uniformly disposed in space and not on one side. This spatial model of bicyclo [2, 2, 2] octadiene represents a theoretical interpretation of the Rule. The double bond is exhibited by the oval-shaped orbital symbols. It is considered to be stable when the orbitals lie in the same plane (left); when they are transversely placed, however, the double bond is held to be transient.

Working with a wave-mechanical model, Heitler and London succeeded in 1927 in calculating the energy content of the covalent bond of the hydrogen molecule. Their example, frequently referred to as the homopolar method because it emphasizes the electron pair type of bonding, attained classical status, and in the years that followed two semi-quantitative theories were projected on a quantum-mechanical basis. These two, the valence bond theory and the molecular orbital theory, make it possible to ascertain physical data such as bond energies, interatomic distances, and spectroscopic properties.

In a series of papers which appeared between 1931 and 1933 under the title "The Nature of the Chemical Bond", Pauling expounded the valence bond theory. According to this theory, a chemical system is described by means of a quantum-mechanical function from which it can be determined whether electrons are likely to be found in certain positions. The theory of resonance or exchange energy, derived from the valence bond theory, uses the customary structural model, drawing therewith upon chemical experience. This theory describes a particular molecule by means of possible hypothetical limiting forms. The molecule as it actually exists is designated a resonance hybrid, possessing less energy and therefore greater stability than the extreme structures between which it is "bracketed".

The molecular orbital theory took shape in the hands of Hund, Mulliken, Lennard-Jones, and Hueckel during the period from 1928 to 1937. It is distinguished from the valence bond theory by its method of approximation to the exact wave function. Instead of working with hypothetical resonance structures, it makes use of a nuclear skeleton or charge-cloud into which it successively fills electrons with different spins in favorable and energetically differing molecular orbitals.

Molecule models based on quantum mechanics enable a profounder interpretation of physical effects. As an example, light absorption and with it the phenomenon of color can be understood as an excitation of the electronic system. Thus interpreted, the results of measurements of ultraviolet, infrared and Raman spectra, nuclear resonance, and similar physical computations are given a significance which goes beyond the formal correlation of structure and physical properties. These data provide valuable parameters for the semi-quantitative electron theory.

Almost at the same time as the new quantum-mechanical interpretation of chemical structural formulae, chemical reactions, too, were given an explanation in physical terms. The transition state theory, which owes most to Eyring (1935) and Hammett (1940), has as the object of its scrutiny the arrangement of maximum energy through which reacting molecules must pass before the products of reation can be formed.

These new views of matter and reaction have opened up fresh pathways of hypothesis and experiment to the chemist. Physical methods which help to save time and material can be applied to an ever-increasing extent. For we have now arrived at the point where the chemist's and the physicist's interpretations of matter constitute a unified body of knowledge.

The overlapping of physics and chemistry has become evident in the chemical industry, too. It is not just that the physicist has now joined chemical research teams; beyond this, the whole area of knowledge encompassed by the anterior discipline of physics provides industrial chemistry with impulses which are directing its attention to new realms of technology.

The techniques of modern physics in the generation and control of energy, for instance, require materials possessing novel qualities, surpassing those of the classical ones, which no longer suffice in the construction of, say, jet engines or atomic reactors.

The evolution of physical technology offers still another possibility in the guise of collaborative technical research and development work. With the aim of developing color picture reproduction, a team of CIBA chemists is improving the material utilized in this technique, while physicists are designing a "picture transformer" which will make it possible to correct electronically color flaws in the photographic and reproductive material.

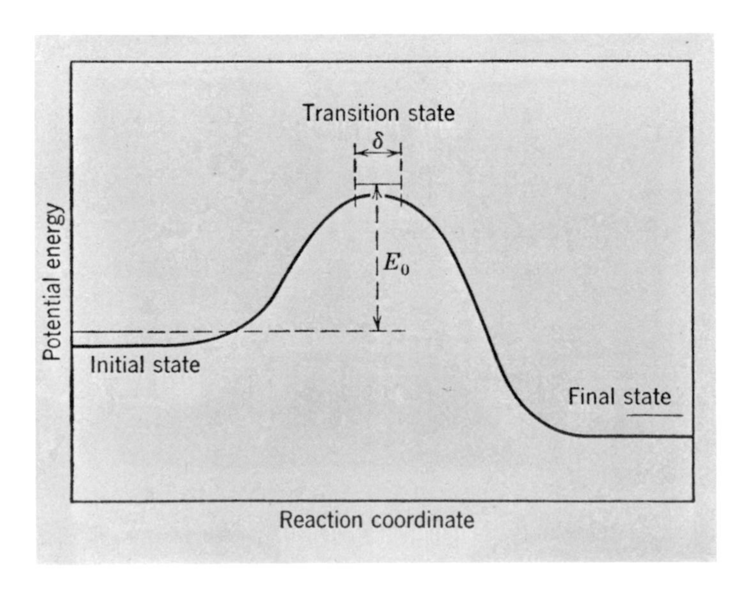

Activation energy (E_0) must be conveyed to molecules in order to cause them to react. The state of increased energy, and thus of actual possibility, is called the "Transition state". Diagram from "Kinetics and Mechanism" by Arthur A. Frost and Ralph G. Pearson; New York and London, 1953.

In Conclusion

Signs of our times: The hearings on automation held in the United States Senate in 1953 evidenced the importance which this revolutionary development has already assumed in contemporary life. Three years later Queen Elizabeth inaugurated the first atomic power station at Calder Hall. Automation and atomic energy spotlight the situation of present-day technology. The machine to release man from manual labor is being followed by highly intricate apparatus designed to "think" for him as well. And the now-classical sources of energy – the steam engine, the internal combustion motor, and hydroelectric power – have been joined by still another: nuclear energy.

These technological successes represent the application of scientific knowledge to practical problems. Modern industry, which is nothing if not dynamic, is based on research equally as dynamic. Experience gained in research institutions all over the world is recorded in countless journals for specialists – 20,000 papers a week. Batteries of tabulating machines and electronic computers are needed in order to keep pace with the flood of data thus turned out. In the process, the boundaries delimiting the various scientific disciplines tend to dissolve and to fuse more and more, with each field proceeding along the same basic lines. The principle of equilibrium which governs chemical reaction, for instance, is not essentially different from the same rule as applied to the business cycle by the economist.

What this survey has attempted to make clear is that every science, strictly conceived, rests upon the rational method which was first engendered in the late Middle Ages and brought to sophistication at the threshold of our Modern Age.

Our epoch is characterized by the tremendous acceleration of research and the expansion of industry founded on science – in short, the growth of every province of human endeavor in which rational standards hold sway. In the West, technology will soon have penetrated to the last hamlet in highland or forest. In Asia and Africa, the people place their hopes in technology as the answer to their problems. The shape of our cities is largely determined by great economic agglomerations and perfected means of transportation. National frontiers, which have come about willy-nilly in the course of a political history that was most certainly not rational, tend to be regarded as obstacles to the ever-increasing exchange of goods. Indeed, the presence of supra-national industrial concerns, the creation of international economic and political structures have already rendered them obsolete in many cases. Where science, economic life, and technology are concerned, the rational attitude has no peer.

The growth of industrial chemistry in Basle provides a striking demonstration of the effectiveness of this attitude when translated into practice. The agglomeration of trim factory buildings, rising one after the other, is the concrete, steel, and glass reflection of a development in the world of the mind also based on the rational approach. Industrial endeavor, in the interests of its own research progress, has need of close contact with scientific trends everywhere in the world. But it must also hearken to the economic order of the day, responding to the challenge of ever-changing market conditions with its performance in research, devoted to indications and applications. Saturation of the conventional sectors of the market compels the undertaking of pioneer work in new domains. At the present time these are to be found in industrial physics, which we have seen joining industrial chemistry as a partner invested with equal rank. Rapid success is not anticipated in opening up new territory; this is an enterprise which demands long-term planning. The constant changes in the economic and scientific picture do not make it easy to draw up such projects, a fact which in turn necessitates a clear-headed and dispassionate analysis of situations and tendencies. Paradoxical as it may sound, in the sphere of industry rational

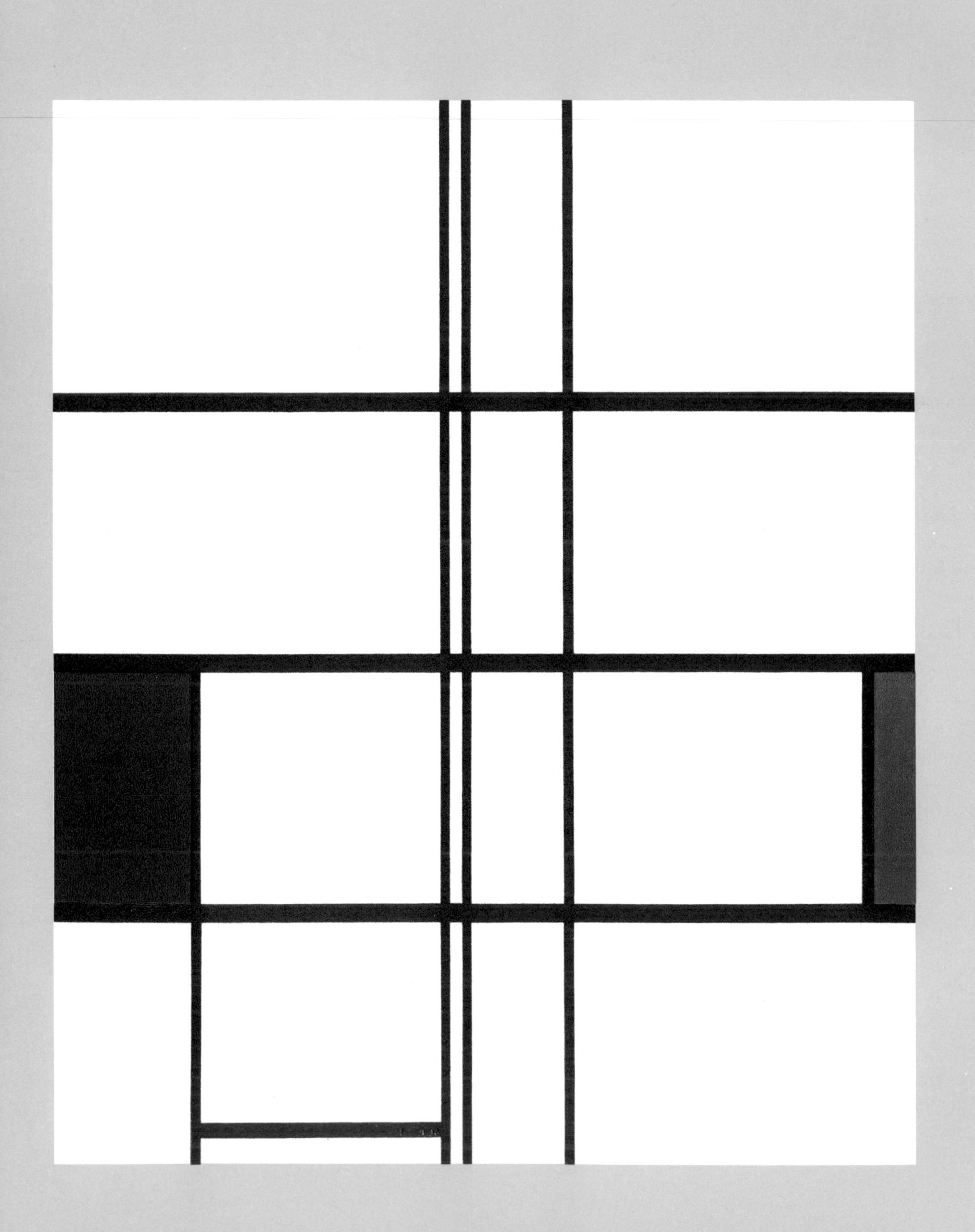

analysis has a significance equivalent to contemplation in the sovereign realm of ideas. Of this latter exercise the Basle historian Jacob Burckhardt wrote: "It is our freedom in the very awareness of universal bondage and the stream of necessities."

The human power of reasoning alone, however, is not capable of embracing the totality of human experience. In the Middle Ages, men of thought were otherworldly in their bias – contemplative in the religious sense. In the Renaissance, cultivation of the revived heritage from antiquity – pious, enthusiastic, nostalgic – went hand in hand with a fostering of the new, scientific attitude to nature. The entry to the technological age is not watched over by René Descartes alone. Flanking it is his contemporary, Blaise Pascal. Whereas Descartes exalted the practice of clear and distinct thinking to the status of a method, laying the cornerstone of what has become the superstructure of today's science, technology, and economy, Pascal emphasized that other realms of knowing also exist. Fragment 282 of his "Pensées", which appeared in 1670, begins: "We know truth not only by the reason, but also and moreso by our heart, and from the latter comes our knowledge of first principles." These first principles – what Descartes understood by "ideas" – have not been discovered through lucid thinking as such, not even by Descartes himself. It is the creative act which discloses them, and only when logical conclusions are drawn from abstract tenets can we speak of truth arrived at through the reasoning faculty.
Logical systems of thought always have the semblance of absolute objectivity. It is easily forgotten that they, too, rest upon axioms. And axioms – what else are they but ideas? Ideas are the foundations of all scientific systems and social institutions. Neither economic factors, nor even the constellations of power politics, and certainly not the might of individual men constitute the mainsprings of history. Always impelling the course of events, rather, are the ideas which creative individuals have apprehended and given a form.
That rational thinking has been of tremendous use is a fact requiring no further demonstration. It justifies the statement that "Technical things should be treated in a technical way". Yet this assertion dangles in limbo if not placed in a greater perspective, which comprises far more than science and technology. Gabriel Marcel has formulated the primary and abiding emphasis in these plain words: "Human questions have to be treated in a human way."

Piet Mondrian. Composition with Red and Blue, 1936. Private collection, Basle.
In 1914 the Dutch painter noted in his diary: "Neither life nor art could one bring forth, were one to trust in the spirit alone. Or in matter alone. The unity of both is what constitutes Creation."

CIBA trademarks and those of other firms, to the best of our knowledge, have been placed in *italics* upon their first mention in the text.

Layout and Production: CIBA Publicity Department in collaboration with Andreas His, design consultant, Basle

Documentation: Erwin Zwigart, CIBA Medical Information Service Archives
English: Stanley Hubbard

Photography: Norbert Bigler and the photographers Marcel Ackermann and Urs Huenerwadel, Photo Section of the CIBA Dyehouse Laboratories

Photogravure: Roto-Sadag S.A., Geneva
Letterpress and Binding: Otto Walter Limited, Olten
Paper: Zurich Paper Mill on Sihl

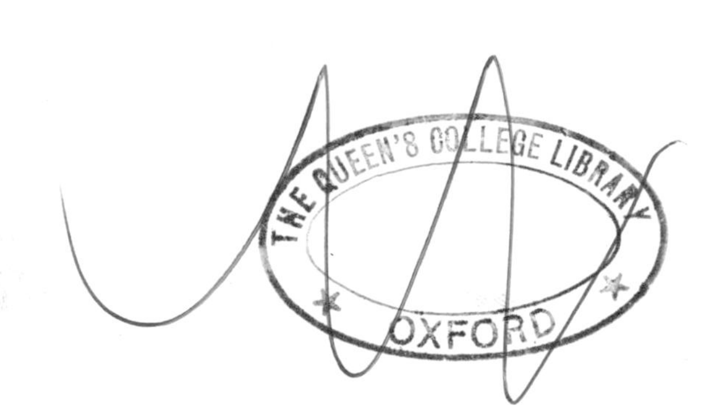